MW00623772

SHADOWS, SHELLS, AND SPAIN

JOHN MEYER

SUMMER NOMAD PUBLICATIONS

Copyright © 2017 by John Meyer.

All rights reserved. No part of this book may be reproduced, stored in or introduced into a retrieval system, or transmitted in any form or by any means (electronic, mechanical, photocopying, recording or otherwise), without the prior written permission of the copyright owner, except in the case of brief quotations embodied in critical articles and reviews.

Library and Archives Canada Cataloguing in Publication

Meyer, John, author
        Shadows, shells, and Spain / John Meyer.

ISBN 978-0-9876703-6-6 (softcover)

        I. Title.

PS8626.E925S53 2017   C813'.6   C2017-900933-8

Summer Nomad Publications
65 High Park Avenue, Suite 2306
Toronto, ON
Canada
M6P 2R7

First Summer Nomad edition published 2017.

Visit the author's website at www.johnmeyerbooks.com

Cover and text design by Tania Craan
Front and back cover images by John Meyer
Front cover shell and arrow images from Shutterstock

Printed in Canada.

SHADOWS,
SHELLS,
AND SPAIN

ACKNOWLEDGMENTS

This is primarily a work of fiction, although some of the minor events related here did happen to me to some degree. However, the major characters are the product of my imagination or are used fictitiously, and any resemblance to actual persons, living or dead, is coincidental.

I am thoroughly grateful to Traci Johnston, Janelle Blair, Natalie Mizuik, and Paul Gurney, who each read the first draft of this book and provided me with invaluable comments and suggestions. I also want to say *gracias* to Jordina Juganera for her help with some of the Spanish language sections.

I also want to thank my new editor, Joanne Haskins, for all her hard work and dedication to detail. And thanks to my book designer, Tania Craan, for once again joining me on this book journey and guiding me along through its visual creation.

And of course, I want to give a big thank you to all my new Camino friends from the United States, the United Kingdom, Spain, the Netherlands, Germany, France, Austria, Finland, Argentina, Australia, and South Africa, who unselfishly shared their stories and provided me with endless inspiration to fill these pages!

CONTENTS

THAT NIGHT IN PALMA

I KNEW THERE WOULD BE trouble the moment I reached the Shamrock Fun Place. I had never wandered that far from the safety of my gloomy apartment. The oddly named Irish pub was completely uncharted territory. I had always turned back as soon as I reached the Hard Rock Café. *Always.* That night, however, I walked in a darker mental fog than I had on most of my other melancholy nights in Palma, and I had foolishly ambled too far.

My trouble came in the form of two Swedish beauties who spilled out of the live-music bar and staggered toward me. And, no, their approach wasn't to be taken as a compliment. I was less an object of their interest and more of a handy target for their inebriated attention.

The brunette in the tight white dress tripped on her heels and reached for my shoulder to steady herself. She giggled and picked at her shoe to determine what possible obstruction had suddenly made feel her so unbalanced.

She was twenty-six, maybe twenty-seven. Every man standing on the sidewalk patio desired her. Every woman was begrudgingly impressed. Even her trailing blonde friend was enthralled. "Look at her! Look at her!"

While the brunette was aggressive, the blonde was softer and more seductive. Her flowery sundress disguised her figure, but her smiling face and piercing eyes were enough to demand one's full devotion. And while the brunette left no doubt you could never satisfy her impulses, the blonde teased you that anything was possible as long as you held her attention for more than a fleeting moment.

The Swedish beauties were a deadly combination and best to be avoided at all costs, unless one had a strong stomach for what was sure to be fast-approaching heartbreak.

I was trapped in the brunette's grip until she regained enough balance to walk away and consider her options. Two men burst out of the Shamrock and approached her. The thin man in the ponytail and his husky friend with one too many necklaces marked off their territory by standing as close as possible to the uninterested brunette.

The blonde remained with me, sizing me up with mischief in her eyes.

"It's our first day in Palma."

"You're making quite an impression."

My own impressions of Palma had been rather limited thanks to my bouts of depression. My nights of melancholy exhausted me, although I was still an alert and functioning human being. No one had detected that I was heavy-hearted and morose. I lived in a shared apartment above the Plaça de la Drassana, where I never *completely* shut out the outside world. Even while I was lying flat on my back in the middle of the floor, I kept my window open to listen to the hubbub below.

And whenever I summoned the strength to get off the floor, I would connect with the activity in the square by watching the various cliques converge and scatter: the indecisive dinner dates studying the patio menus, the packs of Euro-boys grabbing one last beer before heading off to the town's nightclubs, and the marina millionaires hoofing it among the middle class while the crew stayed on board to stock up their ships with champagne and caviar.

When my room above the Plaça de la Drassana finally felt too stale and confined, I would join the mob in the square in search of a meal and a drink. Or several drinks.

Since I had already made the effort to leave my apartment, I inevitably ended up in the appropriately named Corner Bar in the far corner of the plaza. It was a recruitment pub for the unemployed eager to find work aboard a boat. Crew members posted their business cards on the crowded bulletin board while their potential maritime masters advertised job openings.

I just thought it was a great gathering place to hear English—even if it was only from the bratty British bartenders swapping sexist insults with the naughty yachties, dressed in their nautical whites as though they had just gotten off the court at Wimbledon. Other times the mariners talked of the sea and boasted about their adventures in exotic ports like St. Tropez, Capri, and Santorini as though they were subway stops on a typical commute around the Mediterranean.

Whenever I felt particularly adventurous, I would lumber down the bustling Carrer del Apuntadors, dodging the college kids munching on cheap pizza, and avoiding the African salesmen cluttering the corner of Carrer de Sant Joan as they hawked their GSFC (Glowing, Squeaky, Flying Crap).

If I was desperate to escape the foot traffic, I might reach the tree-lined promenade, Avinguda d'Antoni Maura, and slip into the Lennox Pub for English ale served by Spanish locals with lisping Balearic accents. The thing I liked most about the Lennox was the small sitting space across from the bar, where I could tuck myself behind the wall and hide from the chatty tourists and the club kids fortifying themselves with one more drink before they headed to the clubs.

The final frontier of my Palma wanderings would be to join those kids for the long walk west on Avinguda Gabriel Roca. Some were heading home to their posh waterfront hotels; most were sobering up a little before sampling the more fashionable bars and EDM clubs west of the city center.

The busy boulevard was good business for the touts. Artisans sold their cheap jewelry. Gorgeous club girls peddled their low-price nightclub passes. Musicians offered weed and beat their bongos.

I just watched. It was the closest thing to human contact I had—apart from pointing at menu items and nodding at beer-tap handles.

It was only a thirty-minute stroll, but it was enough. It was a shame I had never completely explored the enchanting city. My calculated misery prevented me from inspecting the massive Gothic cathedral or wandering the medieval neighborhoods to feast my eyes on the sixteenth-century mansions or sample the bustling shopping areas.

No, my exploration typically ended after a ramble along the boulevard before I turned back for the secluded safety of my apartment. Anything longer and I might be tempted to try out one of the superclubs. Or visit one of the expensive beach hotels. Or . . . talk to someone.

I always turned around once I reached the Hard Rock Café.

That night, however, I had wandered closer to the colossal hotels and the sleek sailboats at the end of the harbor. I was mesmerized by the patchwork of languages bombarding me on the sidewalk: the slurry Spanish, the drunken German, the fractured French. I had walked past the Hard Rock Café, past the small casino, and past the Three Lions pub, finally reaching the Shamrock, where the pretty boys on the patio watched the inebriated mannequins stumble along the sidewalk.

The Swedish blonde introduced herself as Selina; her brunette friend was Evelina. They were staying for only a few days on the island before they moved on to London, where both girls had studied for a year at university.

"My English is terrible."

"It's perfect, and you know it."

Selina purred when she talked and seemed embarrassed about her shiny white teeth. When she listened to my replies, she would grab her strands of long, shiny white hair and press them against her lips. The gesture might have implied timidity, but it also strengthened the implication that she was actually interested in what you had to say.

"It looks like Evelina isn't going home," Selina noted.

Ponytail and Too Many Necklaces were in heavy negotiations

with the beautiful brunette on where to head next—although they did all the talking. Evelina was too busy gazing up at the moon or staring down at her feet. Occasionally she would laugh and touch Ponytail's arm. Her gestures only infuriated Too Many Necklaces, who now realized he was no longer included in the next stage of the party.

"If she goes, I will be stranded here," Selina sighed. With one glance around the sidewalk patio, I could predict a dozen suitors stepping in to save her from her lonely predicament.

"Maybe you could walk with me home?" Selina asked.

When I hesitated, she added, "It isn't far. Only a short walk."

She slipped away and gestured for Evelina to join her in a private conversation. They spoke to each other in Swedish and punctuated their discussions with bursts of giggles and glances back in my direction.

Too Many Necklaces stared at me with contempt.

Their minds now made up, Selina slinked back to me while Evelina explained her decision to her two suitors. Ponytail was in; Too Many Necklaces was out.

"Is she going to be all right?" I wondered out loud.

"She'll be fine," Selina said as she locked her arm into mine and waved at the oncoming traffic. Two taxis parked outside the Hard Rock Café darted toward us.

"I thought it was a short walk."

"It's even faster with a taxi."

The first taxi stopped in front of Evelina and Ponytail. He held the door for her while Selina pulled me into the back of the other cab. Too Many Necklaces, out of taxis and out of luck, thrust his hands into his pockets and retreated into the Shamrock.

Selina rattled off her hotel's address for the driver, collapsed back into the seat and smiled at me. Then she grasped my hand and nodded, as if to say "This is good; this is happening. Relax."

Without prompting I blurted, "I'm married."

I waited for a sign of attitude adjustment from my gorgeous captor, but Selina continued to nod and hold my hand. In fact, her grip tightened a little.

Eventually she asked, "Where is she?"

"I don't know."

"Oh, you don't know." She said it like a confirmation. I was with her now. It didn't matter where my wife was.

"She left me."

"Your married wife left you." Another confirmation. However, the addition of the redundant word, "married," somehow demanded a further clarification.

"We're separated. But, technically, still married."

"Technically."

It sounded like a hidden proposition. *Technically*, I was married. *Technically*, I was also free to do whatever I wanted with a strange woman in the back of a Palma cab. Selina broke eye contact and stared out the window at the retreating hotels as the taxi approached the old city center, the illuminated Gothic cathedral gleaming from its ominous perch overlooking the harbor.

"My wife left me back in Toronto. There was no conversation. No personal note. No . . . nothing. She just one day picked up her stuff and left me."

Selina kept gazing out the window.

I continued. "She quit her job without telling me. She didn't mention a thing even to her mother. Not at first, anyway. She just . . . left. You understand that, right?"

Selina looked back at me and smiled. She finally released my hand, but only so she could rub my neck.

"I understand."

"She apparently went traveling. Alone, her mother said. Do you know how long I've waited to hear from her? Ten months. It's almost June, and I haven't seen or heard from her since last September!"

"Ten months is a long time."

I slid farther into the corner of the cab, complicating Selina's access to my neck. No worry. She simply slid her hand onto my knee.

My fractured explanation was only adding to her desire and

confusing my own. I wanted to walk again on the street, to bolt in any direction, but Selina's indifference to my wounded words and her constant touch were weakening my resolve.

"Ten months," I repeated. "Ten months of not hearing from her. We're supposed to be *separated*. That means living apart, not leaving the country! How are you supposed to work things out if you're not even in the same country?"

"You cannot work things out," she repeated.

"She came here, you know. Her mother finally told me. She came *here* to Mallorca. So, I quit my job and I followed her."

"And did you find her?" Selina's hand was off my knee and cruising up my thigh.

"No."

"Maybe you did not look hard enough."

"No, I looked, I looked," I snapped.

Selina finally released her grip and sat upright. We were close to her hotel, and she wanted to ensure the driver didn't take any wrong turns. She said teasingly, "You talk a lot."

"The truth is, I never talk about this."

"Maybe you make up for it today, I think."

I certainly had been an exhaustive talker as a high school teacher in Toronto. I primarily taught history, although I was often saddled with another class or two, like Media Studies or PhysEd, to justify my slight salary and fill my days.

I was popular enough in the classroom, thanks to my opening-day speech each semester. "If you give a shit about history, sit in the front and participate. If you don't, sit in the back, shut up, let the students who need this class to get into college do their work, and I'll give you a passable D+." It bought me some peace in the classroom, but those who sat in the front of the room weren't exactly riveted by my lessons. I tried, though; I really did.

My favorite assignment was always the first one: pick a current world conflict from the newspaper and trace it back to its origin—namely, the singular historical moment from which the roots of unrest had since reverberated. The drafting of the Sykes-Picot Agreement was always handy for any dispute in the Middle East. The development of Canada as a resource economy built to supply its European conquerors worked well for any foreign trade dispute.

I used to award extra points for every additional century that a student could trace back a particular conflict's roots. That is, until a Grade 11 smartass cited the biblical story of Jacob and Esau battling over the family blessing from their blind father, Isaac, as the reason Israel and Palestine were still at odds (because Jacob's descendants, the Israelites, later warred with Esau's descendants, the Edomites, who lived near the Canaan border).

I didn't award the smartass the thousands of bonus points he thought he deserved, and his mother wrote letters to the school calling for my resignation, since I was an anti-Semite and presumed Holocaust denier.

It was irritations like these that eventually made me loathe teaching. If it wasn't the alarmist parents, it was their apathetic teenage children.

"But, sir, that happened before my time! Who cares?"

"Before your time? What are you, sixteen? *Everything* happened before your time! The construction of the pyramids was before your time. The painting of the Sistine Chapel was before your time!"

Students heard that outburst more often than I would have liked to admit. It also generated more letters from the alarmist parents calling for my resignation, since I was a bad influence on their kids and a presumed pervert.

"The past matters, people! How many times do I have to tell you this? The past informs you of the present. The past influences your future. 'Those who cannot remember the past are condemned to repeat it.'"

Why was I so desperate for the approval of a sixteen-year-old nuisance anyway? Teach the lessons, assign the tests, mark the papers, and call it a day. But I couldn't. *Somebody* had to care.

It became a miserable daily existence, made worse by a George Bernard Shaw quote that singly gnawed at me: "Those who can, do. Those who can't, teach."

George was right. I had to *do* . . . something. Anything! Teaching teenagers wasn't fulfilling me; I needed to find a more creative outlet—and I thought I had found it when I started writing novels.

I tried several genres. My young adult novels only reminded me of my apathetic students, and my science fiction books always morphed into *Star Wars*. My dystopian novels were too depressing. My horror novels gave me nightmares. My political thrillers gave me headaches. I settled on detective novels starring rugged private eyes and leggy dames.

I wasn't very good at it.

In fact, I never came close to completing any of them. I wasn't clever enough to conceal the credible clues. My attempts at misdirection were too misleading. I was heavy-handed when I needed to be charming, and I was lightweight when I needed to be conclusive. And anyone who read any of my early chapters always deduced the killer right away.

I even gave my early chapters to my brightest students as an extra-credit homework assignment.

"So, what did you think?"

"Sir, I didn't finish it . . . "

"Never mind that. What did you think?"

"What is this, a murder mystery? Am I supposed to guess who the killer is? What does this have to do with my history project?"

"Never mind that. *What did you think?* "

"I don't know . . . Was it the chambermaid with the stutter?"

"Damn it!"

I then gave my early chapters to my dimmest students.

"So, what did you think?"

"Sir, why are you giving me this? You said that if I kept my mouth shut in class, you'd get me that D+."

"Never mind that. What did you think?"

"I don't know . . . Was it the chambermaid with the stutter?"

"Damn it!"

My literary stabs at writing another *The Big Sleep* had induced only big yawns. At my lowest literary point—clearly after spending too many rainy afternoons playing the board game *Clue* as a child—I once wrote that Colonel Dijon did it in the conservatory with the Menorah. And I didn't even know what a conservatory was!

All of this—the drudgery of my school days coupled with the failures of my nighttime literary efforts—made me difficult to live with, I guess. All I know is . . . it made my wife, Pamela, miserable.

We had to get out of the cab now. It was parked on the one-way street of Carrer de Sant Feliu and unable to reach Selina's hotel on Carrer de Vi. The lane was too narrow for vehicles; we would have to walk the rest of the way.

Selina paid the driver and motioned for me to join her outside. Carrer de Vi was more of an alleyway than a residential street, foreboding in its darkness and dependent on the moon to light the way. Because it featured no shops or restaurants, it was neglected by the city and left alone in its scars and blemishes with its chipping paint and exposed gray walls. Unlike the rest of the city center, which was so meticulously preserved, this street whispered, "Proceed with caution ye who enter here."

When Selina interlaced her fingers with mine, I didn't object. We walked in silence to the weathered wooden door that served as the unremarkable entrance to the Hostal Pons.

"Well, we made it," I said. "You're no longer stranded."

"Maybe you could walk me upstairs."

"I don't think so."

"It's dark inside. And a lot of stairs. I get so confused."

"You Swedes sure are fragile," I teased. "How did you even manage to find the Shamrock?"

"I had Evelina."

Selina let go of my hand to open the front door with her large key. She beckoned me to take a look inside.

I hesitated but followed, suddenly petrified that I was slowly slipping down a dark path into something I thought I'd never do.

I followed Selina into the building. The ground level was filled with wooden furniture and large ferns, linking the hotel with the first-floor apartments and making the area more of a community gathering space. Selina's bedroom was up the staircase.

Now that I was no longer standing on the street, Selina stood behind me and blocked my escape.

"It's not so dark in here."

"But you should see up the stairs. And the lock on my door is hard. I'm not strong enough to take it off, I think."

"I'm *not* going in your room," I murmured as I led the way up the stairs.

At the top of the staircase was an open doorway to the hotel. While the building now served tourists, it had once been the home of a large Mallorcan family. Every room was functionally furnished and subtly converted into a guest space.

We headed past a pair of sitting rooms filled with comfortable chairs and little reading nooks the former family might have used to entertain their visitors in. After another flight of stairs, we reached the first level of bedrooms and a small kitchen and dining area.

"We have to go to the top," Selina whispered.

We climbed several flights of stairs until we reached the top two rooms of the hotel. There was also an open entrance to the roof, where the tiled deck welcomed daytime guests who wanted to soak up the sun on a selection of patio furniture and reclining chairs.

"What do you think of the view?" asked Selina.

The overall view, at night, was minimal: just the residential rooftops and backyard patios of other stacked homes, complete with clothing lines and satellite dishes.

I shrugged.

"No. Me."

I shrugged again with a smile.

Selina swatted my chest in protest and backed away toward her room. Only then did I notice we were not alone on the roof. Against the wall were two exterior shower stalls with only flimsy curtains to keep out prying eyes.

Although I couldn't see her in the darkness, I could hear a female guest humming behind one of those curtains during her late-night shower. It was admittedly an open-rooftop concept, but I suddenly felt like we were shamefully intruding.

Selina led me to the door of her room, whose window opened up to the rooftop and whose front wall separated the room from the back of the showers.

She handed me the small key and I opened the padlock. It wasn't as difficult as she claimed, but there was a trick to it since the shackle looped though two hooks mounted on both the door and the frame. Locking it required two free hands; unlocking it was as easy as the turn of a key.

"There, I did my duty—"

Selina slid into the room and turned on the light. It was a simple layout with a single bed, a small closet for her clothes, a nightstand, a small table with a solitary chair, and a sink. Perhaps it had been a former servant's quarters or used as an attic for storage.

The other notable feature about the room: it was as hot as an oven. Selina opened the window, but it did little to diminish the insufferable heat.

"Evelina sleeps in here too?"

"She's across the hall. Are you going to come in?"

"No, I'm done here—"

Just then the shower girl entered the hallway carrying her shoes and her toiletry bag, her towel loosely covering her naked body. She shrieked when she saw me, and the towel slipped a little, exposing some cleavage.

I yelped a little, too, and instantly retreated into Selina's room— and then instinctively unbuttoned my shirt to fight the heat.

"That's better," Selina purred as she hiked up her dress and pulled it over her head in one swift motion.

Seeing she misunderstood my undressing, I buttoned up my shirt again and wiped away the perspiration developing on my brow.

"No, no, no—it's hot as balls in here. Don't you have a fan or something?"

Selina remained on her bed, holding her dress in her lap.

"Listen, I'm only in here because there's a naked girl in the hallway. I just need a minute."

I crept closer to the corridor and listened for a door slam.

"Why don't you sit down here with me?" asked Selina.

"I'm good up here."

Selina pouted. "Is this about the married wife again?"

"Yes, it's about the married wife again."

Selina tossed aside her dress and lay back across her sheets. If it was a sexy gesture, it also was an uncomfortable one. That single bed looked incapable of supporting two full-grown adults.

"She left you, no?"

"I'm sure she has a great explanation. She just hasn't told me yet," I snapped as I leaned into the hallway. Enough time had passed. The shower girl had to be inside her room by now.

"No conversation, you said. No note, you said."

"Well, isn't this convenient; you suddenly have an amazing memory for everything I already said. But you keep forgetting the part where I'm technically married!"

"*Technically*," Selina scoffed. And, then, with a rub of her tummy and an extended hand, she said, "I'm not going to leave you."

2

THAT LIFE IN TORONTO

PAMELA (or Pam—nobody who loved her called her Pamela) had had her own problems with her domineering mother hijacking every holiday, every weekend, and most weekday nights with her histrionics. "I need you here on Halloween. I'm not getting up to open the door and feed those kids candy." "Are you coming over for Easter? If Jesus can rise from the dead, the least you could do is help me flip my mattress."

Even if her mother weren't already haranguing her, Pam couldn't properly relax at home thanks to her stressful job as an advertising copywriter.

"Honestly, Jamie. She says one thing one minute, then completely changes her mind the next. Am I supposed to be psychic or something?"

"Is this that dog food client again?"

"No. Mother." Then, after a beat, "I mean, I'm going to lose my mind any day now, I swear. She never likes any of my ideas, and I'm the one who's always getting screwed."

"Your mother?"

"No, dog food."

Because of my literary failures and her daily creative battles, our conversations in the bedroom were rarely about our relationship and usually about our preoccupations.

"Jamie, would you ever buy a lipstick for men?"

"Never . . . Listen, Pam, do you think it would hurt a lot if I killed you with a shovel?"

"Yeah, probably . . . So, tell me, what's the first thing that comes to mind when I say the words 'fish taco'?"

"Fish with Spanish accents . . . Do you know where someone can buy arsenic? Do you think they have a store for that?"

"Walmart probably has a whole aisle for that. Honestly, Jamie, these clients really expect me to pull rabbits out of my ass every time I see them."

"If you could pull rabbits out of your ass, we could hit the road and make some serious, serious money."

"You'd pay serious, serious money to see me pull rabbits out of my ass?"

"Do you take credit cards?"

Bad novels, indifferent students, an exasperating mother-in-law, demanding clients who expected magic . . . we had no mental escape from our dreary lives or any physical escape from our midtown apartment.

Pam's only reprieve was flipping through the magazines she subscribed to; then she could imagine herself sampling the city's finest cuisine reviewed in *Toronto Life*, wearing the most comfortable couture featured in *Vanity Fair*, and sailing to the world's most exotic ports splashed across *Condé Nast Traveler*.

"Jamie, how about Santorini? It was once a volcano; just look at it!"

Pam would shove yet another travel magazine across my dinner plate.

"See those cliffs? And all those pretty white buildings? Wouldn't you just love to go there?"

"I guess—"

"Or . . . or . . . Bora Bora!"

Pam would fan through the magazine until she found the proper page. "Look, it's our very own beach hut overlooking the water. Are you kidding me?! You wake up, you jump in the ocean. Could you imagine?!"

"Pam, we can't afford any of this. And I can't go anywhere until school gets out in the summer—and then that's *your* busiest season because everyone else in your office leaves for the cottage."

"I don't care!" Pam would say, flipping through the rest of the magazine pages in disgust. "I mean, c'mon; even my mother's been to Maui. She still talks about that fucking luau every time I offer to cook a ham for Christmas."

Soon any faraway island would do for Pam: Tahiti, Fiji, Sardinia, Corsica—it didn't really matter. She just wanted to see a body of water splashing onto a tranquil stretch of soft white sand.

The one island in the world that obsessed her the most, however, was Mallorca.

Mallorca (the preferred Spanish spelling) is off the eastern coast of Spain in the Mediterranean Sea, making up one of the four major Balearic Islands along with Ibiza, Menorca, and Formentera. Now, while the party paradise of Ibiza gets most of the attention, Mallorca is the larger island. It had earned its own unique reputation as a sun and booze destination for the elite while boasting a mixed residential terrain of beach towns and mountain villages in addition to its one vibrant city, Palma.

It was George Sand's nineteenth-century travelogue, *A Winter in Mallorca*, about her miserable season traveling with her lover, the composer Frédéric Chopin, that was largely to blame for Pam's obsession—and not because of Sand's occasional praise for the island paradise, but rather because Sand devoted many more pages to her disdain for the place and its people.

"Jamie, listen to this! 'At the moment I cannot conscientiously recommend this trip except to those artists of robust physique and ardent spirits . . . '"

"I think I have more of an 'ardent spirit' than a 'robust physique.' What about you, Pam? Ardent or robust?"

"This woman's a riot. We *have* to go!"

Then, later, "Jamie, listen to this! 'We nick-named Mallorca the Island of the Monkeys, because, when surrounded by these cunning, thieving and yet innocent creatures, we . . . felt no more rancor or scorn than what the Indians feel toward chimpanzees.' She actually called the peasants 'monkeys'!"

"Well, to be fair, 'cunning and thieving monkeys'."

"And then she wonders why the people of Mallorca were so mad at her when she published the book. She even calls them 'savages'! Oh, Jamie, we *have* to go!"

But we never made it to Mallorca. Or Tahiti. Or Fiji, Sardinia, or Corsica. We barely made it to Centre Island a mere fifteen-minute ferry ride across the harbor from downtown Toronto.

I shared some of the details about my wife with Selina and, while my seducer was polite at first, I had reached the breaking point of her patience.

"You think that is a nice love story or something? It's a sad story."

"The best love stories are always a little sad . . ."

Selina sat up and reached for the dress she had discarded so seductively on the floor.

"I don't want to hear any more about your married wife! You don't find her. You don't even look for her. You are lazy—"

"It's more of a depression thing, really—"

"I don't care. Get out—you lied to me."

"No, I didn't; no, I didn't. I told you about my wife in the cab."

"It wasn't serious."

"Yes, it was!"

"Now you are in my room, I take off my dress—"

"I didn't want you to take off your dress. *You* took off your dress!"

Selina held her dress tightly to her chest and waved me out of the room.

"Get out! You're a lazy liar! Go look for your wife!"

"I don't know where to start."

"Start somewhere else!"

I closed the door behind me, and the house immediately went dark and quiet. A moment later, the sole remaining light peeking underneath her door was extinguished, and I was alone.

The walk home from the Hostal Pons was incredibly short. Walking south on Carrer de Vi, I soon reached Carrer Sant Pere, which emptied onto Plaça de la Drassana.

It was pretty and serene inside the square at that late hour. The

17

chattering cliques had gone home. The bars were shut and silent. The stone benches were empty. The only representation of life was the Spanish plane trees that rose majestically from the gaps in the cobblestone, bathed in amber light from the street lamps.

I reveled in its peacefulness while I reflected on the recent unpleasantness. I resented Selina's assessment that I was lazy. It was hard work to be so idle and shiftless!

The number of questions alone that reverberated in my mind kept me vital and mentally occupied. What went wrong with my marriage? Who was to blame? What could I have done better? What mistakes did Pam make? What warning signs had I missed? Why did Pam suddenly leave me without giving me a chance to change my ways? Where did she go? What should I do next? And when I find her, what should I say to her? And what can I do to guarantee this type of estrangement never happens again?

And then there was that other dreadful question that needed answering, which I kept procrastinating about: should I confront Pam's mother again to see what she knew? Shudder.

My relationship with Pam's mother had started off sour (after all, I had stolen her only child) and had only grown more acidic over the years.

Pam's father had been much more cordial and sweet, although he was also a sickly man, suffering from one ailment after another. It was so commonplace that he was ill with the latest bug or strain of flu that I had stopped asking him how he was feeling; I couldn't stomach the answer. It turned out he was much more ill than he had let on, and he died suddenly from cancer during our honeymoon in New York City.

His sudden death triggered my mother-in-law's transformation into a meddling monster, and Pam and I were left alone to deal with her bitterness and spite.

It only got worse after Pam's sudden disappearance. Of course, her mother had always blamed me for the split. And she wasn't too interested in helping me find her daughter so the two of us could work out our problems.

So, I pestered our friends, I tracked every lead and every suggestion, I searched every place Pam and I had ever visited in Toronto, I called the police; I even attended marriage counseling sessions by myself, hoping for some psychological insight that might suggest my wife's whereabouts.

The only nugget of information I ever received, however, was from her mother during a particularly frustrating phone conversation in early October.

"I'm going to ask you again: where did she go?"

"I haven't the foggiest."

"You must know something. She tells you everything."

"Ha! That's what you think."

"Well, maybe she doesn't automatically tell you everything. But somehow you nag it out of her."

"I do not *nag*."

"Where is she? Her work doesn't know. Our friends don't know. Even if you don't know *everything*, Pam must have given you a clue at some point; you talked to her every day."

"As did you—"

"Not since we separated in the summer and she moved into the guest room."

"Honestly, Jamie; I don't know a thing."

"Was it Bora Bora? She always wanted to go to Bora Bora."

"I don't know. Stop yelling."

"Santorini? Was it Santorini?"

"Why take a Spanish class if you're planning on going to Santorini—"

"Ah haaaa! 'A Spanish class.' So it's Mallorca, then—of course! Wait…when did Pam take a Spanish class?"

"You'll have to ask her! When you get to Mallorca!"

Her mother hung up. I fought with her for days over the phone and outside the door of her house (she wouldn't let me in) about Pam's whereabouts. She had conceded the island of Mallorca but wouldn't reveal anything more. Pam was on the move and didn't want to be disturbed. She had left me for a reason, and her mother wasn't about to arrange a reunion.

So, in the middle of October, I quit my job, packed a suitcase, and headed to Mallorca in search of my missing wife, leaving behind my apartment, my friends, and my life—without a second thought about my future. I just wanted to see Pam again.

The mattress inside my Palma apartment was all I could think about as I entered the doorway of the faded yellow building and climbed the stairs above the Mini Market that so graciously supplied me with chips, ice cream, and, of course, beer and wine.

My roommate, Sneaky Pete, was in Ibiza for the week, which meant I had migrated from his comfortable living room couch to his even more comfortable bedroom.

When my head hit the pillow I forcefully removed any remaining thoughts about my mother-in-law and conjured up the face of my missing wife, lingering on her long chestnut hair, her piercing brown eyes, the faded freckles scattered across her cheeks, her plump red lips . . .

Hours after my Swedish temptation, I climbed out of Sneaky Pete's bed and picked up my clothes and any other damaging evidence suggesting I had ever slept in his room. Collecting errant beer bottles was a sad reminder that I had intended this living arrangement to be temporary. But seven months later, I was still sleeping on his couch.

Pam had announced our separation back in June while I was grading the final papers from my apathetic students. "Announced" was my preferred term, since there had never been any elaborate discussion. She walked into the kitchen and coolly notified me that our marriage was over and that she'd be filing divorce papers in the morning. Before I could protest, she marched out the front door and hopped in her car, and headed straight to her mother's house for the night. When I saw her again the following morning, her lawyer had already drafted the paperwork.

Pam had promised to talk about our issues over the summer while I was off from school, but the conversations were sporadic and rarely scratched the surface as to why we were falling apart.

She repeated many times that she "loved me," but she didn't

offer the vaguest of solutions as to how to fix our marriage. Only later did I realize that Pam's frequent love declarations must have stunned me into submission.

She loved me, so why worry? It seemed better to wait it out and forgo any immediate unpleasantness by keeping busy with our lives. She went for walks; I played pick-up basketball games at the playground. She took classes (like Spanish, I guess); I procrastinated writing my next novel and read some literary classics for inspiration. When I finally suggested marriage counseling, she agreed.

We never did attend any therapy sessions. I had drawn up a list of potential counselors from the internet, and she assured me she'd research them and make a decision. She didn't. Her only decision was to leave me in September, just as my classes started up again.

Of course, the sheer size of Mallorca and its population of eight hundred thousand made any type of personal search next to impossible. After a quick tour of the island, stopping in every sizeable town near a beach or a mountain, I stuck with the capital of Palma in the faint hope of one day spotting my wife.

It was fruitless and depressing. And, yet, I stayed. And, soon, I needed a job.

Pam and I had never had much money to travel, so the cash I brought with me didn't last long. We hadn't established much credit, so there was no banking institution to finance an extended trip. I had no family. My parents were dead. I had no siblings. And I couldn't borrow money from my friends because each one of them sided with Pam in our split and concluded that maybe it was better we were kept apart. Some of them even admired her for leaving on a long vacation "just for herself."

It wasn't incredibly difficult to get a job in Palma. Not at first. Not when you get creative with your resume and lie in your interviews.

I found a job teaching English at The Academy on La Rambla, northwest of the old town's central square, Plaza Mayor. Two statues of Roman emperors greeted you as you entered the walk-way, erected by General Francisco Franco supporters in 1937 as a tribute to fascist Italy. And that's just how The Academy treated me—as a fascist.

Its website promised to teach its students "practical language as it is used in real-life situations." Hey, as far as I was concerned, my separation was a real-life situation, so I brought photographs of my wife to class. "Have you seen this woman?" "If you were visiting Mallorca for the first time, where would you look?"

I guess I was *too* real for The Academy (or I should have stuck to the curriculum).

The Academy then wanted me to take the University of Cambridge examinations to prove my mettle. That would have set me back several months, however, and I declined on the grounds that I spoke perfect English, so what was the difference? I was fired.

However, in my short stay at The Academy, I did meet Sneaky Pete. He was a fellow teacher who was sympathetic to my plight and needed a roommate to help pay for his expensive apartment. His real name was Peter, but nobody ever called him that due to his duplicitous habit of stealing clients from the school and teaching them privately. He also freelanced around the Balearic Islands, often going to Ibiza for days at a time teaching fly-by-night seminars and trolling the superclubs for potential students and possible sex partners. Of course, a potential student who was also a sex partner was the ultimate score.

My next job was at Die Akademie near the cathedral on Carrer d'En Morei. Despite its virtually identical name, this was an international school developed in Germany that practiced something called the "superlearning" method. According to the website, it was English-language study designed for learning in a "relaxed and peaceful way . . . without pressure, in a pleasant atmosphere."

It turned out the seemingly pleasant administration heads were bigger fascists than those at the Academy and fired me within the week—before I even had a chance to bring the photographs of my wife to class.

I wasn't deterred. Taking a page from Sneaky Pete, I began to advertise my own private lessons beneath the Die Akademie sign posted in the school's courtyard.

My notices never stayed up long. Within the hour, someone from the staff would spot them and tear them down. Even with their limited exposure, however, I would often get an e-mail query from a potential client.

I would also get potential clients from English Rob, who ran The English Book Shop across the street. Whenever a Spanish local wandered into the store inquiring about a guide to help them speak better English, Rob would pass along my business card.

The shop was crammed with about fifty thousand publications occupying every available space on each of its four floors. English Rob called it Dickensian because it sounded old and quaint—and not because it suggested the poor social conditions of nineteenth-century England.

English Rob ran the store alone, without any staff. He had few visitors and even fewer customers. Each time I stepped into the store I felt compelled to buy something, whether he had a new client for me or not.

This explained the odd pile of books on the floor of Sneaky Pete's apartment—from Mikhail Gorbachev's *Toward a Better World*, which I plucked from the neglected Russian Literature section, to *Leonard Maltin's Movie Guide 2007* taken because its faded and damaged spine had particularly spoiled English Rob's laughably outdated Entertainment section.

A few days after my Selina encounter, I returned to The English Book Shop to see if Rob had referred any more prospective clients to me. I had to admit his outdoor display did catch the eye with its plush rocking horse, its grand terrestrial table globe, and joyful Marilyn Monroe photo.

Inside the store, however, the eye was bombarded by disorder and antiquated collections that offered no hope of finding anything distinctly useful for the twenty-first century.

When I arrived, English Rob was at his usual post, sitting behind the door, hidden by packed shelves, watching Premier League football on his desktop computer.

"Hello, Rob. It's me. Jamie Draper."

"Yes, yes, hello," Rob mumbled.

"Anything new? Any new clients for me?" I stood quite still, careful not to disturb anything. Over the years, the artistry of shelving books by their specific subject matter had been replaced by an obstacle course composed of random piles of publications scattered over the floor.

"No, no," Rob muttered. After a moment of reflection, he added, "You did receive a package."

"A package? Where is it?"

"On the floor there."

I bent down to consider the various stacks of books, but it wasn't until I turned the corner into the next room that I found a large envelope addressed to me underneath English Rob's reading chair, a green velvet throne that had seen better days decades ago.

"When did you get this?" I asked, turning over the envelope in my hands but not daring to open it yet. It was indeed addressed to me care of Rob's bookshop. I recognized the return address, and I shuddered.

"Some months ago—I don't know. I forgot about it until I stepped on it the other day."

"Months ago? Why didn't you tell me?"

"I'm telling you now. You used my address?"

"I mentioned your shop to a few friends back home. When exactly did you get this?"

English Rob only grunted. I was interrupting his football match, and he wasn't interested in providing any excuses or explanations. I grabbed a book from the top shelf of the Travel Guides section and paid him for it. There was no receipt. There was no exact change. I nonchalantly handed him a twenty-euro note and walked away. I was confused and curious about the package, but I was already late for a class.

I didn't have far to walk. One block north stood the thirteenth-century Santa Eulàlia church, which presided over the Plaça de Santa Eulàlia, a quiet square that served as a nice respite from the nearby shopping streets.

Luis waved to me from the bench under the central patch of plane trees. His dark hair was neatly combed, as always, and his face lit up with recognition and wonder. Dressed in a crisp white button-down shirt and olive chinos, Luis completed the illusion that this was a formal classroom of study with a well-planned curriculum.

This public square would have to do as our intimate classroom, however. Since I didn't want to impose on Sneaky Pete's apartment space, it was the only viable option—and it simultaneously made everything much more pleasant. I even supplemented the class occasionally with a bottle of wine and paper cups.

There were also no textbooks or exams. My curriculum was elementary conversation. I would pick a topic of interest (to me), and we would just sit and explore it for a while. I also encouraged my clients to bring along any English-language newspaper or magazine article they had stumbled upon and I would help them with the translation.

Unfortunately, Luis had arrived empty-handed that day. He simply beckoned me to the bench as though we were two old friends about to chat about the weather.

"Hello, Jamie. How are you?"

"Good, good. Sorry I'm late."

"Why do you say 'Good, good' and not 'Good'?"

"Um…we do that sometimes when we're in a hurry. But you shouldn't do it. Just say it once. It's too confusing to really explain."

"Okay, good, good." Luis smiled at his little joke. He was finishing his first year of university at the Universitat des le Illes Balears and already spoke exemplary English. Reading it was difficult for

Luis, but he spoke it well. He still hadn't determined his academic major, but he did know that he wanted to work in tourism and encourage travelers to visit the Balearic Islands. This made him eager to please people—mostly me.

"You didn't bring anything for me to translate?" I asked.

"No. But you did." Luis pointed to my envelope.

"It's a letter from my mother-in-law." Calling attention to Pam's mother made me shudder again.

"You do not open?"

"Maybe you should." I feigned disinterest and wondered if I could order a takeaway glass of wine from one of the cafés in the square.

"Okay." Luis snatched the envelope and tore at the seal.

"Congratulations, Luis. You're about to learn about passive-aggressive behavior."

He stared at me with concern, trying to work out the meaning of the unfamiliar words.

"The woman who wrote that letter is hostile. Um…she's angry at me without telling me that she's angry. She's sarcastic. But not in a funny way…she wants to hurt my feelings."

Luis nodded and pulled out a smaller package that was tucked inside the larger one.

"It is another envelope."

I grabbed it and examined the writing. The outer package was clearly from my mother-in-law. If I didn't recognize her handwriting, I certainly remembered her return address. But this envelope was written by someone else. It was addressed to me, but the return address was in Gibraltar.

"Gibraltar? I don't know anyone in Gibraltar . . ."

While I was lost in thought for a moment, mentally reviewing the names of every person I had ever met in Spain who might have a connection to Gibraltar, Luis took back the smaller envelope and casually opened it.

Finally there was an actual letter—some handwritten pages torn out of a small notebook—and he immediately began reading it out loud. "Dear Jamie, I am so . . . sorry . . . to . . . wuh-rite to you . . . this way. And I . . . k . . . k . . . k-now . . . you . . . want . . . be . . . lie . . . eve . . . me when . . . I tell you this . . . but I . . . love you—"

I snatched back the letter. "That's from my wife!"

"That is good, good, yes?"

"Yes!" Eager to read everything at once, I scanned the pages for immediate revelations, but nothing was making any sense. It was just a blur of words written in the smooth and steady hand I had seen a hundred times on grocery lists and important date reminders posted on the refrigerator.

"Listen, Luis, I'm sorry. But I'm afraid I can't do the lesson today."

"But I pay—"

"Yes, I know. But this is from my wife—"

"But I pay—"

"Here," I said, handing him the travel book I had just purchased from English Rob. "Read the first chapter and tell me what you think."

Luis opened the book to the second page and traced the title of the book with his finger. "Lazy . . . Tours . . . in Spain . . . and . . . " His finger stopped moving as his lips silently worked out the pronunciation of the final word in the title.

"Elsewhere," I impatiently added. "*Lazy Tours in Spain and Elsewhere*. It means other places . . . Spain and other places."

Luis then pointed to the publishing date. "What is this?"

"That's the year it was published. Eighteen ninety-six."

"Eighteen ninety-six?"

"Yes, it's very old. Have fun with it."

It took me another five minutes to convince Luis that reading a book from 1896 was a valuable English lesson. He still felt an injustice was taking place, and he wouldn't leave until I agreed to give him a free lesson in the future. He's going to make a fine travel agent one day.

Clear from my client commitments and with the shaded bench all to myself, I finally read Pam's letter.

3

THE FIRST LETTER

Dear Jamie,

I am so sorry to write to you this way. And I know you won't believe me when I tell you this, but I love you. Not in the same way when we first met—but I still love you. You were my husband. You were the love of my life. And I'll never regret our time together. Never!

So why am I not telling you this in person? I'll get to that. But first, I have to say I'm sorry. I'm sorry for leaving you like I did a few weeks ago.

A few weeks ago?! There was no date on Pam's letter, so I checked the envelopes. The Gibraltar stamp indicated January, while the mother-in-law envelope indicated February. Obviously, the routing of this package had taken months. But why? And where was my wife now? Could she possibly know that I would receive this letter ten months after she had left me?

And I'm sorry for putting you through any kind of hellish worry or concern.

But I just had to leave. I'll explain why soon, I really will. But right now, Jamie, at this very second: I have to be selfish. Very very selfish. Yes, it's all about me right now. Nobody else. Not even you. And I'm sorry. Just know for now that I have very good reasons for all of this and it will all be made clear to you, I promise. I'll explain everything!

You probably won't believe me, but I really really miss you. Really! It's hard to explain all these feelings and emotions in just one letter. And that's why—there's <u>more than one letter</u>. This is just the first one. (Not the first one I wrote, by the way, but the very first one you'll read.)

I tore through the envelopes again to see if I had missed something. Nope, this was the only letter in the package. The other letters were missing.

Remember when you used to write me letters when we were first going out?

It's true. I used to be romantic. I used to write her letters the moment I got home after our dates. Actual letters. Handwritten. I'd describe every wonderful moment. I'd compliment her. I'd tell her about my feelings and emotions using soothing and suggestive words I could never say to her out loud. She'd receive them in her mailbox a full week later, and it was like she was reliving our date—except this version of me was eloquent and passionate and verbose.

When did I stop doing that? When I asked her to marry me? No, I remember writing her a letter the night before the wedding. That might have been the last time. Once we started living together, I suppose I lost the initiative to capture every tender moment and romantically rephrase every highlight.

Well, I still kept them! I just loved them too much and could never throw them away. Even though that's what I told you I did.

That was true. During the darkest night of my novel writing, I had suddenly snapped and thrown every unfinished manuscript into the garbage. Then I had begged Pam to help me dispose of everything I had ever written—including those letters. I simply had to definitively free the world from all my literary failings. (Of course, my manuscripts were still saved on my computer, and Pam had lied about throwing out those letters.)

    And sometimes after we'd fight, I'd read some of those letters again just to hear you say sweet things to me like you used to.
    Sorry, that sounded bad.

It certainly did!

    It's not like you stopped saying sweet things to me. Or if you somehow said those sweet things to me I'd still be there with you today . . . Aaaargh, this is so frustrating! I'm getting off topic . . .

I still said sweet things to Pam; I know I did...

    Look, Jamie, I loved it when you used to write me letters, so now I'm writing you letters to explain <u>my life</u> over the last few months—in order to explain <u>me</u>. You were so open and honest with me when you used to write to me, so now I'm going to be open and honest with you. And hopefully you'll be able to understand why I had to do this. And maybe you'll forgive me.
    My stuff is really too hard to say, believe me. So I convinced myself that it's really better for me to write it all down. And I can write it all down exactly how I want to say it without stopping and arguing with you and having you twist my words around and stand there with your arms crossed and rolling your eyes or whatever!

Twist her words around? I was just trying to understand them. Maybe I used different phrases in trying to figure out what the hell she was trying to tell me, but I didn't *twist* them!

I did roll my eyes, though. I was doing that right then and there reading Pam's letter.

    I just <u>have</u> to do it this way! Again, sorry!
    So let me start by saying that after I left you, I bought a one-way ticket and flew to Mallorca. It was September in Spain, and it was after the summer tourist rush and the weather was perfect.
    And no, I didn't plan it months ago. I bought it right after you went back to school. I looked on the internet one afternoon and I bought a plane ticket. No plan. No conversation with anyone. I

*just booked it and began packing. It was so crazy. I was so scared
about your reaction and yet so excited to finally go to my favorite
island. Crazy, right?*

I hadn't been able to share in my wife's sudden excitement. I
had gone crazy with worry. Then I went crazy with depression.

*And I did it all, too. I went to Palma; I walked a lot around the
Old City and ate the most delicious meals ever!*

*Then I took the cute little train to Sóller. It's like a hundred
years old and it was paid for by orange and lemon farmers. Isn't
that awesome?*

*I also took the bus to the mountain village of Deià. A lot of
writers and musicians hang out there and they make a big deal
out of Robert Graves's old house.*

*Of course, I went to the hill town of Valldemossa too to check
out the monastery where George Sand and Chopin stayed that
winter. The town's completely slammed with bars and restaurants
now and the place is a complete tourist trap. I thought I was the
only one who read that book!*

*The monastery was nice but a little tacky with the giant stat-
ues in the entrance and all the shitty souvenirs. I couldn't imagine
living in it though. Those cells were smaller than our crappy
apartment. But it was September and warm. Not rainy and windy
like Sand and Chopin's winter.*

Sorry! Okay, so I explored the island. Ha!

Yes, thank you, I get it. You had a good time. I was probably
rolling my eyes again.

*But then I got back to Palma and met this British woman,
Nicola, at this English pub, the Lennox.*

The good ol' Lennox. Just reading that name gave my heart a
jump—like my wife and I were secretly connected again. Our vis-
its to the pub may have been months apart from each other's, but
it still was a shared experience of English ale and Balearic accents.

And I was talking about walking around the north side of the island in Sóller and Deià and then she told me that she just got back from the Spanish Camino. Look it up—it's amazing! You basically follow this thousand-year-old road across Spain. And thousands of people do it from all over the world. The way she described it, it was all so incredible. So I had to do it too!

Now Pam was losing me. She wasn't exactly a trekker around town. She had never asked to go hiking in the woods. She wanted to relax on island beaches. Sun, margaritas, hammocks, ocean. Not blisters, mosquitoes, poison ivy, mud.

I blamed her sudden enthusiasm for walking across Spain on her new friend, Nicola. Pam had always liked the Brits and their music. She dragged me to every Britpop night at the Velvet Underground on Queen Street.

So I'm doing the walk! Me! In fact, this letter is from the Camino. In fact, all my letters are from the Camino. So now here's what I'm asking you to do: walk the damn Camino!

I read Pam's previous paragraph over again. Then I read it again. Then I said out loud, "Are you crazy?"

Don't call me crazy. You won't be able to completely under-stand me and everything I've been going through until you do this walk. Seriously, Jamie; it's the best feeling ever. Walking across Spain has really opened up my mind. You meet all these great people, you stay in all these great towns. The food's amazing. The walk's amazing. It's so beautiful every day but yet no two days are alike because the towns and the landscapes keep changing. You're around people all the time but then suddenly you're all by yourself on this strange and wonderful road with all these arrows and signs guiding you along the way so you don't get lost. It's unbelievable. Thousands of people are walking along this ancient road and yet you can still be alone for miles and miles without anyone else in sight!

You have to do it! You have to!!

"No, I don't." I was now talking directly to my wife through her letter. I had completely shut out the rest of the world. It was just my wife and I having a private chat beneath the canopy of the plane trees planted in Palma's Plaça de Santa Eulàlia.

Listen, only by walking this Camino will you understand— maybe—what I was going through. So, yes, you really do have to walk a mile in my shoes to understand me better. In fact, hundreds of miles.

I know you never wanted to go anywhere when we were together, but maybe now you can.

That's not really true. I had wanted to go places. We just didn't. That's all. There was school. And work. And our mortgage. And we didn't have the money. Or the time . . .

And before you make up some other excuse, think about this: Don't you want to read more letters from me? Don't you want to read more letters from me where I explain everything? Like, why the marriage ended? What I was feeling? Why I left you when I did? Why I'm here?

"Well, yeah, of course…"

Then you have to walk the Camino! I know, I know: I'm a terrible manipulative bitch for asking you to drop everything and do this. But, seriously, Jamie; you'll grow to love it. I know you will! You'll have so much time to think and meet so many people who might inspire you. It's just fucking incredible!

I stopped reading for a moment and considered her proposal. Pam had written this plea thinking I was still in the middle of the fall semester back in Toronto, struggling to teach my indifferent students.

Little did she know I was actually in nearby Palma, several months later, only a short flight away from the start of the Spanish Camino. I didn't have any formal English classes on my slate. I was a free spirit who could do anything he wanted. I slept on the couch in Sneaky Pete's apartment. There wasn't even a rental agreement. I just gave him cash from time to time.

So, what was preventing me from immediately embarking on this journey—other than the unwillingness to suddenly walk hundreds of miles? My wife had even tried to make the strenuous exercise sound fun. The simple truth was: nothing.

Plus, the only way to find the answers to all the nagging questions that kept me awake at nights and fuelled my frequent bouts of depression was to actually follow her siren call and fucking walk the walk.

> *Think about it, okay?*
> *Meanwhile, here are some clues about where you'll find the first bunch of letters: Hemingway, donkey, bunny, Landerrain, Red Rock, typewriter, pilgrim. Messed up, right? Don't roll your eyes!*

"I'm not!"

> *I'll give you more details about those clues in the next letter, I promise. But you have to go to Pamplona to get them. That's where I started my walk.*
> *C'mon, this is fun! You used to do this kind of stuff all the time! Remember, when I turned thirty-five?*

For Pam's thirty-fifth birthday, we had suffered through the indignity of standing in the stifling holding area waiting for the ferry ride across the Toronto harbor to Centre Island. Hours earlier, I had taken the trip alone and rented a dinghy on the island, which I then illegally moored near the ferry docks. Arriving on the island with my wife, I attempted to row that dinghy along the shoreline to a secluded picnic spot I had previously scouted.

I didn't know how to maneuver the boat properly, however, and we splashed around in circles for about an hour. We finally gave up, left the dinghy behind and walked to my secret picnic spot, where I had tied up a basket full of Pam's favorite foods to the low-lying branch of an old willow tree.

Unfortunately, the windy afternoon had loosened my Boy

Scout knot, and the basket had fallen to the ground, scattering its contents and providing a feast for the ravenous squirrels.

Still, Pam had loved the effort, and we stripped off our clothes to have sex right there on the grass—until a curious boy and his screeching mother stumbled upon us during their afternoon stroll.

Remember, when that mom screamed at you?

"How dare you defile the park?! Help! Help! He's defiling the park!"

It was hilarious!

Hilarious for Pam, maybe. For the next several weeks, every time we had sex, all I could hear was the screeching mother: "Help! Help! He's defiling the park!"

Pam continued her letter with an inventory of recommended gear. Then came her final plea for the Camino.

Listen. Honestly, Jamie; this is not about you proving that you still love me or anything. This is about finally learning about me and what I've gone through over the past few months. I'll share everything. I've already written the other letters, so I know I did. Yes, this is manipulative. And, yes, you deserve better. But please please please consider this request. Beyond connecting with me again, you'll get soooo much out of it, I swear. And, hopefully, you'll get out of it what I got out of it. Peace. Jamie, after all that has happened, that's what I discovered most about myself. I'm finally at peace. So come to Pamplona and come to the Camino.
    Love, Pam

Under her name she'd written the whereabouts of her next letter, with the "Hemingway" clue, in noticeably much sloppier script—as if it were an afterthought, hastily written.

I sat on the bench for another ten minutes, staring at the ground and absorbing her thoughts and appeals. At the moment, the instructions and clues didn't make much sense, while the walking exercise alone seemed quite daunting.

After ten more minutes of careful rumination, the cross-country journey then seemed somewhat attainable. However, I couldn't make a definitive decision about my best course of action. Not yet.

I had to read the entire letter again. By the time I reached the part that read *"This is about finally learning about me and what I've gone through over the past few months,"* I knew what I had to do. And I was at peace with it.

I called my mother-in-law for the first time since I had left for Mallorca to find out what she knew about the letter and why it had taken so long to reach me. But she didn't answer the phone, and I was repeatedly greeted by her answering machine. (Yes, she still used an answering machine. It was my job to buy her a cell phone and teach her how to use it, but I had neglected her request.)

Despite its long delay in getting into my hands, I was impressed she knew where to send the package. I hadn't spoken to her in months or given her my street address or e-mail address (like she had a computer, ha!). She must have asked my friends—the few I had actually updated on my pathetic life in Palma.

Next, I e-mailed my students and informed them I had to cancel my upcoming appointments due to an emergency. Most replied within the hour and wished me well.

Only Luis wanted to know if he would be compensated with a free lesson at some point, so I gave him the assignment of reading another chapter of *Lazy Tours in Spain and Elsewhere*.

Using Sneaky Pete's desktop, I booked my trip to Pamplona and then struggled with the spotty internet connection to research the Spanish Camino the best that I could.

Officially, it was called the *Camino de Santiago*, or the Way of St. James, the patron saint of Spain.

To refresh your memory of biblical history, James was one of Jesus's disciples and part of his inner circle. After the death and reported resurrection of Jesus, James actively preached the gospel around Judea—with some early scholars suggesting he eventually went westward, all the way to present-day Spain. Apparently, he had little spiritual success, however, and soon headed back home to Jerusalem.

What can be confirmed is that he was the first of the original twelve apostles to be martyred for his faith. The local Jewish authorities didn't appreciate these new "Christians" publicly preaching about a divine man who was resurrected from the dead. King Herod Agrippa, a friend of Emperor Caligula and a strong supporter of the Jewish state, subsequently beheaded James in the year 44 AD.

Following James's death, the legend goes, his remains were transported by two of his disciples by boat back to Spain, where they landed on the coast of Galicia and buried him in a cemetery near present-day Santiago de Compostela.

Eight hundred years later, the bones of St. James were discovered by a hermit who said he was guided to the very spot by a shower of shooting stars (*compostela*, derived from Latin and meaning "field of stars"). And once the local bishop concluded that the bones of St. James were indeed buried alongside the bones of his two disciples, a small chapel was constructed to preserve the apostle's legacy.

Later, the local king, Alfonso II, never missing a chance to promote a viable tourism option, ordered that a church be built in Santiago de Compostela to further honor the grave of St. James.

Then the Church authorities, never missing a tremendous marketing opportunity, upgraded a Roman trade route across northern Spain so that believers could travel to Santiago to see the relics of St. James. Pilgrimages to Jerusalem and Rome were already in vogue, so the Church had just added one more city to the holy itinerary.

These became the "busy" years for dead old St. James, as several military leaders battling the Moors in Spain claimed to have visions of James as a mighty warrior, astride his steely steed, crushing their Muslim enemies. St. James was now the rallying cry for the entire Christian army, and the legend of St. James the pious apostle-turned-Catholic-superhero was born.

Stories of miracles, both big and small, soon emerged from the Camino experience. Some were directly attributed to the ghost of St. James; others were credited to penitent pilgrims walking along the Camino. Each insignificant town seemed to have at least one supernatural story. It didn't matter if none of these tales could be proven. The damage was done. Each mile of the journey was now considered mystical and magical.

Medieval pilgrims, thirsty for heavenly guidance during the Dark Ages, heeded that spiritual call and began to travel to Santiago on foot and on horseback. Churches and hospitals were built, and monasteries opened their doors to overnight guests. New towns sprung up along the route and old ones evolved into commercial centers. And if the citizens of independent districts like Navarre and Castile were a little slow in embracing the Camino's commerce potential, monks and settlers from France filled that void with the encouragement of eleventh-century leaders like Sancho the Great and Alfonso VI. Even military orders like the Templars and the Knights of Santiago got into the community spirit by protecting the poor pilgrims from roving gangs of thieves.

By the twelfth century, the Camino pilgrimage business was booming. It became so established that the world's first travel guide, the *Codex Calixtinus*, compiled by the French monk Aymery Picaud, provided recommendations and warnings about traveling the Camino. Picaud, while helpful, was certainly not above racism, portraying the French pilgrim as noble and the Navarrese, in particular, as barbarians who sodomize their women...and their donkeys.

Then in 1189, Pope Alexander III declared Santiago de Compostela a holy city on par with Jerusalem and Rome. He even sweetened the deal and promised an escape from purgatory if one were to complete the journey in a Holy Year (although the time would only be cut in half during a non-Holy Year).

This get-out-of-purgatory pilgrimage continued unabated throughout the ages despite major obstacles like the Black Death, the Protestant Reformation, and the continental wars of the sixteenth century.

In the Middle Ages, half a million pilgrims a year walked across Spain. With the arrival of the enlightened eighteenth century, the numbers slipped to about thirty thousand a year—which still amounted to a sizeable sample of the European population.

The only event that seriously threatened the Camino was the confiscation of church lands in 1837 during the civil war between the monarchists and the liberals who fought over the future of the Spanish sovereignty. Many churches and monasteries were closed, and the Camino accommodations and ancillary industries suffered tremendously.

However, the Camino experience bounced back into a big business during the twentieth century—especially for the small towns along the route that would otherwise see few to no tourists. For Roman Catholics, it might have something to do with Pope John Paul II visiting Santiago de Compostela in 1982. For many others, UNESCO's declaration in 1985 that the Camino was an important cultural route and a World Heritage Site spurred further funding and restoration of many of the churches and inns along the trail.

Today, however, it's less of a spiritual quest and more about the search for an alternative vacation. Church attendance might be down and cynicism about the role of religion might be up, but none of that affects the thousands of pilgrims from all over the world who walk across northern Spain every single day of the year, through every season and through every extreme weather warning.

"What do you mean you're leaving?" asked Sneaky Pete. It was the following morning, and he had just returned from Ibiza, which was odd, since it was a Saturday and Sneaky Pete did his best business on Ibiza weekends. He was watching me pack my duffel bag as he sucked back a beer and tugged on his beard.

"I told you. I'm following my wife on this Camino."

"Ibiza, mate. That's where you need to go."

"My wife's not in Ibiza."

"Is that all you're taking?"

My bag was only half full of clothes; I was leaving the rest of it scattered on the floor.

"For now. I figure I'll check out what she's got to say in Pamplona and then go from there. I mean, I could be back here in a couple of days."

"Pamplona. That's the place where they run the bulls. Are you going to run with the bulls?"

"That's in July. It's June tomorrow."

"I'd stay for those bulls."

"I'm leaving now."

"I'd go to Ibiza and then run with those bulls in July."

Sneaky Pete had never been too sympathetic about my search for my wife, so our parting was quick and impersonal. And, despite my shaky promise to return to Palma soon, I would never see Sneaky Pete or my discarded clothes again.

I walked down the stairs to emerge on the eerily quiet Plaça de la Drassana. The millionaires were now safely tucked aboard their yachts. The local beauties were still sleeping off their vodka cocktails. The packs of Euro-boys were just heading home after another night of sexual conquests.

The first sign of life was at la Plaza de la Reina, where several cabs waited to whisk travelers away to the airport, or to the port for ferry rides to the Spanish mainland or the islands of Ibiza and Menorca.

I instructed my driver to take me to the airport and began to worry about Pamplona. What would I find there? Would Pam's initial instructions work? What would her next letter say? Was I really considering walking the Spanish Camino?

I considered my travel bag. Pam had provided a list of recommended gear, but I, woefully, didn't own any of her suggested items. While I stuck to her clothing rule of three—three shirts, three underwear, three pairs of socks, just two pants—the items weren't entirely suitable for the Camino.

The shirts had to be polyester tees with wicking material. So did the underwear. The socks had to have a double layer with a thin wool exterior and a wicking liner. The pants had to have extra pockets and be convertible to shorts with the pull of a zipper around your thigh. It was all about wicking away any moisture from your body, keeping everything as dry as possible to avoid blisters and rashes. I wasn't ready. I was a blister-and-rash disaster waiting to happen.

At the Palma airport, I called my mother-in-law every twenty minutes on my shitty cell phone. Finally someone answered—a friend of hers who was picking up the mail and watering her plants. She was tired of all the ringing and explained to me that my mother-in-law had left for an extended vacation.

"Where did she go?"

"I don't think it's appropriate for me to say. Who is this?"

"Her son-in-law."

"Well, if *you* don't know, I don't think it's appropriate for me to say."

"How long is she gone for?"

"I don't think it's appropriate—"

"Well, what *can* you tell me?"

"I'm done in here in twenty minutes. Why don't you call back and leave a message?"

I hung up the phone and ignored her suggestion. I had left enough pointed messages accusing Pam's mom of withholding information and failing to help me find her daughter. Now I had my first solid lead, and I was going to follow Pam's thorough instructions through to their proper conclusion.

4

PAM IN PAMPLONA

THE MORNING FLIGHT to Madrid was quiet and uneventful and only ninety minutes long. Staring out the window at the dull blue blanket of the Balearic Sea, I continued to contemplate the Camino and the reasons people would leave the comfort of their homes to hoist a twenty-pound backpack over their shoulders and trample across an unfamiliar country.

My Camino research had told me the original religious reasons were now increasingly less common. Few pilgrims believed they were on a mad march to see the actual bones of St. James. Fewer still suspected they might witness a modern-day miracle to reignite their faith. Today, no one would admit they were walking across Spain to reduce their waiting time in purgatory.

Since two-thirds of the pilgrims listed themselves as Roman Catholics, however, more than a few walkers were seeking some kind of heavenly guidance for their problems or, conversely, thanking God for a perceived blessing—like the birth of a child or the surprise recovery from a debilitating disease.

Nevertheless, the majority of pilgrims were walking the Camino simply as a break, challenging as it might be, from their modern-day lives. In the Middle Ages, because of the inherent dangers of travel, a pilgrim would have to settle his financial affairs before leaving on this type of journey. He had to pay off his debts and forgive debts owed to him. He had to draw up a will and even make clear arrangements with his wife that if he died along the way, she could remarry without the stigma of scandal.

(Yes, almost all of the ancient pilgrims were men. Women traveled only if they were accompanied by their husbands.)

Instead of wrapping up their fiscal affairs *before* they boarded a plane bound for Spain, many pilgrims today were walking the Camino *because* of their financial troubles. Maybe they had just lost their job. Maybe they hated their job so much they needed a mental break. Or maybe they were changing careers and just wanted to have a little adventure before they settled into a new working environment.

And never mind the medieval task of making remarrying arrangements for their spouses left alone at home. Many modern pilgrims were walking the trail to *get away* from their wives and husbands. Many were mourning—or celebrating—a divorce and walking the winding road to re-establish their independence.

Whatever the personal problem or issue, the long walk gave a modern-day pilgrim time to think and re-examine his or her priorities. And because all their essential belongings were strapped to their back, it also challenged the capitalist compulsion to buy more and more gadgets to fulfill an empty life.

This walk was about letting go of your connection to material goods and your monotonous routine at home to refocus on what was truly important. It was about changing your perspective and adopting a new attitude. It was about learning about yourself and confronting your comfort zone.

The Camino journey was a demanding, month-long exercise to feed your mind and soul while testing the limits of your body. No two pilgrims were alike, so no two Camino experiences were alike.

The only real and tangible concept that was universal among pilgrims now was this: as long as you opened your eyes to the power of what the Camino could do for your life, you'd return home a changed and better person.

So what was Pam's original reason? She felt trapped in her monotonous life? She was planning on divorcing me and needed to regain her independence? She felt she had to finally focus on what was truly important to her mind and soul—which apparently wasn't our failing marriage? I didn't know. I had to read her next letter to find out.

Meanwhile, as the plane descended into Madrid, I knew my initial reason for considering this Camino adventure. I just wanted to find out what the hell went wrong with our relationship and see my wife again!

Waiting for my afternoon flight to Pamplona I passed my time in the Madrid airport searching every bookshop and magazine kiosk for anything written in English about the Camino.

The best I could find was a general guidebook to Spain that, sadly, contained little useful information about the Camino, since it catered to the filthy-rich traveler and not the dirty-poor pilgrim.

It did, however, mention the complicated network of modern-day walking routes that crisscross Spain toward St. James's alleged resting place in Santiago de Compostela.

Now, while there are ten major trails (and many more minor ones), when most people discuss walking the Camino they are probably referring to the most popular route, the French Way, the eight-hundred-kilometer trek that begins on the French side of the Pyrenees in Saint-Jean-Pied-de-Port and runs across the top third of the country through the cities of Pamplona, Logroño, Burgos, and León.

Four more major routes begin in the southern cities of Madrid and Seville and the eastern towns of Tortosa and Valencia. And while each route winds its way through the country in distinct directions, each one of them eventually intersects and connects to the French Way.

Another popular path is the Northern Way, which begins in the border town of Irún and runs along the northern coastline, but even that road ultimately joins the French Way in Arzúa—making the last hundred kilometers of the most popular Camino route the busiest section of the entire journey because all the Spanish paths eventually converge onto the indomitable *Camino Francés*.

Now the Camino pilgrimage isn't limited to the country of

Spain. For hardier pilgrims who want to extend their trip and begin their journey in France, four major routes also cross that country out of the cathedral cities of Paris, Vézelay, Le Puy, and Arles.

Other starting points are located in Belgium, the Netherlands, Germany, Switzerland, Italy, the Czech Republic, and Poland. However, almost all of those trails, including the aforementioned French routes, eventually meet in the French town of Saint-Jean-Pied-de-Port, further establishing the French Way as the most popular Camino path.

And, no matter where you begin, the destination is always the same: Santiago de Compostela in Galicia.

To some pilgrims, the journey begins the moment they leave their homes for their pilgrimage. My journey began on my afternoon flight to Pamplona, which was cramped and uncomfortable and, thankfully, only sixty minutes long.

Although Pamplona was a sizeable city, the airport was tiny and catered only to passengers traveling to and from Madrid (although it did provide summer seasonal service to Barcelona and the Balearic Islands). Waiting for my bag at the lone baggage carousel, I noticed I was the only traveler in casual clothes. The other men wore business suits, while the women were smartly dressed in their Saturday best.

Perhaps that's why I was immediately approached by a frazzled woman dressed in hiking boots and carrying a large backpack.

"*Peregrino? Vas a Roncesvalles?* "

She was embarking on her Camino journey and wanted to share a taxi with me to the border village of Roncesvalles.

"*No, no soy peregrino.* "

Three words into my new adventure and I was already testing the limits of my Spanish vocabulary. Since my English-language classes were conducted entirely in English, I had never really absorbed much of the local vernacular. Even after living for several months in Palma, most of my acquired language skills were employed to purchase food and drinks.

The frazzled pilgrim nodded and proceeded to approach everyone else inside the tiny airport.

By her choice of Roncesvalles as her starting point, the pilgrim was clearly walking the French Way. The village represented the final destination for Day 1 of the recommended thirty-three stages of the Camino route.

While the French town of Saint-Jean-Pied-de-Port was traditionally the starting point of the Camino, it was a trusted tradition only among foreign travelers.

The Spanish pilgrims, who represent fifty percent of the Camino walkers, don't believe in leaving their country in order to begin their spiritual journey. Why cross the border and briefly go to France when the Spanish Camino is clearly a Spanish rite of passage that requires you to walk across Spain?

So, only foreigners (those who stick to the established route recommended in most Camino guidebooks) begin on the French side of the Pyrenees. However, since it's a convergent point for most of the other international routes across Europe, Saint-Jean-Pied-de-Port also serves as a kind of a melting pot for the experienced walkers and the new, bashful beginners.

And what a courageous start for those beginners! While most of the Camino trail is majestic and manageable through pastoral farmlands and rolling hills, the first day walking out of Saint-Jean-Pied-de-Port is dire and demanding, sending you up and down a mountain. Any pilgrim dubious about his or her stamina would certainly be severely tested on their first day out.

The good news is that the rest of the exhaustive walk would be much easier without the stubborn obstacle of a lurking mountain range. The bad news is that any injury suffered on that first day, like a strained knee or a twisted ankle, would likely remain with you for the rest of your pilgrimage.

I didn't have to face that Camino conundrum of whether to start my journey in Saint-Jean-Pied-de-Port or in Roncesvalles. Pam started *her* adventure in Pamplona, so *I* was starting in Pamplona (if only to read her next letter).

If Pamplona had a tiny airport that predominately served Madrid, its taxi stand outside the airport was even smaller, serving no one. Eight of us stood on the sidewalk with no cab in sight. All the other airplane passengers were whisked away by family or friends in waiting cars. We were the lost and ignored, fending for ourselves without even the option of rail or bus service to take us to the city center.

"Don't the taxis know about us?" I murmured. "I mean, they must know the arrival schedule? How many planes are flying in from Madrid?"

Fortunately, my complaint caught the ear of a college student waiting at the front of the line.

"You have to call them," she said, waving her cell phone. "I called ten minutes ago and they said someone was coming."

"Tell them to send a lot more cars," I answered.

"You can share with me. I go to the Old Center."

I readily agreed, shaking off the embarrassment that I had unfairly jumped to the front of the line.

Our taxi soon arrived, and I scrambled into the back seat. The college student gave her destination to the driver before collapsing into the seat beside me. She was Paula, an Italian student studying at one of the local universities, and already fluent in both Spanish and French while she improved her English with a private tutor.

When I mentioned that I was considering walking the Camino, she shook her head. "There is no time for me. Between school and work and my boyfriend, there is no break for me to do this."

"Well, I have all the time in the world right now."

"It is a difficult walk. You have to train. Did you train?"

"Well, no—"

"Everyone in Europe trains. So, in America—"

"I'm Canadian—"

"So in America . . . Canada . . . you have to train more."

"Well, I didn't train—"

"Even *I* would have to train. But there is no break for me to do this."

The taxi stopped just outside the Old City Center at Calle Leyre and Calle de Amaya. The Plaza de Toros loomed ahead on our right. The plaza served as the endpoint of the Running of the Bulls during the city's San Fermin Festival in July—and the arena of death for the forty-eight bulls forced to fight during the nine-day celebration of Pamplona's patron saint.

On this day in June, the arena was ignored and forgotten; its bright-red entry doors were locked, its outside grounds free of fanfare. That would change in five weeks when twenty thousand patrons would enter en masse and scream for the savage artistry of the *matador de toros* in the epic showdown between man and beast.

Paula paid the driver and we both slid out of the cab. After I paid her my share of the fare, she asked, "Where do you have to go?"

"Café Iruña."

It was the precise location noted in Pam's addendum to her first letter. "*Go to Café Iruña and find the Hemingway.*" I didn't know what her clue meant exactly, but I trusted it would become clear once I walked through the door.

Paula pointed straight ahead, past the bullring. "Two minutes. Inside the plaza."

I waved goodbye and followed the curve of the road until I was dumped into Pamplona's central square, Plaza de Castillo. It was the city's social hub, framed by fashionable cafés and impressive mansions built in various styles from the eighteenth and nineteenth centuries, with the universal presence of arches and porticos shading the residents from the blazing summer sun.

North of the Plaza de Castillo lay the original domains of the ancient city, while the modern metropolis stretched far and wide toward the south. Despite the development of newer and more distant suburbs, the pleasant plaza remained the beating heart of Pamplona.

When I arrived, the prevailing atmosphere was bargain hunting as the view of the popular square was blighted by large white tents set over tables displaying the modest wares of a Saturday flea market. While the keen consumers haggled and the indifferent browsers grazed, I sidestepped my way across the square to the fabled Café Iruña.

The small city boasted seven hundred drinking establishments, but none of them was as famous as the Café Iruña. Opened in 1888, it was the first public property in Pamplona to operate with electricity. Not the city hall, not a civic community building, not an upscale hotel—but a bar. The thirsty citizens had their priorities.

The celebrated café boasted the city's largest terrace, but it was its opulent interior that impressed me most. When I crossed the threshold, it took my eyes a moment to adjust. The etched glass, the chandeliers and vintage lamps, the *arabesque* wooden columns, the large mirrors that gave the illusion of unlimited space, not to mention the long sturdy bar, the marble tables, the handsome armchairs, and the black-and-white checkered floor. It felt like an exquisite ballroom, not a blue-collar bar. It deserved a gentleman in a suit holding a premium scotch, not a desperate tourist in a T-shirt clutching his duffel bag. This was a drinking institution of class, not a letter depot for tourists.

Now, where was that Hemingway? "*Go to Café Iruña and find the Hemingway.*" Suddenly, Pam's clue didn't seem so straightforward.

"*Dónde está el Hemingway?*" I only had to ask three customers before I received a nod of recognition and a point in the right direction.

There was an Ernest Hemingway statue installed in a side room that used to be the bar's smoking area. There he was: the beloved writer in bronze, standing at the end of the bar. He looked relaxed but determined. His right foot was resting on a step, his right elbow leaning on the bar, his face turned away from the ruckus in the room as he stared into the entrance hallway, egging on all comers to buy him a drink or challenge him to a boxing match.

He was the 1950s Hemingway, stocky of stature and thick of beard, and not the 1920s Hemingway, with the trim build and the first-rate moustache, who placed Pamplona on the international map by writing about its San Fermin Festival in his first and arguably best novel, *The Sun Also Rises*.

I stared at the bronze for a long time. What was I supposed to do now? Was Pam's letter taped to his body? I started patting him down from his head to his feet. It was only when I was bent down groping Hemingway's firm bronze ass that a young bartender towered over me.

"*Lo siento*," I apologized.

He shrugged. He was remarkably dressed in a crisp white shirt with a black vest and black bowtie, his black mane slicked back without a hair out of place.

Despite my Spanish apology, he detected my English accent and mimicked a camera in his hands and gestured toward the statue. "Photo?"

"Oh, no, no, no. *Habla usted Inglés?*"

The young bartender shrugged again. "Little."

Whether the Spanish locals spoke a little English or a lot, they always confessed to knowing just a "little."

"I'm looking for a letter. From Pam Draper. That's my wife. It's a letter?"

Now I was mimicking the process of handwriting a message, folding up a sheet of paper, and stuffing the contents inside an envelope. I even licked the seal.

"A letter. It's here, I think. My wife told me to come to Café Iruña and find the Hemingway. Well, this is the Hemingway. *Lo entiendes?* It's a letter from Pam Draper. Pam."

The young bartender blinked and stood his ground. It was unclear whether he understood any of my explanation, and I was dreading that I might have to repeat my mime routine. Then he said, "*Un momento.*"

The young bartender walked to the other end of the bar and discussed my situation with an older bartender who, with his stout stomach and woolly beard, looked very much like a reincarnated Hemingway.

He patiently listened to the younger man's story and didn't move a muscle, only allowing his eyes to drift in my direction as I leaned against the bar like my bronze companion.

Finally, the older bartender boomed, "Pam Draper?"

I nodded.

He held up one finger. "Un momento."

As he slipped into a back room, the younger one returned to me with a wide grin. His story had been a success.

"Drink?"

The posh location warranted a single malt scotch, but I demurred and weakly pointed to the beer tap for the San Miguel.

My drink was soon in hand, and the older bartender emerged from the back room with an envelope and a small white bag.

I thanked him and tore open the envelope. Two folded sheets of paper fell onto the bar. It was Pam's handwriting, all right.

I read through the letter quickly, consciously reminding myself to slow down and absorb what she was confiding in me. It was similar to her first message, likely written in the same feverish session.

> *Dear Jamie,*
>
> *You made it! Congratulations! I'm so so excited that you'll be coming on this journey with me! You're going to love it, I swear.*
>
> *Maybe not at first. But soon!*
>
> *Once you've embraced the whole concept of the Camino and what it can do to your life, everything just becomes so clear and meaningful. It changed me completely for the better and gave me so much peace. And I'm sure it will do the same for you.*

While Pam's first letter had been long and earnest, this one was to the point with a reintroduction to the task at hand. It offered absolutely no further insight into our marriage. She had earlier promised "I'll explain more in the next letter," but that didn't hold true. Where were her ruminations on our relationship? Why had she left me?

> Only by walking the Camino will you begin to understand what I'm feeling. The Camino really opened my eyes to our relationship, which I can finally put into words. It will all be explained in my future letters, I promise.

Oh sure, I'd heard that one before.

Then a new, troublesome question emerged: how did this letter even get to the Café Iruña? Had Pam returned to drop it off? Did anyone on the staff remember her? And where was she now?

As I read on, other curious staff members joined the two bartenders. I appeared to be the subject of much debate and analysis.

"Do any one of you remember the woman who gave this to you?" I held up the letter. "Anyone? Does anyone remember? She's my wife. Do any of you remember her?"

Now the small group broke up and walked away to perform their barroom duties. Nobody wanted to talk to the man with the "Dear Jamie" letter.

There was more helpful information on the next sheet of paper listing the towns where I would find her first batch of letters. I hesitate to describe these as "exact" locations, since the clues were about as vague as Pam's instruction to "*go to Café Iruña and find the Hemingway.*" However, each tip expanded significantly from her first list of clue words: Hemingway, donkey, bunny, Landerrain, Red Rock, typewriter, and pilgrim.

I called this the Clue Sheet and studied her next location closely: "donkey." It appeared that this letter would be found on a hill a few hours west of Pamplona. It was conveniently stuck in between two towns, which suggested there was no rail or bus service to reach it. I would have to walk to it in order to find it.

Pam's pledge to have me walk this Camino certainly didn't lack subtlety.

I returned to her Pamplona letter, where she asked, *"So, Jamie, have you got your gear yet? No problem, if you don't. There's a pilgrim store in Pamplona."*

Then came that familiar, final plea again.

> I hope you're ready for this. Not just in terms of the walking, but in terms of what I'm about to tell you. Even if it hurts some-times, the walk will heal you and give you peace. I discovered a lot about myself, and I'm sure you will too.
>
> So do you still have any doubts?

I . . . guess?

> Well, forget them and listen to me! Just do it, Jamie! You're already in Pamplona, right? You might as well start the Camino. It only takes a few more steps.
>
> Love, Pam

When I was done, the young bartender approached me with a broad smile and nodded. Perhaps he knew something about the letter's contents, because he asked, "Walk the Camino?"

I hesitated for a moment but then let out a long sigh. "Looks like it...yes."

I paid him and stuffed the letter and the Clue Sheet into my bag. There was no time to waste. I had work to do.

When I turned to go, the young bartender called out, "Señor?"

He reached inside the forgotten white bag and produced a small hand shovel. I would need that.

5

THE CAMINO'S FIRST STEPS

ALL RIGHT, so I was walking the Camino . . . the next morning. No one walks in the evening. It's an after-dawn pursuit fueled by tradition and strategy. After all, it was preferable to walk in the cool morning hours before the sun burned away the afternoon (much of the trail's terrain was without shade). Plus you needed a place to sleep each night, and that meant arriving early enough in the day to secure a prized spot in one of the inexpensive *albergues* along the pilgrim route.

That evening in Pamplona, I was much too late for any of the albergues. I would need a hotel. I asked the younger bartender for a recommendation, and he gave me directions to Hotel Yoldi, a modern business hotel a half kilometer south on Avenida de San Ignacio.

The hotel was accommodating. No reservation, no problem. There was a small room left for me. Riding up the elevator, an American tourist commented that the hotel was a favorite among bullfighters. When I surveyed my cramped room I surmised that bullfighters were likely short of stature and easily satisfied.

My room secured for the night, it was time to assemble my gear. The hotel recommended the pilgrim store near the cathedral. That meant returning to the Plaza del Castillo but exiting through the northeastern lane of Calle Bajado de Javier and joining the crowd on Calle de la Estafeta, Pamplona's most famous street.

In the nineteenth century it was named after Pamplona's first post office (an *estafeta*), but its international fame was now due to its prime position along the route for the Running of the Bulls.

During the early mornings of the San Fermin Festival, the street would be jammed with panicked runners trying to avoid the horns of the charging bulls. It was straight and narrow and the longest section of the run, sloping upward so that the bulls and the runners had to race uphill before entering the bullring.

During my night in Pamplona, this medieval street was jammed with hungry and thirsty locals enjoying a Saturday evening stroll. At the end of the street, I turned right, onto the calmer Calle de la Curia, and soon found the one-stop pilgrim store just as the tired old proprietor was locking its doors.

Through the glass window, I presented Pam's list of items and explained that I would need everything on that recommended inventory. At first, the old woman was annoyed that I had arrived so close to closing time. Once she calculated how much money she was about to add to her cash register, she gladly reopened her doors.

We started with the walking shoes. Not hiking boots. This was a trek, not a climb. They had to be waterproof and half a size larger than my usual shoe measurement to leave room for the inevitable swelling of my feet. I tested three different pairs around the store (pacing, twisting, jumping) while we assembled my new pilgrim uniform: the three polyester T-shirts, the three pairs of double-layer socks, the three pairs of polyester under-wear, the two pairs of convertible pants. All made with wicking material, meant to keep one's body as dry as possible.

I also needed a fleece pullover for the potentially cool nights and chilly mornings. And an oversized plastic poncho to drape over my clothes in case it rained.

I also needed comfortable shoes for the relaxing evenings after my long day's walk. I pointed to my worn-down deck shoes. The proprietor nodded. They would have to do. And I was happy to finally contribute to the excursion.

Now it was time to gather my Camino gear and haul it around in my new backpack. Just like the walking shoes, I tested three different knapsacks, each with a superfluous number of adjustment straps and secret compartments. Color and style weren't a consideration. The only requirement was that it be the best fit for my body. Again, it was an unsteady workout throughout the store with much pacing, twisting, and jumping.

"Are we done now?" I asked.

Pam's recommended list was out of my hands and in the firm grip of the old woman. She chuckled and shook her head. Not even close . . .

I also required a thin sleeping bag for the albergue beds, a money belt to hide my valuables, a quick-drying towel, and a hat to shield me from the sun. I ignored the fedoras and the floppy hunter's hats for a basic baseball cap.

Next on the checklist was a detailed guidebook.

"It has to be in English."

The proprietor stared at me as though I had just insulted her. "Of course."

There was not much choice in the reading material. There was only one reputable Camino guidebook written in English. And every person who spoke English on the trail carried it.

We moved onto blister repair. The old woman gathered a set of needles to drain blisters, a box of bandages to cover them, a tiny jar of Vaseline to coat them, and an anti-blister stick that you rolled on your feet and toes like a bar of deodorant; this was meant to prevent them.

"Maybe all you need is the stick," she shrugged.

She then went through the rest of the store's inventory and lauded the benefits of each small item. I declined most of the paraphernalia but did acquiesce to the tube of sunscreen, the plastic cutlery set, the water bottle, the small bottle of detergent to clean my clothes, and the palm-size flashlight.

"Are we done now?" I asked. "I really feel like we're done."

The cagey proprietor swept her arm toward the pharmacy section of her store.

"I have my own toiletries!" I proudly objected.

Satisfied with my purchases, we packed everything into my backpack and weighed it. It was only twenty-two pounds, about ten percent of my body weight, the perfect load for a pilgrim to carry across the country.

Stepping into the street with my new gear, I felt almost inspired to begin my journey immediately. But there was more work to be done that night. I still needed my *credencial*.

The credencial is the pilgrim's passport. To spend the night in any of the pilgrim-only albergues, you need to present your credencial to the albergue's host as proof that you are indeed a pilgrim who deserves the budget benefits of a simple bed and an inexpensive three-course meal.

You then get a passport stamp in your credencial as proof of your stay. At the end of your journey, you present your stamped credencial to the Pilgrim's Office in Santiago de Compostela in order to receive your *compostela*. Now the compostela was a diploma that proved you did indeed walk one of the official Camino routes (and earned your reduced time in purgatory). Today, it's a prestigious certificate of accomplishment that is less magical than it once was in the Middle Ages but just as coveted by any exhausted pilgrim.

Now you don't have to walk the entire eight hundred kilometers from Saint-Jean-Pied-de-Port to be eligible for your compostela. Not even close. According to the Pilgrim's Office, you only need to walk one hundred kilometers (or bicycle two hundred kilometers) along any official route in order to receive it.

This goes back to that ongoing debate of where to begin your Camino journey. What do you do if you don't have the five weeks of vacation time needed to walk the recommended route from Saint-Jean-Pied-de-Port? Begin your trek in a town farther along? Skip sections of the route and take a bus in between some of the stages? Or do you do what many of the Spanish pilgrims do: start from Roncesvalles and walk as far as you can in your allotted time before packing up and continuing your journey the following year?

Having said all that, limited time or not, many pilgrims pass over much of the dreaded Meseta, the two-hundred-kilometer stretch of barren plateau that lies in the center of the country. Pilgrims complain of its dry heat, lack of shade, limited food resources, non-existent landmarks, and drab scenery.

Pragmatists with a restrictive schedule recommend a Meseta miss. Purists preach that every single step of the Camino is equally important, and that only through conquering the punishing Meseta will you fully appreciate the entire experience of your Camino. I was neither; I just wanted to find my wife.

The tired old proprietor recommended I pick up my credencial at the Albergue de Peregrinos de Jesus y Maria, located around the corner on Calle Compañía. It was one of several albergues in the city, but it was endowed a special status by pilgrims because of its proximity to the cathedral.

I entered the gloomy lobby, and the frustrated man behind the reception desk waved his arm in protest. "*Completo*! " He was eating a large hero sandwich and having difficulty keeping its contents from spilling onto his desk.

"I'm not looking for a bed."

"English? Full!"

"No, I know. I just need a passport." That was my first mistake. I couldn't remember the word, credencial, and thought of the document as a pilgrim passport.

"Passport? No. Tourist office."

"No, not a passport. That pilgrim thing that you need. What is it called? A compostela?" No, that was wrong too, and only made matters worse.

"Compostela? No. Santiago."

"No, not a compostela. Hold on . . ." I lowered my backpack to the floor and rooted through it to find my new guidebook. Of course, now it looked like I was looking for a room again.

"No! Full! No bed!" His sandwich collapsed in his hands and fell apart over his desk.

"No, I know. I need that compostela or whatever it's called—"

The clerk then explained in both Spanish and English how Santiago de Compostela was where one earns one's compostela. And an easy way to remember that was to understand that the word "compostela" was mentioned in the name of the city.

"Yes, yes, I know—oh, here it is!" I had found the mysterious word inside the early pages of my guidebook. "Credencial! That's what I need."

"Ah, credencial." The clerk immediately calmed down and gestured for me to have a seat. Our linguistic impasse was instantly forgotten. "Passport, please."

He proceeded to write down my name and passport particulars inside my new credencial, noting the date of my arrival, crossing off the box indicating I was indeed walking, and awarding me my first stamp. Considering all the bits of cheese, tomato, and deli meats scattered on his desk, I was impressed he managed to avoid soiling my credencial.

Moments later I was standing outside the albergue, completely outfitted to walk the Camino. I wanted to explore the town, but it was approaching ten o'clock and I had to wake up early. I also hadn't eaten anything since my insignificant snack on the flight to Pamplona.

I returned to Calle de la Curia and ventured toward the Cathedral de Santa Maria la Real. It was closed and had a haunting air, currently abandoned by inquisitive locals or tourists.

Behind the cathedral was the Navarreria, the oldest part of the city, once populated by farmers and craftsmen and the original citizens of Pamplona.

I wandered to the Paseo del Rédin, a few steps north from the cathedral, and peered over the city wall into the Arga River valley below. Early that afternoon, the day's pilgrims would have marched through Old Pamplona from this very entry point.

Pamplona (or more likely its suburb of Cizur Menor) would mark the end of Day 3 of the traditional thirty-three stages of the recommended route. Those that started in Saint-Jean-Pied-de-Port would have left the French border town to march up and over the Pyrenees for breathtaking panoramic views (provided there was no fog or rain or wind to ruin the experience) before making the steep descent into the sleepy hamlet of Roncesvalles.

There, they would have joined the Spanish pilgrims on the start of their journey and likely stayed in the single dormitory *refugio* (if they couldn't find a bed in one of the two available hotels).

From there, on Day 2 (or Day 1 for the Spanish), they would have walked up and down the hills outside Roncesvalles before stomping downhill across the Arga River valley to the tiny village of Larrasoaña, which boasted only one available bar in which to eat and drink.

The next morning, they would have followed the Arga River, strolled through lush forests, tiptoed along the highway, and then plunged through the busy suburbs of Villava and Burlada before they approached the city walls of Pamplona.

Once they reached Pamplona, the Saint-Jean-Pied-de-Port pilgrims would have already walked a total of 73.4 kilometers.

I, instead, walked the meager four hundred meters back to the chaos of Calle de la Estafeta for late evening tapas and beers. Each restaurant featured an unruly lineup of customers and an unstructured policy of serving whoever was able to articulate their order above the din.

My method of silently pointing to menu items was inadequate here. Plus my bulky backpack drew angry stares and concern from everyone around me.

I entered and failed at four different bars before finally managing to wedge myself in front of a tapas display case on my fifth attempt. I then yelled and flapped my arms and received four separate plates of tapas and two distinct brands of beer. I ate and drank what I was given without complaint.

The Camino wasn't really respected here, not like it was in most of the towns and villages along the route. Cities like Pamplona,

Burgos, and León didn't need Camino commercialism to survive. They had their own industries centered on commerce and other attention-grabbing attractions.

For instance, the San Fermin Festival in Pamplona draws more than two million visitors a year over its nine days of celebration. Every hotel is booked months in advance. Every bar and restaurant does booming business.

The Camino trade, by contrast, only attracts one hundred thousand pilgrims during the course of the entire calendar year. And virtually none of these pilgrims are lavishing money around the city. They're not seeking a party; they're searching for a cheap meal and an inexpensive place to rest their heads before they leave at the break of dawn for the next bargain bed.

Walking back to the Hotel Yoldi along Calle Estafeta with the crush of Saturday night revelers, I could only imagine what the medieval street must be like during its summer festival when the small herd of bulls would be released from their corral and forced to rush up the street to the bullring while thousands of hungover souls scrambled ahead of them.

To many onlookers, it was cruel entertainment. To almost everybody else, it was state-sanctioned madness. However, more people die annually on the Spanish Camino than during the *entire history* of the Running of the Bulls.

Since 1924, a total of fifteen people have been killed during the annual run (although hundreds more have been injured). Meanwhile, the modern Camino incurs about twenty deaths a year due to heart attacks, falls off the trail, and traffic accidents along the highways and busy city streets. I would have to be careful.

Safely sequestered inside my hotel room, I emptied my backpack and repacked with purpose, careful to memorize where everything resided so I wouldn't have to unpack my gear every time I needed something.

Now…what to do with the items I brought with me from Palma? After a quick calculation, I decided to leave it all behind in my room. (Well, except my toiletries.)

That was certainly in the spirit of the Camino, wasn't it? Isn't that what Pam wanted me to do? Leave my mundane routine behind and enter a new chapter of my life?

I even gave up my cell phone with its nefarious links to the outside world. It wasn't difficult. It was an old BlackBerry with an untrustworthy data plan, few worthwhile apps, and a failing keyboard that no longer capitalized letters or typed the letter "t."

The next morning, a quiet Sunday, the first day of June, I readied for my Camino with the speed of a Formula One pit crew. I washed in minutes. I slathered my virgin feet with my anti-blister stick. I dressed with pride, like a penitent priest draping himself in his ceremonial vestments. It was six-thirty, and with no experienced pilgrim in my room to guide me, I had no idea if I was early or late after my new morning ritual.

I disregarded the elevator and stomped down the stairs. At that early hour, my heavy footfalls were the only sound in the hotel. My sudden presence in the lobby even startled the drowsy reception clerk. I slid my hotel key across his desk and headed for the door. There was no time for breakfast or conversation; I had to find my pilgrims.

"*Buen Camino*," the clerk called from behind his desk.

"*Gracias*," I replied as I emerged onto the street.

It was overcast, with billows of dark clouds threatening to dampen my first day of walking. It was chilly, but once I started trudging through the city, my body warmed up and felt more comfortable. The only disconcerting component of my morning walk were the obnoxious drunks littering the streets on their way home from their Saturday night revelries.

I received my fair share of "*Peregrino!* " taunts and a full complement of plastered Pamplonese as they asked me where I was from and pointed me in new and odd directions to confuse me. "Camino this way, my friend!" "Peregrino, where you from? *Alemania? Estados Unidos?* " "Peregrino, why you no talk to me?" "Camino closed today, I swear!" "Peregrino, you want a drink?" "Buen Camino, *bastardo!*"

No one bothered to approach me as long as I kept my head down and my pace quick. I had memorized the first few steps of my route, and I wasn't swayed by their misleading directions. Never straying from the border between the Old City Center and its southern expansion, I circled the exterior of the ancient quarter until I reached the official Camino path, where the medieval Calle Mayor intersected with the modern Calle de la Taconera.

It was outside the fortified Church of San Lorenzo, with its notable chapel dedicated to Pamplona's patron saint, San Fermin. It was the perfect Camino crossroad: old meets new with the remnants of military might and religious ritual on equal display.

Apart from the occasional car cruising along Calle de la Taconera, the entire area was deserted. Was I late? Where was everyone? I peered down the narrow Calle Mayor, anxiously hoping for someone to join me. But no one came.

Following my guidebook map, I crossed the street to walk along the edge of the Parque de la Taconera. At the end, I crossed the street again to another park, the Parque de la Vuelta del Castillo, where I encountered my first Camino marker.

It was a yellow sign, pointing north, with a silhouetted walking figure and the words "Camino de Santiago," followed by the symbol of a scallop shell. On the ground more shell markers were implanted into the cement walkway that crossed the park.

Why a shell? Some disciples avowed that St. James wore one around his neck as a reminder that he was a "fisher of men." Other myths contend that his dead body, or his coffin, or perhaps the beach where the Christian martyr washed ashore in Galicia, was covered in scallop shells.

More important to the Camino cause was the yellow-arrow system developed in the 1980s once the Camino was designated a European Cultural Route. You can find the yellow arrows everywhere: on sidewalks, on signposts, on building walls, on trees, even on large rocks at your feet. Each and every arrow points pilgrims toward Santiago. While non-pilgrims may view the arrows as unsightly specks of yellow graffiti, they remain beacons of support for lost peregrinos.

Crossing Parque de la Vuelta del Castillo, I was glad the shell markers were placed only a few meters apart. They served as a constant reminder that I was on the correct route out of town—until they stopped.

Approaching the edge of the park, I found only an intrusive roundabout on the street suggesting several alternative routes to follow. I tried each and every road, looking for a symbol to show me the way. Where were the shells? Where were the yellow arrows? Where was the crucial Camino sign?

I was thirty minutes into my Camino trek to re-connect with my wife . . . and I was hopelessly lost.

I consulted my guidebook, hoping it would point me in the right direction. It was written by a religious scholar named Joseph Burnsley, and I had begun to refer to it as my "Burnsley." And not in a flattering way.

"Halfway round the park watch out for arrows that veer off right . . ."

Wait, *right*? We were traveling in a diagonal. What arrows?

". . . pass under the busy ring road along the university campus . . ."

Under the road? How do I get *under* the road? And which buildings were the university campus?

"Continue to the roundabout veering right along the main road and left across the stone bridge . . ."

I'm in the suburbs! There's a stone bridge? Where was the river? Burnsley!!

I stood in the middle of the roundabout and surveyed my options again. Maybe this particular roundabout was the *wrong* roundabout. Maybe I had to retrace my steps into the park to find out if there were, indeed, arrows that pointed to the right that would lead me to the *correct* roundabout . . .

The problem was that there were no street names mentioned in many of the descriptions. That would have been helpful. Don't tell me to "follow this road" and "go under that road." Give me street names. Left on Easy Street; right on Obvious Avenue. Burnsley!!

Finally, a homeless man pushing an empty shopping cart emerged from the park. Even under the self-imposed duress of too much drink and too little sleep, the old man could sense my desperation from fifty meters away.

"Camino?!"

"Yes! I mean . . . *sí!*"

He gestured that I had to make a hard right turn and follow the main street that intersected with the park.

I walked along Avenida de Sancho El Fuerte on the lookout for anything that might get me back on track: a busy ring road, a university campus, a stone bridge, a river, a Camino sign, yellow arrows, shells in the sidewalk . . . anything. Ten minutes in, I felt the panic return. Was this even the correct street? Had the homeless man with the shopping cart misled me, like the Old Pamplona drunks had tried to do? Should I abandon the Camino and hail a taxi to take me to the next town? Where were the other pilgrims? Burnsley!!

Then I spied a garbage collector making his morning rounds, his yellow jacket a beacon of hope amidst the stench of the streetside trash.

Giving him little credit for knowing the English language and fearing a frustrating conversation, I kept it simple. "The Camino?" I added a shrug and a sad frown.

The garbage collector brightly nodded and pointed to the next block. Take that road.

As I headed for it, I saw it was Calle de la Fuente del Hierro. I recognized that name from my Burnsley. Mention of it had been buried under all the other descriptions about nearby albergues and alternate routes—but it matched up, and the shell markers were once again embedded in the sidewalk. Hallelujah! Forget Burnsley; give me garbage collectors and homeless men with empty shopping carts to lead the way.

Now, with my first Camino crisis under my belt, I deserved a caffeine boost to celebrate.

With the comforting shell markers under my feet, I kept my eyes peeled for the first sign of an open restaurant. A few doors down, a café window beckoned. I peered through the glass; it had the requisite coffee urns and pastries on display. The shop also had two customers carrying large backpacks. My first pilgrim sighting!

6

THE MOUNT OF FORGIVENESS

I ENTERED THE PAMPLONA café and was immediately greeted with a smile and a hearty "Hello!" from the pilgrims. That was more like it!

Soon armed with a cappuccino and a croissant, I shuffled to their table and asked if I could join them.

"Absolutely."

Kate and Janet, two English professors from Columbia University, were on a year-long sabbatical while they toured around Europe together. Kate was chatty and asked a lot of perfunctory questions about my life as Janet applied generous gobs of white sunscreen to her face and neck, even though the sun was not threatening to burn through the overcast sky.

I answered Kate's questions as briefly as I could, conveniently skipping over any discussion about my missing wife or my depressive days in Palma. I changed the subject once I noticed Kate's Burnsley on the table peeking out from under her napkin.

"You have that Burnsley too, huh? It got me lost this morning."

"Oh, we don't use it much," Kate replied.

"Just for accommodations," Janet confirmed.

"All you have to do is follow the arrows."

"Yeah, well, I apparently missed some arrows and ended up in some strange roundabout—"

"I hate those roundabouts!" agreed Janet.

"We've been walking since Saint Jean; you'll get used to it. Stick with us."

That was settled. I had befriended my first pilgrims. All I had needed was a Pamplona coffee shop.

We left the café together and found the rest of the route that morning well-marked; it was incredibly easy-going. Every few meters we spotted another shell or yellow arrow pointing us in the right direction.

And we did eventually pass "under the busy ring road along the university campus" and continue "to the roundabout veering right along main road and left across the stone bridge."

I stopped to reread that Burnsley passage again. Why had I been so confused? Was it me? Or was it Burnsley? He made it all sound so suspiciously close to the citadel park when, in fact, all these landmarks were kilometers apart, and the guiding information was buried in extraneous descriptions about alternative accommodations. Burnsley!!

I followed my new companions, unsure of the pilgrim protocol for walking along the trail. None of us felt compelled to engage in conversation. The only sound to break the silence beyond the occasional suggestion to "Look at that" or a status inquiry like "How you doing?" was the clickety-click of Kate and Janet's trekking poles.

I had seen the poles listed in Pam's recommended gear, but I had ignored them. They were meant to stabilize your body going up and down the steep slopes while easing the impact on your knees and legs. Some pilgrims swore by them. Some pilgrims couldn't be bothered. Some pilgrims preferred a large wooden stick (either purchased in a pilgrim store or discovered along a wooded trail). I dismissed them all as extraneous items that limited my mobility and unnecessarily filled my hands.

Clickety-click, clickety-click, clickety-click. They couldn't be ignored. Clickety-click, clickety-click, clickety-click. This could become annoying. Clickety-click, clickety-click, clickety-click. I would eventually tune them out.

Soon there were other things to concentrate on. Now that we were leaving the city, I could see new pilgrims farther up the path and more walkers strolling far behind us. We were ants in a single-file mission to reach Santiago de Compostela, spread out randomly along the endless Camino trail.

We began ascending into Cizur Menor, a sleepy suburban community about five kilometers outside the Old City Center and a short two kilometers from the University of Navarre. With its newly paved streets, red-brick sidewalks, and red-gable-roofed homes, it offered a cozy respite from the medieval madness of Pamplona.

Burnsley recommended it over the ancient city as the Day 3 stopping point. While it did boast modern conveniences and a suitable albergue, Cizur Menor clearly lacked the magnificent marvel of bustling Pamplona.

That's the moment I demoted my guidebook from respected Camino bible to a glorified suggestion box. How could anyone endorse somnolent Cizur Menor over medieval Pamplona? Burnsley!!

As we left the dreary bedroom community, the route shifted to a narrow footpath bordered by waist-high grain and grass. It was a gentle climb, for the moment, as we rambled through placid plains and over manageable mounds of earth toward the towering hills ahead.

Pilgrims now appeared in front of us and behind us. If they were slow, the three of us soon passed them on the path. If they were faster, they eventually caught up to us and carried on.

However, unlike the typical lack of manners demonstrated by freeway drivers during a rush-hour commute, showing respect on *this* road was sacrosanct. No one hogged the Camino highway! If someone was slower than you, you politely passed them on the left. If someone was faster than you, you moved over without incident.

And it was all done so cordially. None of this choreography was managed in silence. The passing pilgrim always offered a gracious greeting of "Hola" or "Buen Camino." Always. It was simple Camino courtesy. And the trailing pilgrim always replied with his own "Hola" or "Buen Camino." Always.

Now, what happens if you meet the same pilgrim along the path several times over the course of the day? (It happens more than you think. Everyone walks at different speeds and takes their meal and bathroom breaks at different times.) Are you required to once again greet them with a "Hola" or a "Buen Camino?" It's a judgment call. But, as I learned over the course of my Camino, there had better be eye contact and some sort of visual acknowledgment, like a wave of the hand or a nod of the head. Not responding to every single "Hola" or "Buen Camino" was downright rude and bad Camino karma.

So, like a long and tiring game of "Marco Polo" in someone's swimming pool, the words "Hola" and "Buen Camino" are infinitely repeated along the pilgrim path all day long. And, just like the clickety-click of the omnipresent trekking poles, those bursts of pilgrim politeness are soon tuned out and ignored.

The narrow footpath now pointed us to Zariquiegui. The Camino course was rising, and the fields of grain were replaced by heather and mountainous shrubs sprouting along the path. Beyond the village, wind turbines lined up on the approaching hill, and—right on cue—the breeze intensified and sent a chill down our backs.

We entered Zariquiegui after having walked over eleven kilometers; we had about twelve kilometers left to go before we reached the day's destination of Puente la Reina. We faced a steep ascent, so most pilgrims paused to rest and refresh themselves for the next push.

Without announcement or ceremony, Kate and Janet peeled off their backpacks and unloaded their lunches for a roadside feast. It was the distraction I needed, because I was nearing the location of Pam's next letter and I longed for some privacy.

With Kate and Janet content to sit on the street and eat their sandwiches, and many other pilgrims lining up for food inside the open café, I fortified myself with a chocolate bar and a cup of burnt coffee from a pair of vending machines outside the nearby grocery store.

Outside the store and the café, village life in Zariquiegui on a Sunday was non-existent. The hamlet housed just two hundred souls, and I suspected they were all hiding in their homes or possibly praying inside the thirteenth-century Church of Saint Andrew.

According to Burnsley, grand medieval churches like Saint Andrew's were prominent in every town along the Camino. While most of these historical landmarks were probably worth inspecting, few pilgrims took the time. We were saving our spiritual appointment for the final holy house in Santiago de Compostela to mark the end of our journey. Sorry. The other churches would just have to make do with the religious locals.

Boosted by my caffeine jolt of chocolate and coffee, I slipped away from the pilgrim pack and wandered on my own out of Zariquiegui. It was certainly a haunting little village, marked by the absence of its people and the separatist graffiti that scarred some of its buildings.

While Spain's constitutional monarchy represents the fifth largest country in Europe, the kingdom is, in fact, made up of over a dozen distinct regions that enjoy varying levels of power, autonomy, and self-government. Pamplona, for instance, is the capital city of Navarre, a former kingdom with its own traditions and institutions that retain a strong Basque influence.

The Basques are descendents of the Vascones, Europe's original aboriginal population, who have lived on the western side of the Pyrenees for thousands of years. When the Romans settled in Pamplona, the Vascones were allowed to continue their traditional way of life and retain their language and culture. After the fall of Rome, the Visigoths, the Franks, and then the conquering Moors tried but failed to drive them from of the mountains and wipe them out.

Eventually all the Basque tribes united under the banner of the Kingdom of Navarre, which pledged support to any major power that would leave them alone and let them self-govern. (They were even ruled by the French between 1234 and 1512.)

Finally, in 1513, the Spanish crown united the various territories across the country, including Navarre, and granted the region its own special privileges. The territory thus evolved over the centuries with a workable mix of Basque and Spanish cultures living peacefully together, who jointly opposed any national government that would try to take away their distinct rights.

This arrangement and understanding would get severely tested during the Spanish Civil War. The Basques supported the ruling Republicans, who promised more self-government opportunities, while the assimilated Navarrese supported the rebel Nationalists, led by General Francisco Franco, who were staunchly Catholic and anti-separatist. When Franco won, the dictator punished the Basques by banning their language. Later, the Basques struck back and assassinated the prime minister and possible successor to General Franco, Admiral Luis Carrero Blanco.

Today in Navarre, the Basque minority still exerts a strong influence in the region and regularly holds demonstrations to demand separation from Spain.

Meanwhile, on the Camino, the pilgrims are quite oblivious to such partisan politics, with every Camino sign and every Camino host conducting business solely in Spanish.

Nevertheless, on the walls of old buildings sprinkled along the rustic road, there was often a graffiti reminder that some in Navarre wanted nothing to do with Spain and its unifying Camino.

I separated myself from the village and marched steeply toward the imposing line of wind turbines, the roadside shrubs bowing their heads in the breeze.

Half an hour later, I was on the peak of Alto del Perdón, the Mount of Forgiveness, which represented the highest point of the day and probably its most spectacular setting. Forty wind turbines commanded the ridge, twisting and wheezing in the blustery breeze and supplying Pamplona with a large proportion of its electricity.

The lofty location was worth a long look, not only to mark my morning progress from Pamplona but for its panoramic view of the rest of my hike to Puente la Reina, with the villages of Uterga, Muruzábal, and Obanos dotting my descent.

The area was also significant for its cast-iron sculptures dedicated to the pilgrims. Erected in 1996, the silhouettes of medieval peregrinos on foot and on horseback, along with two donkeys and a dog, pointed westward toward Santiago.

Many pilgrims paused only briefly to gape at the sculpture before turning back to the trail. Others stopped just long enough to take a quick photo of themselves among the cast-iron cut-outs.

I, however, was in no rush to reach Puente la Reina. I had an assignment. I produced Pam's Clue Sheet from my pocket and verified her next hint. *"Dig under the second donkey."*

There were only two donkey figures, and I assumed it was the beast of burden posing on the right side of the sculpture. As I inspected the ground, I noticed a small patch of dirt had been overturned and tilled between the donkey's hind legs. How long ago, I couldn't be sure, but it was the only strip of soil surrounding the sculpture that was free from stones.

I lowered my backpack to the ground, retrieved my small hand shovel, and began to dig. I didn't get very far.

"Excuse me. Do you mind taking a picture of us?"

I soon became the unofficial photographer of Alto del Perdón. Pilgrim after pilgrim approached me to request that I take a photo of them standing among the silhouettes. Individual pilgrims. Groups of pilgrims. Some spoke English. Some spoke Spanish. Some merely pointed at me and then at their cameras. Everyone posed; everyone smiled; everyone nodded their thanks when I was done. Nobody seemed to mind that they were interrupting my mini Indiana Jones expedition.

After a dozen or so requests, I finally fell to my knees and began digging in earnest. Breaking through the surface of the soil, it took only a few jabs of my shovel before I struck something solid.

"Hiya! . . . Excuse me. . . Hellooo! I know you can hear me."

I pivoted to find a pleasant-looking pilgrim leaning against her trekking poles and swaying against the wind. She was pale and lean with a mess of sandy curls that completely covered her forehead and obscured the top of her face. What could be seen were her big hazel eyes below thick eyebrows that presided over her thin lips and the deep dimples in her cheeks.

"You leavin' somethin' behind?"

"Actually, it's kind of the opposite."

She was British with a surprising set of shiny, perfect teeth. London, maybe. Not posh or upper class—but definitely far removed from the Cockney environs of an Eliza Doolittle.

"Well, when you're all sorted, you think you can take my photo?"

Moments later, I had uncovered a wooden cigar box. Although I was anxious to open it and devour Pam's next letter, I was compelled by the pale pilgrim's intrusive curiosity to slip it into a pocket of my backpack for a later peek. I wanted to read it in complete privacy. This letter was for me and me alone, and I didn't want to share its contents with anyone.

"What is that?"

"Nothing."

"Go on, give us a look."

"I'll look at it later."

"How did you know it was there?"

"Look, do you want your photo now or what?"

She dropped the questioning and posed where I had been digging. Intent on the perfect photo, she brushed away the drooping strands of hair from her eyes. Each time I pushed the button on her camera, however, her hair fell to cover the top of her face. After six or seven attempts, she finally accepted one of the shots.

"You should consider a haircut."

She shrugged at my suggestion and stumbled ahead; I noticed a significant limp hampered her step.

Unfortunately, my indulgence of the curious Londoner compelled several other pilgrims to recruit me to document their own moment on the mountain with a personal photo.

Eventually escaping my paparazzi duties, I trekked down the mountain; I was careful not to trip over the loose rocks on the trail or bump into the walking wounded who plugged up the path, wincing with every swivel of their knees and every twist of their ankles.

While most pilgrims prided themselves on their courtesy, swiftly stepping aside for faster walkers and extending a friendly "Hola" or "Buen Camino" to everyone on the trail, the same can't be said for those *other* pilgrims on the path: the notorious bikers.

Obviously, they were much quicker than the pedestrian pilgrims and, unfortunately, seemed to have little respect for the rules of the road. Speeding down the hill, they announced their sudden appearance with the ring of a bell or an indecipherable holler.

As I climbed up Alto del Perdón, their presence was less surprising but just as intrusive. We walkers were expected to scramble out of their way because they were on a bike. Why should they slow down? Why should they steer to avoid hitting a hiker? You couldn't expect them to actually stop and dismount for a moment, could you? They were on bikes, so they must have the right of way!

They were, after all, part of an exclusive Camino club. They spoke only to other bikers. They ate their meals only with other bikers. They always roomed together in separate albergues and hotels. And they all seemed to shop at the same tawdry bike shop stocked with loud neon shirts and lurid Lycra pants, now wedged into every available crevice.

To be fair, they were a fleeting nuisance—because, unlike the other walking pilgrims you might see several times throughout the day, you were assured you'd never see them again. While we were struggling to achieve twenty to thirty kilometers a day, the breakneck bikers were covering that same distance before they broke for lunch.

It was while I was scrambling out of the way of a pair of biker bullies that I ran into the nosy Brit pilgrim again.

"Oh, sorry!" I cried as my shoulder nudged her backpack. The impact was minimal, but the effect was more significant as her foot slid off the path and her body braced for a tumble into the shrubs lining the path.

I planted my feet and grabbed her arm, saving her from a fall.

"Sorry," I repeated as she pushed off her slender legs and precariously regained her upright position.

"Bloody bikers," she snapped.

"Are you all right?"

"Well, you saved me from a bit of nastiness, so cheers."

"I mean, you have a limp."

"Courtesy Saint-Jean-Pied-de-Port. Massive blisters and a poxy knee on the first day; I should get a medal or somethin'."

"Well, you do get a certificate at the end—"

"Too right!"

"*If* you make it."

"What?"

I immediately regretted my pragmatism. "Nothing."

"No, you said something."

"Well . . . not everyone makes it, right? Some pilgrims get too hurt, so they can't finish. Some just give up…"

Her quick smile melted into a lasting look of disapproval. "You can let go of my elbow now."

I apologized for suggesting she might not complete her Camino, but it did little good. She shrugged off the apology, and I followed her in silence until the potential for a tumbling descent was over and the trail leveled off again.

Finally, we could lift our heads away from the hazardous loose stones and soak up the stunning valley. Grasslands broke up the almond trees and vineyards that spread across the basin in patches of gold and all shades of pale and pastel green. The sky was breaking up, too, sending us heavenly sunshine that soon made us thankful for the overgrown shrubs along the path offering occasional pools of shade.

"So, my name is Brie," the nosy Brit finally announced.

"Brie. Like the cheese—"

"French cheese, thank you very much. Bit of a clanger from me mum, since we're not too keen on the French—oh, sorry! Are you French?"

"Do I have a French accent?"

"You can never be sure."

"Well, I'm Canadian."

"Well, that's half-French, innit?"

"So, I guess you're only half-sorry."

"Let's go with that, then." Brie smiled. "I absolutely blather on about the dumbest things; that's the truth, don't mind me at all. I'm always getting my mouth into loads of trouble."

"No prob—"

"My husband was always telling me to shut it. 'Shut it, Brie,' he'd say. 'Just shut it.' But I didn't listen; I kept rabbiting on and on. It didn't matter what I was on about. Sometimes it seemed important. But sometimes it was just to fill the silences, you know? Oh, he hated it, that's for sure. And then I'd rabbit on some more."

"Right—"

"Martin. That's my husband's name. Not a bad bloke, I guess. Well, not in the beginning, of course. He was decent then. Or maybe he was; maybe he wasn't—being in love and all that, who could tell? That all changed later. That's just the way it is, innit? You're in love and everything's fine one minute and then suddenly it's not fine and you're not in love anymore and you wonder, 'Hold on! Where did my life go?'"

Was I supposed to answer her? Brie's pause was just long enough to function as a demand for a response, but I was too late.

"I guess that's why we're here on this walk: trying to figure it all out, yeah? Trying to figure out what went wrong and what went right? Well, not all of us, of course. I can't speak for everybody, that's for sure. Nobody else on this walk was married to Martin—"

Brie stopped walking and grabbed my arm.

"You hear that?"

"No. What?"

"I just said '*was.*' Was married to Martin. Bloody hell, that's the first time I ever said *that* out loud! That is massive, that is!"

Was I supposed to answer? Brie paused again, but all I could manage was a nod. That was enough. She let out a loud whoop and surged ahead. And for one brief, euphoric moment, her limp disappeared.

Then Brie turned back to me in horror.

"What's your name? Bloody hell, I didn't give you a chance."

"It's okay." Her shocked expression was so amplified in relation to such an insignificant gaffe that, for a moment, I completely forgot her question.

"Well?"

"Oh! Umm. Jamie. Jamie Draper."

"Jamie Draper. That's a fine name, that is, Jamie Draper."

With that settled and my name approved, Brie resumed her slow pace along the path. Her limp was back, too.

"Now what am I going to call *myself*? That's the new question, innit? Brie Baxter, that's the old me. Well, the married me. 'Martin's wife,' that's what his friends called me. Never Brie. Never Brie Baxter. 'Martin's wife.' 'The missus.' My own name didn't matter. 'Martin, you and the wife going to have us over for drinks?' Well, bollocks to that—those days are done. Now it's going to be 'I'm going to pop down to Brie's.' 'Which Brie?' they'll ask. 'Why, Brie Bletcher. She's taken her own name back. Martin's out of the picture.' And good riddance too!'"

This one-sided conversation continued through the villages of Uterga and Muruzábal. I waited for an opportune moment to escape, but Brie never took a breath. Her conversation was full of whimsical observances and rhetorical questions that didn't require input from me, apart from nods and meaningless phrases like "I see" and "I guess so" just to prove I was listening. I didn't retain much.

Martin sounded like a ghastly husband who had mistreated Brie, showing rude indifference and a preference for late-night pints with his mates. Her older sister, Marigold, wasn't much help. She was wallowing in her own loveless marriage to a mechanic named Clive and didn't approve of Brie's divorce. Splitting up was too easy, she thought. Marriage was meant to be a lifetime of compromises amid a steady slog of chores. Brie's parents were even more divisive, with Mum pitying Brie and blaming herself for being an unqualified mentor while alcoholic Dad sided with Martin and his thirst for late-night brew.

My continued audience to Brie's exhaustive monologue was likely due to the lingering guilt I felt for suggesting she might not reach Santiago de Compostela. Limping or not, she certainly needed to complete her Camino, if only to prove to herself and everybody around her that she was indeed strong and independent again, free to focus on any personal mission she felt worthy to accomplish.

It was only when we entered Obanos that she noticed her sluggish pace was causing me to practically limp myself in order to justify our slow speed.

"You can walk ahead, you know."

"I don't want to be rude."

"Oh, please. I've been blathering on and on, and you deserve a break. Plus, you never opened your prezzie from the hill."

I hesitated to leave her behind. It felt like the Titanic was going down and I was jumping the lifeboat queue in front of the women and children.

"Go on. You've been gagging for it ever since you took my picture."

"I'm sure I'll see you around," I said, even though it felt like a permanent parting.

"I'm sure of it!"

I waved goodbye and propelled myself ahead.

Brie yelled, "You've been good company! And that's the truth."

I waved back at Brie again and searched for a convenient space to be alone. I found it in Obanos's medieval town square. Patient pilgrims gathered by the water fountain to take photos of the neo-Gothic church while the anxious ones darted through the adjacent archway to secure their beds in nearby Puente la Reina. Locals lazed in the shaded periphery, indifferent to all the Camino fuss.

I headed for the church's shadowed cloister. It was a Sunday afternoon, but the front doors remain shuttered. The tourists didn't dare to inspect its interior; the locals didn't bother with its cooling cover.

The skull of St. William was housed here. The legend goes that in the fourteenth century, the Duke of Aquitaine and his children embarked on the Camino. His daughter, Felicia, was so moved by the experience that she gave up her life in court and chose to live the rest of her days in Navarre as a hermit. Then her brother, William, located her and grew so incensed by Felicia's rejection of her royal duties that he killed her in a fit of rage. Naturally, the remorseful brother then walked the Camino himself for penance and returned a changed man. Mirroring his sister's sacrifice, he also gave up his privileged life in court to spend the rest of his life living in poverty and helping the poor pilgrims.

There is little record, however, that any of this actually happened. Still, William's body (or somebody's body) is buried in the monastery on the hill, while his skull (or somebody's skull) is kept inside a fancy case in the church. And he's worshiped as a saint. I guess we're supposed to forgive and forget the fact that he once killed his own sister!

Seated alone in the church's cloister, I removed the wooden cigar box from my backpack. I sat against the front wall of the church and caressed the fine finish of Pam's prop. This was the first of my wife's proper letters. The previous messages were motivational speeches designed to compel me to join the cult of the Camino. Here, finally, was her assessment of our marriage; this was her maddening method of avoiding face-to-face confrontation.

I finally opened the lid and unfolded her handwritten letter. I took a long breath and skimmed the first page, looking for clues to the content and its overall tone. As my eyes danced over the words, I knew Pam's apologies were over. This wasn't going to be a very pleasant read.

7

THE LETTER OF CONFESSIONS

Dear Jamie,

Well, you're in it deep now, aren't you? Welcome to the Camino! Didn't you just loooove the walk today? Sure, it was mostly uphill, but didn't you love that view? You just can't get views like that in Toronto. Windy too, I bet. Luckily, I had sunshine on my day. Some of the others on the Camino had showers. I'm sure it's a whole different experience in the muck and the rain.

All right, stop rolling your eyes; I'm getting to it!

How did she do that? My wife was probably hundreds of miles away and yet she always knew when I was rolling my eyes.

Listen...I have to start at the beginning. Hear me out here, be patient for a second. The beginning of our marriage was wonderful and beautiful and exciting. To be honest, the beginning was my favorite part!

Now, now don't start thinking that our marriage was a chore, <u>because it wasn't</u>! It's just that we weren't madly in love anymore. We were once. I want to say we once were "lovers" but it sounds so dirty—but that's what we were! Sex in the car, sex in the park, sex at my mother's house, sex on that ugly Italian furniture with the plastic covering!!

And you were always so sweet! That's what made me fall in love with you. It wasn't the sex and the late-night talks and the romantic letters—although that was part of it too.

It was the little things you did. Remember that Smart Set job I had when we first met? Remember when you first showed up at my work? I had just had another bad day fighting with Mrs. Barkley about God knows what. I fought every day with that woman . . .

Pam always hated her jobs. If it wasn't that retail gig at Smart Set, it was the secretarial pool at the temp agency, or when she was tending bar on King Street, or when she was writing those ads for that miserable ad agency. Come to think of it, I always hated my jobs, too. Misery certainly loves company.

So what did you do—without even knowing it? You surprised me at work holding flowers and didn't say a thing. You saw that I was upset and you just gave me those flowers and held my hand. I'm not going to lie: my heart melted that day. It was <u>those kinds of gestures</u> that made me fall in love with you. You knew me. You <u>got</u> me! If I started talking about my stupid day it would have just led to tears and stupid shit that I probably would have regretted. You did the one thing that made me feel better. And loved. You showed that you were thinking about me, that you couldn't wait to see me, and that you wanted to surprise me with something beautiful. You know what? I actually kept those flowers for weeks and weeks and even dried them and put them in a scrapbook—which I eventually lost in the move to our apartment, but whatever.

She kept a scrapbook? I think I found that scrapbook when I unpacked the boxes. And I think I threw it away, too . . .

So what happened to all those moments, Jamie? Let's face it. Everything changed the moment we got engaged. I'm not saying my mother was right—she's wrong about just about everything else—but she nailed it when she said we weren't ready. All that wedding planning sucked the romance out of our relationship.

Why did we have to go so big? Why did I have five bridesmaids? You know how many of them I still see today? One! Janet. But only when she finds a babysitter for a couple of hours and we can have a quick brunch.

Now she tells me! I had a hell of a time finding five grooms-men. It was difficult enough finding three men in the whole world I actually liked. I had to bribe two other teachers at school just to stand with me in the church to complete the set. I even had to rent their suits.

We should have eloped or had a small ceremony in a small church with no bridesmaids and just a couple of witnesses. At least the wedding wouldn't seem like such a waste of money right now.

Our marriage was fine—don't get me wrong. You were a great husband. You were attentive, you made me laugh, you did all the things you were supposed to. But I have to be honest: it isn't enough. Not anymore. Not for me.

The magic just . . . ended. It was like suddenly we were just friends-with-benefits living together. And then the benefits stopped. And then what were we? Companions? Business partners tied to a mortgage with a TV that was too big for the living room?

"The TV was fine! The room was just too small." Why did that bother me? She was kicking the shit out my heart and I was suddenly defensive about the size of my TV.

It's my fault too, of course. I lost the magic too. I don't know; maybe it was the job, maybe it was my mother, maybe it was that shitty apartment. But everything about my life started to depress me.

And we both got so complacent. Is that fair? I think we both lost the will to do all those sweet little special things that used to mean underline everything. We were just sooooo tiiiiiiiired all the time!

Janet says she and Brad have a date night once a month. Why didn't we do that? We didn't have any kids. We didn't have to find a babysitter. We had the time.

And why didn't we go anywhere? Damn it, Jamie; I got paper cuts from all those fucking travel magazines.

Look, I know, date nights and trips to tropical islands might have only been temporary solutions to our problems. But at least I would have better memories to look back on now. I'd rather remember a romantic week in Santorini than feeling helpless because I lost a scrapbook with dead flowers in it.

But hey, that stuff's on both of us. We both failed at this marriage thing. I didn't try either. I got too comfortable and lazy and stuck to the same routine, just like you.

I didn't insist on anything. I didn't want to start a fight with you. But you know what? Maybe I should have. Maybe I should have fought you on this complacent bullshit. We both should have fought for our marriage!

I know, I know: there was this past summer after we separated. But by that time I had already given up. I still loved you but I hated our life in that apartment. I just wanted to get out of that building every chance I got and just go for long walks and take my Spanish class and take my cooking class or whatever.

Yeah, I took a cooking class! Just to get out of that damn apartment. But I certainly didn't use anything I learned. You know why? Because every time I went to the grocery store and thought about the food I needed to cook to try out a new recipe, I just couldn't be bothered.

It was that apartment. Not as an actual living space or any-thing—and not as the place where _you_ lived. But just as a stupid symbol of what was bothering me. It was a couple of rooms on a noisy street with ugly gray walls—and they were crushing me. Does that make sense? I needed space!

I appreciate that you found some therapists to check out, but I already knew what I needed without some expensive, pointless therapy. I had to get out. Have an adventure. Have time to think. Have time for me—and only me. Bottom line.

Well, nooooo, wait a minute. That's not entirely true. That's not the bottom line. There's more, Jamie. And you'll find out about that in the next letter.

Right now just think about what I said. If you disagree, you've got plenty of time to argue with me and get it out of your system before the next letter. But that's how I felt.

> *Take care, Jamie. I love you. Try to enjoy the Camino. Make some friends. Get drunk tonight.*
>
> *Love, Pam*

Holy . . . shit. . . . "If I disagree?" How could I disagree? If that's how Pam felt, that's how she felt.

I couldn't move. I sat against the church wall for five minutes . . . ten minutes . . . thirty minutes . . . maybe more . . .

I was numb. Not angry. Not despondent. Numb.

"Try to enjoy the Camino"? "Make some friends"? Neither seemed possible. "Get drunk tonight"? I could possibly manage that.

Stuffing the letter into my pocket, I hoisted the pack onto my shoulders and retreated through the town square without the usual routine of untwisting the straps, fastening the clasps, and fiddling with all the length adjustments. I even forgot the cigar box.

I was only about two kilometers away from my day's destination, but I couldn't enjoy any of the scenery, compelling as it was. There was a dirt track running alongside a farm; that's the last thing I remember. I don't recall my approach to the outskirts of Puente la Reina.

The letter's hurtful themes kept replaying in my mind. "Sucked all the romance . . . the magic ended . . . business partners . . . tired all the time . . . date nights . . . paper cuts . . . dead flowers . . . already given up . . . cooking class . . . pointless therapy . . ." And then this gem: *"I had to get out. Have an adventure. Have time to think. Have time for me—and only me. Bottom line. Well, nooooo, wait a minute. That's not entirely true. That's not the bottom line. There's more, Jamie. And you'll find out about that in the next letter."*

What the hell was that? Pam's cruel idea of a cliffhanger?

Outside Puente la Reina I was greeted by a metal statue of a pilgrim. He looked peaceful in his hat, his right hand holding a wooden staff, his cloak blowing in the wind, his smiling face showcasing an impressive beard. No backpack, no worse for wear. Damn, he even looked smug.

The metallic pilgrim was standing alone on a traffic island where two roads intersected, merging the Camino Francés with the Camino Aragonés (which originated in the French city of Arles and entered the French-Spanish mountain pass of Sombort).

I could see no pilgrim from either route. It was just me and the smug statue. Pam's comments vanished from my mind as I took a physical inventory. I was thirsty and out of water, I hadn't eaten since the Zariquiegui vending machines, and I needed a bed for the night. The bed was the priority. It was only early afternoon, but I was probably too late for a favorable albergue booking. I retrieved my Burnsley and scoured the Puente la Reina pages.

"Jamie! Hiya! Over here!"

Brie was waving at me from across the road. Her backpack was gone. Her clothes were clean. Her hair was wet.

I walked back along the road, mustering a fake smile to hide my ongoing disappointment about Pam's confession.

"There's a spot back there at the albergue. It's full, but I saved it for you. Didn't you see me wave? You walked right past the entrance; it's right behind those trees. Did you already have a place? Are you staying in the hotel? I got it all sorted for you in the albergue if you want it."

"Thanks, but—"

"I saw you at the church but just kept walking. I thought you'd catch up to me but, nope, you were too slow. So I just walked into that albergue and said I needed two beds. I promised him you'd come, but it's your choice and all that, so don't feel any pressure or anything. But if you don't come there's going to be a lot of people disappointed. He's turned away loads. So…what do you say?"

What could I say? I nodded and followed Brie.

It was the first albergue mentioned in Burnsley, located in the basement of the Hotel Jakue. Hotel guests paid for queen-size beds in private rooms with maid service. Pilgrim guests paid for a mattress on an underground bunk bed where everything was do-it-yourself.

The albergue had its own reception pavilion outside the hotel. Several pilgrims milled about the benches, discussing their options. These must have been the pilgrims turned away by the *hospitalero*, the official host of the albergue, a volunteer who had previously walked the Camino and wanted to give back to the community.

The young man with the bucket of unruly hair seemed agitated by those lingering walkers outside his office until he saw me approach with Brie. She had been true to her word and hadn't made him a liar to the others.

We were asked to sit down across from his desk, and I presented my passport and my credential. Slowly and oh so diligently, he wrote my personal information into his registry. There were no computers on the Camino. Not yet. This was a handwritten procedure. And damn it if he wasn't going to take his time with the paperwork.

I paid my ten-euro fee and received my first earned stamp in my credential. It was a handsome stamp advertising the Albergue Jakue with a caption across the top that read, *"Y desde aqui todas los caminos se hacen uno"* ("And from here all the roads become one").

I admired my stamp, which symbolized more than an ink stain in my pilgrim passport. It represented the introductory 24.1 kilometers (according to Burnsley) of my potentially life-changing journey.

After securing accommodation and paying in advance (no one would be around in the morning to take your money), it was important to verify the curfew situation . . . just in case.

Yes, the price you paid for your budget bed was to be treated like a child. Ten o'clock was the usual bedtime. That meant the front door was locked up for the night at exactly nine fifty-nine. You're late? Come back at dawn. That also meant the lights in your room would be extinguished at precisely one minute after ten. Want to read? Suffer the scorn from your new roommates.

Those were the rules. You paid very little for that bed, so lie in it and shut up.

The truth is, most pilgrims welcomed the strict nighttime routine. It meant a proper sleep before the next day's walk. Most were exhausted by ten o'clock anyway. They had been walking since dawn; they had been drinking since lunchtime; they were ready to lie down, close their eyes, and dream of Santiago.

"So, curfew's ten o'clock?" I asked…just in case.

"Sí, sí, sí," the hospitalero nodded. "I show you the bed."

"No, I got it," Brie proposed.

The hospitalero handed me a plastic bag containing a sheet for my mattress and a pillowcase for my pillow.

I followed Brie down the stairs and obeyed the posted sign to remove my shoes and place them on the outdoor rack. The pilgrim way requires you to have faith that your shoes will be there on your return. I wasn't worried. I had big feet.

The albergue had the usual amenities afforded to the do-it-yourself pilgrim: a kitchen, a dining room, a bathroom each for women and men, a laundry room, an outdoor clothesline around the back, and a sleeping area. This particular sleeping area was comprised of two rooms containing twenty bunk beds separated by dividers into four-person cubicles. Not bad for ten euros.

After the long walk, there was no immediate rest for the weary. It was time for the daily chores, which everyone did without hesitation or complaint.

The first task was to make your bed. If you were one of the first pilgrims in the room, it served as a proper claim to your territory. At the Albergue Jakue, however, I didn't have any bedding options. I was sleeping above Brie.

"They always give the healthy blokes the top bunks. I'm always at the bottom. Maybe on account of my dodgy leg, maybe on account of me being a lady—I don't rightly know—but I can't complain. I get up to widdle at night sometimes and I don't want to fall and break my leg—the dodgy one or the other one."

"It's fine."

"If you have to get up to widdle tonight, don't mind me. I can sleep through anything. Martin used to toss and turn like a firecracker all night and I still slept just fine. I just budged up to my side of the bed, that's all."

After tucking in my sheet and covering my pillow, I spread out my sleeping bag. Every pilgrim had one. There were never any blankets inside these albergues, and you only got one bed sheet per person.

Next, I burrowed through my bag to grab my clean clothes, my quick-drying towel, and my toiletry bag. Then I stored my backpack in the one empty locker near my bed. I found out later during my walk that lockers were actually a luxury. Usually you stored your backpack at the base of the bed or against the wall. Again, the pilgrim way requires you to have faith that your backpack and its contents will be there on your return.

I headed for the bathroom and took a long shower, preoccupied with Pam's unflattering opinion of my marriage rattling around in my mind.

The fact there was another letter the following day kept me hopeful. Perhaps the next day's message would show a change of heart. Perhaps Pam would offer some form of an apology. Perhaps she had a more positive spin on the gloom and doom of her initial assessment of our marriage.

"Hey, Jamie, I don't need my space anymore. After all, I walked the Camino! So let's check out those therapists you found online. And you know what? It wasn't a shitty apartment; I was just lashing out. And the size of the TV was just fine. Let's go home and I'll show you what I learned in cooking class."

Perhaps I was laying it on a little too thick . . .

Clean and comfortable for the first time since I left my Pamplona hotel, I found Brie sitting on her bunk bed. Not napping like some of the other tired pilgrims. Not reading. Just sitting there. Smiling. Waiting.

"Right as rain now, aren't you, Jamie Draper?"

She followed me to the laundry room as I washed my clothes in the sink. She followed me outside as I hung up my clothes to dry. She followed me back to my bed as I snagged my Burnsley to read more about Puente la Reina.

All the while, she talked and talked and filled in more details about her dysfunctional family.

Martin had been a carpenter until he fell off a ladder and hurt his back. Now he collected disability pay and did odd jobs around the neighborhood—when he wasn't sitting in his local pub playing the video slot machines.

Marigold and Clive had never left England, although Clive always promised to drive Marigold to Edinburgh for New Year's Eve. Each year, however, he'd drink too much the night before and spend the last day of the year battling a hangover and yelling at the local children to stop banging pots and lighting firecrackers.

Meanwhile, Brie's mother had cultivated the fear that Brie would eventually become a lesbian because her marriage had fallen apart. The same thing had happened to her cousin's next-door neighbor, so she had it on good authority. Now Brie's mother was on a mission to get her married again, as soon as possible, before her so-called "lesbian instincts" took over her body.

I finally tossed my guidebook aside and jumped down to the floor. "Let's go eat."

"You inviting me along?"

"Of course."

I still hadn't eaten since the Zariquiegui vending machines. And Brie was going to follow me anyway.

Our search for food and entertainment would be compromised, since it was still the middle of the afternoon. That meant we were trapped inside the notorious Spanish siesta period, when most of the stores and restaurants would be temporarily closed. Most of us pilgrims came to hate the dreaded siesta.

It was certainly ill-timed for the visiting pilgrim. After your long walk and your mad scramble to secure a bed, the town of your choice would now ignore you for a few hours during its daily hibernation. It felt like a Spanish conspiracy. "Hey tourist, you need medical attention? You'll have to wait. You want to go shopping for supplies? You'll have to wait." The confounding thing is, the smaller the town, the more things that were closed. (Only the cities could accommodate you. While many stores and restaurants would be temporarily closed, a few go-getters relished the reduced competition and stayed open for the wide-awake tourists.)

Brie and I agreed that the first place we found open that served food—any food—would be our desired destination. This was no time to be picky. Walking along the service street (the road that followed the Camino Aragonés), we soon found a lonely bar packed with pilgrims and inebriated locals.

Brie was in her element. All the pilgrims seemed to know her, and all the inebriated locals wanted to *get to know her* and buy her a drink. Deftly fending off her new admirers, Brie managed to round up a few tasty tapas and a round of beers while I secured a table for us on the sidewalk.

Soon we were joined by other pilgrims Brie had met along the way since starting out in Saint-Jean-Pied-de-Port.

There was Wendy, the lawyer from San Diego who broke up with her boyfriend after he brought home a gun. He said it was to protect them from home invaders. She said it highlighted his increasingly violent nature.

There was Brian, the unemployed New Yorker who had traded walking around Manhattan in search of a job for walking across Spain in search of a higher purpose.

There was divorced Colleen from Melbourne, who hated her administrative job and had threatened to quit unless she received a six-month leave of absence. She had already developed a crush on Jock from Edinburgh, who, the previous year, had walked the last leg of the Camino from Sarria and now had a pilgrim girlfriend waiting for him in Santiago. (This revelation failed to dampen Colleen's ill-advised crush.)

There was also Sarah, the interior designer from Amsterdam who had left her friends behind in Larrasoaña because they walked too slow and argued too much.

Then there was Holly, the nineteen-year-old college student from Mississippi whose grandma had cajoled her to walk the Camino to gain some valuable life experience—without any training or proper walking shoes. Four days into her journey, Holly's feet were so blistered and battered the Albergue Jakue took pity on her and insisted she rest there for a few days. (It should be noted that her naive grandma had never walked the Camino herself.)

Even my first pilgrim friends, Kate and Janet, joined us. And they knew Brie too!

I was introduced to each one of them as Jamie the quiet Canadian. It wasn't exactly accurate, and it didn't remotely reflect my personality. However, Brie's tidal wave of conversation limited my output, so I must have made no further impression upon the Brit beyond my name and my home country.

Watching Brie engage with everyone in her own bubbly way did enchant me. Alone with her, she was a leaky verbal faucet that you couldn't turn off. Surrounded by pilgrim friends, she was a volcano of energy that made everyone feel engaged and comfortable. It was like taking the most popular girl in school to the prom. Everyone watched her and everyone tried their best to attract her attention.

The distraction was welcoming. Rather than brooding in my bed about my wife's harsh criticism of our listless marriage, I was meeting new people from around the world—each person with their own set of problems back home as they slogged across Spain.

The state of our feet dominated the early discussion. It was the one thing that bound us all together and gave us the most concern. "How's your feet?" was a legitimate first question to anyone you might meet on the Camino. "How's your blisters?" "What cream do you use?" "Have you seen a pharmacist?" Those of us without blemishes were envied. Those of us with podiatric problems were pitied. Holly from Mississippi was worse than pitied. She was feared. "That could happen to *me*!"

Our foot deliberation was closely followed by the question "How did you sleep last night?" Everything apparently worked against you to achieve any kind of bedtime bliss on the Camino. The early curfew, the unfamiliar town, the uncomfortable bed, the lack of privacy, the nagging injuries to your legs and feet, the nightly worry about where you were headed next day, the early risers, the loud talkers, and the most notorious of all: the snorers. I hadn't slept one night on the Camino and I was already growing anxious about the approaching darkness.

Next came a recap of everyone's daily diet. What they ate that day, where they ate it, what they liked, what they didn't like, where they planned to eat next, and, from the Americans, what food they missed from home. That's when the diet discussion usually ended. As soon as they started complaining about the lack of ketchup in Spain or how they craved a McFastFood joint here and there, the Europeans teased them into silence.

After all the body talk came the actual Camino experience. This was when the group often broke into smaller pilgrim pods, and it became more personal. "Where did you start your Camino?" "What do you think so far?" "What did you think of today?" "What have you heard about tomorrow?" "Are you walking the whole thing?" (Scottish Jock had already walked the last leg and was now walking the first leg. New York Brian was walking only as far as his dwindling money would take him. Mississippi Holly was unsure if she could ever walk another step.)

This was closely followed by everyone's own walk of life. "Where are you from?" "What was your job?" "What did you leave behind?" And then the big question: "Why are you walking the Camino and what do you hope to get out of it?"

Moments ago, we were complete strangers. Soon we were advertising our deepest and darkest secrets. Then we were admitting our faults and our failures. And then we were articulating our hopes and dreams for the Camino and beyond.

It felt strangely safe. While friends and family back home might ignore you or judge you, these new Camino friends listened intently and embraced you—and your flaws. You could be physically hurt, mentally damaged, spiritually suffering; feeling empty, lost, angry, depressed, or just adventurous—all was accepted and all was entirely valid. It was, after all, the Camino: the most engrossing and rewarding therapy session of your lifetime.

At our Puente la Reina roundtable, I didn't have a personal pod. It wasn't intentional or anything. I hadn't contributed my opinions in the preceding group discussion, so I was largely left out of the one-on-one confessions. I didn't mind.

I was actually relieved to be left out. It was only my first day. The others had walked for three or more days and were already in the habit of sharing their private lives. I wasn't ready. No one needed to hear about my broken marriage and my mission to reunite with my wife. Not yet.

Someone from our roundtable announced it was five o'clock. Siesta was officially over. It was time to explore, shop for supplies, take some photos, and choose a dinner destination.

It didn't take long. There wasn't much to explore in Puente la Reina. The town consisted of one major street with two parallel lanes lined with houses and places of worship. Then there was the service road that led to the nearby highway.

We paid our bar tab and walked as a group down the main street, Calle Mayor, which was charming enough, with each ancient building identified with a coat of arms either mounted on the brick walls or on the solid iron doors. The street's Iglesia del Crucifijo was also briefly admired, and someone noted that its twelfth-century foundation was built by the Knights Templar. The church was equally famous for its fourteenth-century wooden crucifix, which hung in the northern apse. No one, however, ventured inside to check it out. Siesta alcohol had taken its toll, and a sumptuous dinner became the new priority.

Scottish Jock and Melbourne Colleen walked ahead to check out the famous bridge the town was named for—Puente la Reina means Queen's Bridge. The rest of us turned for Calle Mayor's only public square to order more drinks from the first available restaurant.

Soon we were joined by a few more pilgrim friends—each one at the behest of the prattling Brie. Everyone knew Brie!

Now there was April, the humble violin player from Harvard University. Betsy, the posh South African den mother, who made it her mission to take care of all the girls and ensure they were safe and eating well. And Abram, the grumpy Dutchman, who had walked the Camino two years ago but didn't want to talk much about it.

Because there were new faces at the patio table, we had to recycle through all the usual topics—much to the loud disapproval of Grumpy Abram.

First, there was the state of our feet again.

"Always, the feet!"

Then the trouble with sleeping.

"You don't go on Camino to sleep!"

Once again we discussed the day's culinary adventures.

"Eat good at home! Here, you eat what they give you!"

By the time we reached a repeat of our reflections on the Camino experience, Grumpy Abram had stormed off to smoke a cigarette.

"It is my filthy habit," he whispered to me in confidence, although I guessed that he also used his nicotine addiction to separate himself from any annoying group.

Throughout the dinner and the subsequent Camino reviews, I again added very little. I was satisfied with the table's tall tales and Grumpy Abram's outbursts. It was entertaining enough without my contributions—and the hubbub sufficiently drowned out my nagging concerns about my missing wife.

Only once did Brie stop the conversation to ask me, "What do you think, Jamie?"

I was so flustered by her intrusion that my mind went blank, and I excused myself to hide in the restaurant's bathroom.

Following the dinner, each pilgrim peeled off from the table to retreat to his or her own albergue or hotel.

The parting was always the same. A hug for Brie. And a cheery "Buen Camino" to one and all, with the added hope we would all see each other on the road the following day.

Eventually there was only Brie and I...and Grumpy Abram.

"We better go," grunted Abram. "Soon they lock us out!"

It was nine forty-five. The three us scampered down the service street back to the Albergue Jakue.

"Did you have a good time?" Brie finally asked. We were pushing our luck and retrieving our dry clothes from the clothesline while Grumpy Abram desperately inhaled his final cigarette for the night.

"Yes."

"You were very quiet."

"Brie, it was my first day. I had a lot to think about."

I would have a lot *more* to think about on my second day. My missing wife would certainly see to that!

8

THE LORCA LETTER

ALL THE WARNINGS were true. It was next to impossible to sleep more than twenty minutes in a row in my albergue bunk bed.

Brie was well-behaved enough, although she did toss and turn with abandon and she did slip out for her nightly "widdle," which caused a mild earthquake in our flimsy beds.

No, it was the snorers. There were only two of them on the entire floor. But two were all that were needed to make one's life miserable. Heaving, snorting, growling, rhythmically snarling, non-rhythmically snarling, loudly, then softly, then loudly again.

Where were the culprits? In the next cubicle? In the next room? The uproar was overpowering and all-encompassing.

And where did these dream snatchers obtain the tremendous gall to sleep among us? These sleeping sociopaths knew they snored! Of course they did! They were full-grown men with partners and families and college roommates. Somebody in their lives, at some point, somewhere, must have told them, "Dude, you snore!"

And yet . . . they still chose to sleep among the silent majority, denying thirty-eight other exhausted travelers the right to a good night's rest.

What happened to the pilgrim spirit? What happened to the Camino camaraderie? This was anarchy!

At first, I only wanted them kicked out of the room. Perhaps a sleep marshal could be hired to wake up the snorers and escort them out to a padded dungeon for the rest of the night.

As the night wore on, I wanted the offenders to wear a badge that read "I hate people. I'm a snorer." That way they could be separated from the Camino crowd and forced to sleep in private prisons devoted to snorers.

Hours passed, and I wanted these sleep assassins kicked off the Camino completely and denied the right to approach the glory of Santiago de Compostela. They ruined the pilgrimage for others! They were not worthy of the Camino's embrace and its path to positive change!

Holy shit, was I tired . . .

Around five in the morning, it stopped. The two snorers had either flip-flopped into more peaceful positions or my exhausted mind had found enough inner calm to slip away and dream.

The sweet serenity didn't last long.

At six o'clock, the morning madness began. Weary pilgrims, many without the aid of an alarm clock, one by one rose from their beds.

Each morning ritual was brief: a short bathroom break, a quick change of clothes, a bed strip, and a hasty packing of whatever wasn't already buried deep inside their backpacks. And they were off.

Once a few pilgrims were up, everybody got up. And although no one talked (for the benefit of the remaining sleepers), there was enough noise now to prevent anyone else from returning to dreamland.

I got up, too. I couldn't defeat the snorers, so how could I compete with the early risers? I inspected my body for signs of injury. Everything checked out. My arms were burnt but my feet were soft and blister-free. My mind was exhausted but my legs felt fine. Perhaps all my melancholy walks back in Palma had provided adequate training after all.

I noticed Brie had already vacated her bunk. Her bedding was gone. Her locker was empty. Just as well, really. I couldn't walk that slowly again. Not when there was another letter from Pam waiting for me.

Everything else was where it was supposed to be. My pack was undisturbed in my locker. My walking shoes were waiting for me on the outdoor rack.

By the time I reached Calle Mayor, I was thinking of breakfast. My Burnsley said the next town was almost five kilometers away, so it was wise to fuel up now.

A street café was open, and I pointed to what I wanted. It would soon become standard fare on the Camino trail: a cup of *café au lait*, a glass of orange juice, and a plate of buttered toast (or a plain pastry if one were available). That was it. There was no need for a menu. What you saw was what you got.

The narrow street abruptly ended at the bank of the Arga River. Its only escape was across the peregrino bridge spanning the lazy waterway. The Romanesque link was impressive, worthy of the postcard pictures it inspired. Some called it the finest medieval bridge in Spain.

The six-arched stone overpass was built in the eleventh century as a gift to the poor pilgrims who previously had to cross the river by boat and pay unscrupulous ferrymen for the pleasure.

One thousand years later, it was still a gift to the pilgrims, or any pedestrian, since cars were forced to use the mundane modern bridge farther down the river.

I reached for my Burnsley for an overview of the day. I was promised a steep climb in the early morning followed by a pleasant stroll up and down rolling hills all the way to the town of Estella.

The village of Lorca was my greater concern. There was my answer to Pam's literary cliffhanger, the critical conclusion as to why she had embarked on her "selfish adventure."

All I had to do was uncover her next clue: "*Underneath the bunny between the two tiny scarecrows.*" Did that mean the letter was outside Lorca? In a field? On a farm? I could only assume that the secret would manifest itself closer to its actual location.

After crossing the Puenta la Reina bridge, I found the rest of my early morning amble less impressive but still refreshing. The dirt track gave me splendid views of the Arga River and its greenbelt of grass and grain.

The steep hill that followed tested the hardy hiker in all of us as we thinned out along the ravine. Chats ceased, and the "Buen Camino" greetings were muted as we saved our energy to dig in for the challenging climb.

I crested the hill and stopped to take a breath and admire the view before following the yellow arrows down to the roundabout and over the bridge into the forgettable village of Mañeru.

I noticed there were two major groups of pilgrims: those who were fresh out of university and those who were near retirement. It made sense. Both groups represented the only people who could afford to take a full month off from their busy lives to walk across Spain. Both groups worked less (or not at all), and both groups probably didn't have small children to care for back home. It was the Freedom Fifty-Five crowd and the Time on My Hands college kids—along with a healthy mix of pilgrims in between.

However, the two groups didn't mingle much with each other. The near-seniors tended to walk slower and drift in and out of smaller couplings all day long. The post-grads, accustomed to the herd mentality of school, stuck it out as one large marching group, walking en masse, shouting and laughing together, and occasionally stopping to wait for the slowest member of their entourage.

The only other subgroup that noticeably fused together like the college kids were the single women. It was either out of sisterhood or out of safety, but the various women walking alone often attached themselves to other singletons along the trail in order to form fast friendships. The Camino was, after all, a unique experience that begged some form of sharing and bonding between the long bouts of introspection.

Moving past untended fields of grass and wheat plastered with poppies that blazed in shades of red, the dirt road rose sharply into the heart of the hilltop town of Cirauqui.

The small burg's name, in the Basque language, means a "nest of vipers," but the only evidence of anything serpentine about

Cirauqui was how the Camino trail snaked through the cobble-stone streets.

When the streets spit me out on the other side of town, the route ran along a tree-lined track that dipped downhill into the remnants of an ancient Roman road. While the stone was mostly eroded, revealing a dirt floor, there were clear cuts of rock here and there, and even a single span bridge, that suggested it had been a far superior pathway two thousand years ago.

Soon the dusty path carried me over gentle hills and through open farmlands before it turned onto a country road that passed under an anemic aqueduct and over another medieval stone bridge. Tired pilgrims picnicked along the roadside, and the sight of their sandwiches made my stomach growl. The thought of coffee made me yawn. I suppressed my cravings and pressed on. Lorca was close. And so was Pam's next message.

A few minutes later, I entered the village of Lorca. I walked delicately. Not because I was tired, but because I was on high alert for my wife's clue: "*Underneath the bunny between the two tiny scarecrows.*"

There were no farms outside Lorca. And no fields. So where were these scarecrows? The letter had to be hidden inside the town. But where? Outside of the twelfth-century church, the settlement seemed more contemporary than most of the other small towns on the Camino. Was that helpful? Would that make the sight of two tiny scarecrows that more obvious?

Since the pilgrim trail briefly formed Lorca's main street, I inspected every storefront and every home.

I suddenly noticed that one house was much more floral and festive than the rest. Pots and planters of glorious red bego-nias and white petunias packed each windowsill. More planters crowded the front door and lined the face of the house, accom-modating a sprawling vine that crept all the way from the street to the roof.

And then I saw them. There on the ground-floor windowsill, two smiling scarecrows stuck out of two pots of purple petunias.

In between stood a white ceramic bunny with a big aqua bow around its neck.

I tiptoed to the window and lifted the rabbit without fear of being spotted by anyone in the house, since the flower arrangements obscured my presence. Nothing there. I traced underneath the windowsill with my fingers. I felt something soft and stooped to have a look. A clear plastic sandwich bag was taped under the frame. It was wet and the tape was peeling off, so it was easy enough to remove.

But I was caught.

"Found another prezzie?"

Standing behind me, Brie was drinking deeply from her water bottle, her trekking poles folded and strapped to her pack. I had to admit, I was happy to see her.

"I suppose you want another photo?"

"Not today."

"You sure? A lot of pretty flowers here…"

"I'm more interested in your little secret."

While I felt no urge to divulge my life's woes like the rest of the prattling pilgrims, I did feel a twinge of wanting to share a little of my mysterious ways to Brie. But just a little.

I approached her with the plastic bag in my hand. "They're letters. From my wife. She walked the Camino a few months ago."

"How lush!"

"Not really."

"Please! You think I ever wrote a letter to Martin? The only thing he'd read is the newspaper. But only for the football scores and the page-three girl with the big tits."

"My wife and I are separated. She left me."

"Oh. Sorry. I do blather on . . ."

"In the last letter she said she needed more space. She said the walls of our apartment were crushing her." I stopped. That was all I was willing to say for now. Was that enough to satisfy Brie's curiosity?

"Well, at least you're getting it all sorted now, right? Me and

Martin never talked about our problems. If I wanted to talk, I'd have to bob down to the local and arse about with his mates. So, you must be relieved, yeah? You get the scoop and get to move on."

"No, I want her back."

"Oh. Well, I do blather on . . ." She tapped me on the shoulder and forced a smile. "I'll let you to it, then. I'm sure you'll catch up to me soon enough."

While Brie limped away, I carefully pulled open the plastic sandwich bag and noticed the seal wasn't perfectly intact. Moisture had got inside the bag and made the pages wet in places, smudging the handwriting here and there. Blowing on it didn't do anything constructive. The pellets of moisture just trickled down the page. I dabbed the papers with the dry folds of my shirt. That was better. But large sections of the message were now unreadable.

Pilgrims streamed past me and acknowledged me with their "Buen Caminos." I nodded back and smiled, but my heart wasn't in it. I just wanted to read what I could from Pam's letter. I contemplated sitting against the floral house, but when the front door suddenly opened, I retreated down the Camino path.

I walked toward the next town of Villatuerta and read what I could, stopping occasionally to decipher the damaged sections.

> Dear Jamie,
> It's only day two, but I really hope you like the Camino!
> Meeting other pilgrims helps if you haven't figured that part out already. But you better not be sulking and keeping to yourself—despite what I said in that last letter.

"How could I *not* sulk and keep to myself? I haven't heard from you in months and then you suddenly lay it on the line like that? Without me around to say anything back? That's not fair. It's my Camino now—and I can sulk if I want to!"

I can't recall if I said that out loud to my missing wife or kept it inside my head. But it was forceful and heartfelt, and I'm sure some of the bitterness escaped from my mouth.

It might have been harsh to read, but c'mon, Jamie; a lot of this stuff was kind of obvious, wasn't it? We were unhappily cruising along in our marriage and nothing was getting any better.

Like I said, this wasn't about you being a bad husband or anything. When I talk about us to the other pilgrims—and yes, I <u>do</u> talk about you—and us—on the Camino, I <u>never ever ever</u> say anything bad about you. If anything, I say bad things about <u>meeee</u>—and how I was just as much to blame for letting the magic die in our marriage and not caring enough to change anything.

And no, I don't mean the therapist stuff you dug up in the summer. I mean, when it mattered. When we were in it! Not when we were looking back and trying to figure out what the hell went wrong.

So I think the breakup was ultimately for the best, don't you?

"Now it's a breakup?! I thought it was a separation. I thought it was a moment to take a breath and figure things out for a while. I can change for the better and make this work; I know I can!"

I mean, seriously? How could we recapture our early days when we were so naive and stupid . . .

The next part was smudged, so I stood in the middle of the road holding the letter up to the sunlight then scurried to the side of a tree for the benefit of the shade. I did everything to change the sun's glare and alter the angle in order to read the streaked section better. Nothing helped. Pam's memories from our naive and stupid days were lost.

I picked up the plot a couple of paragraphs later—but, sadly, not much legible content remained.

So I needed my space and have this adventure. <u>Have time for me.</u> And I still feel guilty and horrible about it—even though I'm loving the walk and all the nice people around me.

"C'mon, Pam—get to the point!"

I wasn't dismissive about her feelings—far from it; it was just more of the same refrain. I now understood her frustrations about our marriage. In two consecutive letters, she had made those very clear. But where was that "bottom line" she had teased me with in that previous message? What changed? I only had a few more sentences to go before the next part became illegible again.

But this separation between you and me is still painful. It still hurts. And not just because our marriage is essentially over. But it's because I've been sick. And I didn't want to tell you.

"Sick? Sick with what?!"

Now I couldn't read it! Pam had begun to explain it and I couldn't read it, thanks to the DAMN WATER DAMAGE!

I read the rest of her smudged letter the best I could. She seemed worried that telling me about how she was *really* feeling while we were separated that summer would have ruined her newly formed independence. Her mother and I would have worried about her too much and smothered her and crushed her restless spirit. Leaving me and leaving the country might not have been the wisest thing to do in terms of her physical health, but it was the healthiest thing she could do in terms of her mental well-being. After years of suffering inside those claustrophobic walls of our apartment, her mental well-being trumped her physical health.

I could make out only a few more sentences.

Me being sick shouldn't be a reason to get back together. None of our initial problems would have been addressed. They'd only be replaced by new ones. And it would have made things worse. Because the only thing I needed more than anything else—my freedom—would have been taken away.

So I kept it a secret from you and my mother and our friends. And I decided against any treatment and escaped instead.

And if that seems harsh, I get it! Believe me, I do. That decision deserves its own explanation. And I'll give you more of it in the next letter. I'm tired now and I think . . .

That was it. I couldn't read any more of her letter outside her final words: "*Be well, Pam.*"

I scoured her letter again for missed words and phrases that would give me more of the details. And I found only one more legible word. The word I probably dreaded the most. *Cancer.*

Where was I? Somewhere between Lorca and Villatuerta. Closer to which town I wasn't sure. In my agitation, I had been walking quickly down the winding Camino track with little awareness of my surroundings.

I now focused on my feet and barreled down the road to my destination. Hungry? It didn't register. Tired? It didn't matter.

Soon I was plodding downhill through a tunnel beneath the highway bypass, crossing another medieval bridge, and entering the modern village of Villatuerta.

Several pilgrims had paused for photos outside the town's twelfth-century church. I stopped just long enough to determine that Brie was not among the Camino tourists.

I charged ahead through Villatuerta. *Cancer.* That's what kept careening through my mind. Not cornfields, medieval ruins, sacred churches, or deserted towns. *Cancer.* How was Pam feeling? And where was she now?

My entire perspective on our marriage now tilted in her favor. I didn't know enough about her diagnosis, but suddenly I felt very selfish about my own feelings about our marriage's inadequacy.

Pam was right. If I had fought harder to save our relationship when it actually mattered, she might not have made her Camino escape. She would have shared her pain; I could have helped. We could have braved this thing together. But Pam had been so fed up with her languishing life, she had singularly focused on her own flight to freedom.

I no longer blamed her for leaving me. She was right. I *would have* smothered her with care and concern during the most incredibly painful and awkward moments of our marriage. She was right, she was *right*.

God, I hoped she was doing okay. Was that a prayer? Was that anguish? I didn't know as I plowed ahead.

I just wanted to reach Estella. I just wanted to ignore everybody else on the road and get to the town to rest and think.

I could talk to Brie. That's it. She had left her husband; she understood. It had been under different circumstances, but it was enough. Beggars can't be choosers; sorrowful pilgrims can't pick out more convenient pilgrims.

I thought more about my wife's cancer. It was the early stages, too—at least, that's what it looked like. There was still time for treatment, right? There were drugs—and easy access to more drugs in most of these Camino towns. Pam could seek medical help whenever she wanted. But where was she? What kind of cancer was it? How much longer to Estella?

I convinced myself it wasn't bad as it sounded. She planned to walk the eight-hundred-kilometer Camino, which challenged even the healthiest of hikers. She had to be okay. Yes, that was it. It was a terrible diagnosis, but she was okay. Bottom line.

My eyes glazed over as I stormed the path outside Villatuerta. Wild hedgerows bordered the roadway. Tracts of trees and faded grasslands popped up in between the flowering shrubs. Descending the winding path, I crossed the pedestrian bridge over the trickling Ega River. I was close now. Past the campground, through the riverside park, past the abandoned church.

Estella's first albergue, the Hospital de Peregrinos de Estella, was directly on the Camino route into town.

I entered the albergue and found a pleasant hospitalero sitting behind a large desk. It was early enough in the day, but he was eager to stamp my credencial and assign me a bunk before the anticipated crowd invaded the albergue. While he wrote down my information, I scanned the page for Brie's name. Hers was nowhere to be found.

A notice board was mounted on the wall that featured a map of the town with other hotel accommodations. There were also handwritten messages from pilgrims asking their missing Camino friends to e-mail them or meet them at their hotels. I scanned the board for a message from Brie. She was nowhere to be found.

"Señor?"

The hospitalero, clutching my passport and my credencial in his hand, waved in earnest as the predicted lineup of pilgrims began to form at his desk.

After arranging my bed and washing up, I grabbed my dirty clothes and headed for the courtyard for the daily laundry tasks. The washing area was behind a bold red wall covered with sacred symbols and images of holy men, like a Buddhist lama, a Catholic monk, and a Hindu priest. I guess at the Hospital de Peregrinos de Estella cleanliness was indeed next to godliness.

As in Pamplona, Romans had built up Estella after it was initially settled by those early Basques, the Vascones. The settlement was then called Lizarra (which is Basque for "ash tree") and spread throughout the slopes of the hills north of the Ega River.

With its nearby mountains encircling the river, protecting the area from wind and foul weather, Sancho Ramirez, the King of Navarre and Aragon, believed he had found the perfect spot to build a riverbank castle to dissuade the invading Moors from encroaching on his territory.

The town was renamed Estella (which is Spanish for "star") and Sancho Ramirez cleverly diverted the Camino trail, which was initially three miles away, to run through his new town to encourage local commerce and provide hospitality for the traveling pilgrims. Then he populated with it with French, German, and Jewish settlers on the south side of the river, who together created the Romanesque architecture enjoyed today in the town's surviving palaces and churches.

By the twelfth century, Aymery Picaud was praising Estella for its "good bread, excellent wine, much meat and fish and all kinds of pleasures." It even became the occasional royal residence for the kings of Navarre during the Middle Ages.

After two hundred years of growth and prosperity, Estella eventually faded from prominence, and the riverfront castle was dismantled so its stones could be used to fortify Pamplona's city walls. However, it remains one of the highlights of the Camino. Even Burnsley tempts his readers to rest in the town for an extra day.

But there was no rest for me. I was on a mission to find Brie and unburden myself of my wife's confession.

Around the corner from the albergue was the steep little pedestrian bridge, the Puente Picudo (Beaked Bridge). And while the delightful overpass was featured on all of the town's postcards, it was only a faithful recreation of the original Roman bridge.

Most of Estella's bars and shops were on this side of the river. The other side, where my albergue was, was historical. This side was practical. So I headed straight for the most practical place to find someone in Estella: the town's main square, the Plaza de Los Fueros.

Throughout all the square's manifestations, from bullring to marketplace, the space had always been home to the moneyed mansions and private apartments of the town's elite alongside the Gothic Iglesia de San Juan Bautista.

Today, the Plaza de Los Fueros is a wide-open space with only a few acacia trees planted in the cobblestone cracks to accompany its uninviting wooden benches. The main activity is along its fringes as the locals and tourists prowl the square's encircling passageways looking to wine and dine in the outdoor cafés.

Brie was easy to spot. Instead of scouring the patios for food options, she was sitting alone on a bench facing the church, her eyes firmly closed as the afternoon sun warmed her beatific face.

I marched toward her until I blocked the sun's glare, casting a long shadow across her body and spoiling her peaceful moment.

Brie opened her eyes with a start but then eased into a smile.

"There he is! What's the story?"

"Cancer."

"What?"

"Cancer. My wife's got cancer."

9

ESTELLA ERUPTION

BRIE GAVE ME thirty full seconds of respectful silence before her maddening questions started. "Is it lung cancer?"

"I don't know, I couldn't read her whole letter—"

"I hope it's not lung cancer."

"I told you, I couldn't read—Wait, why?"

"My neighbor had lung cancer. Well . . . not quite the neighbor. She lived three doors down from me. Wait, was it two doors? No, probably three. Yeah, three. But we talked all the time, so it was like she was living right next door to me—"

"What about the neighbor who lived three doors down from you?"

"Well, she had lung cancer."

"And?"

"Oh, she died. Very suddenly, too—oh, sorry." Then, after a moment, "Listen, you don't exactly know what cancer she has, do you? Did she smoke?"

I shook my head.

"Well, then, see? She probably doesn't have lung cancer." Brie managed a small smile, as though *probably not* having lung cancer signaled some sort of victory. "Now, why can't you read her whole letter?"

"It was damaged by rain or something. Anyway, I can't make out much of it."

"Can I see it?"

I passed her Pam's letter and Brie squinted at it, flipping the pages over a few times as if she were trying to solve a riddle.

"Yeah, that's unreadable, innit?" Then, after another moment, "Could be liver cancer."

"Now why would you say that? Can you see the word 'liver?'"

"Well, no. But you don't want liver cancer. That's a nasty one."

"Is there a good one?"

"Fair play." Brie handed back the letter. "Sorry."

She gave me a few more seconds of respectful peace—until the awkward silence was too much for her to bear.

"There is another letter though, right?"

"Yeah, there's a few more—"

"Well! She'll probably tell you more about it then. Mystery solved eventually. That's something. That's everything!"

"I suppose—"

"So, no need to panic just yet; there's more on the way. I'm sure it's all sorted out in the next one. *Then* you can have your proper heart attack."

Brie meant that as a joke. Perhaps it was poorly timed and a little dark, but I appreciated it all the same.

We were then interrupted by other pilgrims beckoning Brie to their patio table.

"Brie! Over here!"

After the usual greetings and pleasantries were exchanged, Brie and I were once again part of a pilgrim roundtable for afternoon drinks and gossip.

There was Lawyer Wendy again, plus Den Mother Betsy. Scottish Jock and Melbourne Colleen were back.

Amsterdam Sarah was there with her two new pilgrim friends, Paola from Madrid, who was less captivated by the Camino and more enamored with her new smartphone, and melancholic Linnea from Finland, who missed her family terribly but was equally miserable about abandoning the Camino in a few short days for the return trip home.

And then there was the impossibly cute couple, German Lukas and Argentine Camila, who fell in love during an arduous hike in the Andes and now flaunted their affection on the Camino.

Names exchanged and drinks ordered, the customary Camino rants began with the introductory update on everyone's feet. "Did your blisters get any better?" "I poked it with a needle, and you should have seen the pus." "Have you heard of this anti-chafing stick? The pharmacist mentioned it, and it's unbelievable."

I drifted off to ponder Pam's cancer and the health signals I must have missed the previous summer.

The first thing I considered was the day my wife walked into the kitchen to notify me that our marriage was over. She was so calculated, so cold . . . like it didn't matter. Did she already have her diagnosis? There was no room for discussion about the separation; she had delivered her stark announcement and beat a hasty retreat to her mother's house. She must have known.

Pam had promised to talk about our issues over the summer, but the conversations as to why we were falling apart barely scratched the surface. That made sense now. She had much bigger concerns than me. *Than us*. It was all about her—and her health. Like it should have been. The rest of our problems didn't matter for the moment. Of course they didn't.

Pam had repeated many times that summer that she "loved me," but she didn't offer anything remotely resembling a solution as to how to fix our marriage. I don't blame her. She was trying to fix herself. There was no time for marriage counseling. There was no time for my needs. And Pam, naturally, felt guilty about it. Marriage counseling would reveal *everything*, and she wanted to suffer alone. I couldn't be a part of it. That was her brave and difficult choice—and she was sticking to it no matter what the consequences.

When we exchanged our wedding vows, I had promised to take care of Pam and honor her and cherish her and nurture her and grow with her. And while I told myself that I did all that in my heart, I didn't do it in action. I didn't do my job. I had taken her for granted. Love was an action word, but I had let it stagnate into an immovable force. I didn't do the work. I got lazy. Pam told me repeatedly what she wanted, but I didn't listen. I didn't take it seriously. I didn't take *her* seriously. And then when she needed me the most, when she was diagnosed with some form of cancer, she chose to separate herself from me and go it alone. "In sickness and in health" didn't apply to her. Our once-healthy relationship had slowly declined, and she couldn't count on me to comfort her anymore.

Just then someone at the table blurted out, "How did you sleep last night?" Immediately, everyone chimed in about the usual inconveniences of the early curfew, the uncomfortable bed, the lack of privacy, the nagging injuries, the early risers, and the loud talkers. When someone snickered about the notorious snorers, I finally contributed to the conversation.

"These people shouldn't even be here! They should be kicked out of every albergue from Pied-de-Port to Santiago! Why are they sleeping in our bunks? Why do they get to ruin everyone's sleep?"

Lawyer Wendy meekly offered, "Well, maybe they don't know—"

"What are you saying? They don't know that they snore?! Of course they do! You don't think their wife or their girlfriend or their roommate or someone else in their lives ever told them? How can you be so naive?"

"Look, I'm not being naive; I'm just saying—"

"These people don't belong with us. They shouldn't even be walking the Camino. They should stay at home and get their polyps ripped out or whatever they do to chronic snorers. We should put their heads on spikes to warn everyone else who snores to stay away. This is our Camino! You snore? Get out!"

Lawyer Wendy instantly paled. German Lukas and Argentine Camila stopped massaging each other. Den Mother Betsy looked like I had just murdered her children. Melancholic Linnea looked like I had just murdered *everybody's* children. Madrid Paola even looked away from her smartphone. Where was Grumpy Abram when you needed him?

Brie tried her best to diffuse the situation. "Sorry; he heard some awful news today."

I tried to recover. "Yeah, sorry. It's been a bad day. I didn't mean that part about putting their heads on spikes . . . or the polyp ripping . . ."

It took a few uncomfortable seconds for order to be restored. Scottish Jock and Melbourne Colleen were the quickest to forgive me as the rest of the roundtable broke off into smaller group discussions.

"Yeah, so, what happened? If you don't mind me asking?" said Scottish Jock.

"I'm not ready to talk about it yet. Not in front of everyone."

"Fair enough, fair enough."

"Yeah, fair enough," agreed Melbourne Colleen.

Thankfully, my tirade about the snorers was soon overshadowed by something more profound and scandalous: Scottish Jock's admission that he didn't actually carry his backpack on his back!

"Listen, I am still walking the Camino. I just get my hotel to send my bag ahead to the next town—"

"*El tramposo! El tramposo!*" cried Madrid Paola.

This was Camino heresy. The only pilgrims disliked more than the bikers were *los tramposos*, the cheaters—those who used the Camino-wide backpack-shuttle service. Of course it was completely convenient, and it cost Scottish Jock only seven euros a day. However, the very existence of that service disrespected the fine pilgrim tradition of carrying all your possessions on your back. It felt like cheating. And it felt like contempt for the rest of us hardworking peregrinos who slogged our belongings up and down the same Spanish hills.

"But I have a bad back," Scottish Jock protested.

"But your bad back is good enough to share your bed with other pilgrims," joked Amsterdam Sarah.

"Fair enough," agreed Melbourne Colleen.

Our siesta-time drinks led to an early dinner, which ended just as the stores opened up again for the evening trade. Then, of course, there had to be numerous group photos with everyone's individual camera followed by a lengthy e-mail address exchange just in case we never saw each other again. (In reality, most of us would see each other again the very next day. And, for the record, nobody asked me for my e-mail address.)

While our small band of pilgrims wandered off to explore Estella's landmarks, Brie and I stayed behind to further discuss my wife's latest letter.

I told her about Pam's previous letters, our relationship, and our subsequent separation. I didn't stop talking until we had drunk another bottle of red wine. Each.

Through red-stained teeth and purple lips, Brie emitted a long "Whew!"

"Sorry."

"No, no, don't be daft. But from someone who didn't say 'Boo' at the beginning, you sure made up for it."

I was now in a melancholy mood; half dazed, half ready for bed, no longer in any frame of mind to explore the town.

"I used to be romantic."

"I'm sure you were wicked."

"Then I apparently stopped."

"It usually does, innit?"

"It didn't have to."

"You think being romantic makes cancer bugger off or something?"

"I guess you're right. But she might have stuck around."

Brie looked skeptical.

"I could have helped," I proposed.

"It's not just about you, mate. It's about you, her mum, her job, everybody, everything. She just needed to be alone."

"I guess."

"You know what is romantic, though? This Camino."

"Which part? Your bad leg or the snorers?"

"I mean…the Camino sounded romantic *to her*. That's why she came. The romance of the road and all that."

I nodded and surveyed the square. The lively patios, the sturdy San Bautista church, the local children kicking a deflated soccer ball against the helpless trees.

And then I assessed Brie again. A slight burn from the afternoon sun. A tiny smile curling her wine-purple lips. My first impression of her was that she was a chatty Brit with bad bangs. Now she was the wisest pilgrim since Burnsley. Probably brighter than Burnsley. She didn't get me lost in Pamplona.

"What about you?" I finally asked.

"What about me?"

"You left your husband."

"So I did. But we're having a proper chat about you."

"You talk a lot about your family and your marriage, but you never mention what actually broke you two up. What happened?"

"Why does something have to happen? It was just buggered from the start. Just a massive list of stupid shit that eventually becomes one big bin of bollocks until you can't take it anymore."

I was suspicious, but I understood. I finally felt safe enough to share my relationship woes with Brie, but Brie didn't feel secure enough to reveal why her own marriage had ended. Not yet.

"Well, then. That's sorted." She got up to leave. "Fancy a look 'round?"

"You go ahead."

"Where you staying?"

"I'm at the albergue by the bridge."

"Had a long queue when I showed up. I'm the one in the woods. Say, what's the next clue from the wife?"

I already had it memorized from Pam's Clue Sheet. "*Knock, knock, who's there? Landerrain on Saint Anthony.* "

"Not much cop in that one. What does it mean?"

I shrugged. "I'll find out in Los Arcos."

"Want me to tag along?"

I hesitated.

"No, Jamie Draper, you don't have to walk with me and my busted leg. I'll meet you in the square."

"Which square?"

"It's Los Arcos. It only has one."

Brie dropped some money on the table and left me to my misery. "Oh, and Jamie?" she yelled back. "Don't have another shit fit with the peregrinos!"

I sat alone on the Estella patio for a long time, waving off the waiter's insistence that I sample some more wine.

My walk back to the Hospital de Peregrinos in the advancing darkness was quiet and composed, and the moment my weary head hit my pillow I fell asleep—and eluded the rustling roars from the nearby beds. I had discovered the antidote to the snorts from my selfish Camino compatriots: shameful amounts of alcohol.

At six o'clock, the mad scramble began in earnest once again. Without comment and without concern, each of us rose from our beds, anxious to hit the road as quickly as possible.

My body check revealed my feet were still blister-free. The red exposed skin was turning into an acceptable tan. My head was groggy but without the pulsating pain of a hangover. Good.

The day's destination was Los Arcos, 21.1 kilometers away. According to Burnsley, it was an eight-kilometer climb through pines and oaks, followed by a generous twelve-kilometer descent through vineyards and open country. An "easy" day for your average pilgrim.

I wanted to separate myself from Estella as quickly as possible. It was a new day, and I was determined to treat it as a breath of fresh air brushed with hope—and not another sad march as I seethed with a morose meditation on Pam's possible suffering.

Steps away from the albergue, I passed the twelfth-century Church of San Pedro de la Rúa with its sweeping staircase leading up to a damaged cloister.

This is where the kings of Navarre once took their oaths. This is also where the alleged shoulder blade of St. Andrew was interred. In 1270, the bishop from the Greek city of Patras carried it with him during his pilgrimage for good luck. He didn't make it very far, however, and died in Estella. (So much for the good luck.) He and the unlucky shoulder blade were then buried in the church's cloister. After his funeral, a mysterious light suddenly appeared over his tomb. Once the priests investigated his grave for the source of this illumination, they rediscovered the apostle's bone and gave it a more prominent place inside the church—as one does when a dead bone emits a supernatural light.

Hundreds of years later, in 1626, after several miracles had been attributed to the martyred apostle, St. Andrew was finally proclaimed the patron saint of Estella. To seal the deal and thank everybody for the thumbs-up, a fiery vision of St. Andrew's x-shaped cross allegedly hovered over the church after the first public Mass in his honor.

Unfortunately, there were no levitating crucifixes when I walked along Calle de la Rúa. I strolled virtually alone through Estella, with only a glimpse of bobbing backpacks in the distance, both in front of me and behind me.

The previous day I had welcomed that solitude. This day I was determined to welcome some Camino company.

Outside of Kate and Janet in Pamplona, and Brie herself on Alto del Perdón, everyone I had met on my pilgrimage was a friend of the easygoing Brit. It was time I made an effort to make my own Camino connections—not only to prove to myself and others that I could be as affable as anyone, but also to take my mind off Pam's cancer for a while.

I had my first opportunity for Camino companionship when two pilgrims caught up to me walking uphill through the Estella suburb of Ayegui.

The younger man was a German college student wearing aviator sunglasses and sporting dusty shorts. Few pilgrims wore shorts. Shorts meant more exposed skin and more surfaces to apply sunscreen. Shorts were for relaxing in the afternoon shade, not for marching down the unforgiving open road.

The older man, an Englishman, carried a hefty walking stick and wore blue jeans. Nobody wore blue jeans. Jeans meant extra weight and extra-long wait times for them to dry in the afternoon sun. Jeans were for home.

They were discussing the upcoming World Cup football (soccer) tournament. The event was a gift for football fans on the Camino. Suddenly, every Spanish town along the road would become infinitely more interesting during the lazy evening hours. Every bar and restaurant worth its mettle would tune their TV screens to the World Cup to entertain the international cast of Camino characters clamoring for the latest score. Thankfully, Brazil 'played ball' by scheduling most of their games for the early afternoon, so the time-zone shift meant evening entertainment for the pilgrims.

I fell in step with the two men as each summed up his country's chances in the tournament. Germany was always a threat, so the student seemed confident, bordering on smug. England would probably, sooner or later, implode, so the Englishman remained hopeful, bordering on delusional.

Canada didn't have a team in the tournament, so I could share in neither the confidence nor the hopefulness. I had to improvise.

"Well, at least you two have teams playing in the World Cup."

The German and the Englishman looked back at me without a hint of surprise. Intruding on conversations on the Camino was as common as bland pastries and milky coffee for breakfast.

We proceeded to dissect the competition and became fantasy football experts on the soccer skills of distant lands like Algeria, Ecuador, and Bosnia and Herzegovina.

This much-needed camaraderie produced a couple of Camino oversights. Not only were my two new friends entirely focused on discussing sports—ignoring all the scenery—they also walked incredibly fast. When we approached the famous monastery of Irache outside Ayegui, we stomped right past without a sniff of interest.

While the monastery itself was abandoned and had been converted into a woeful museum, the bodega beside it offered free wine. And it couldn't have been more convenient. A pair of stainless-steel taps stuck right out of the wall of the winery—right along the route! One offered red wine, the other, water. You could help yourself. You just needed a container. Hell, some thirsty pilgrims even cupped their hands while a friend turned the handle.

We trudged right past the bodega, however, and right through the hamlet of Irache that followed. The precedent was set. This was a mid-morning march, not a sights-and-sounds tour of the Spanish countryside.

I soon lagged behind the pair. As our path penetrated the pine and oak forest, I slowed down to develop my own comfortable pace. I didn't make an announcement, nor did my friends appear to notice my absence.

I even thought about turning back to claim my gift of wine, but the morning sun was already threatening my skin and I appreciated the shade offered by the tracts of trees.

Whenever the forest cleared, tall grass poured down the hillside to more patches of oak and pine, exposing a long lineup of cliffs across the valley floor. The clearings would be brief, the searing sun would be unfriendly, and then the forest would swallow up the path again—until the next glade of grass.

It was here I caught up to a young Aussie named Jasmine. She had traveled halfway across the world to complete the Camino on the cheap. Like…very cheap.

"What do you mean you don't sleep in albergues?"

"Too expensive."

"They're only ten euros a night. Sometimes six!"

"I can't afford it."

"You can't afford six euros? Where do you sleep?"

"Outdoors mostly."

"Outdoors?!"

"I have a small tent and a sleeping bag. It's no big deal."

"The albergues are just six euros! They're even cheaper than those pilgrim dinners!" I insisted.

Many restaurants on the Camino trail offered a basic pilgrim dinner for a price of ten euros. It was a fixed menu usually consisting of a sad salad, a cheap piece of meat, a handful of French fries, and a tart for dessert—with a bottle of wine for the table. If you sat by yourself, the entire bottle was yours!

"Oh, I don't eat those dinners. I just buy food from a store and make my own meals."

"What meals?"

"I don't know . . . sandwiches . . . fruit . . ."

"All the time?"

"All the time. It's cheaper."

"So you just eat fruit and homemade sandwiches and sleep outdoors every night?"

Jasmine shrugged.

My line of incredulous questioning continued until we reached the village of Azqueta. If Jasmine hadn't initially been concerned about her frugal ways and her disregard for safety, she probably was by now. Her only line of defense against my inquisition was a steely commitment to her thriftiness and a repeated shrug of her slender shoulders.

We found the German and the Englishman eating breakfast outside a café in the village square. It was out of necessity, since there was only one more town before the thirteen-kilometer treeless descent into Los Arcos.

We ate together in the shade, all pastries and jams along with creamy coffee and cans of iced tea. Then there was the pasting of sunscreen upon our skin, along with the donning of caps and hats to cover our heads.

The German student, Karl, was already contemplating walking right through Los Arcos to the next sizeable town of Torres del Rio. He didn't like crowds and preferred to stay in villages where the pilgrims didn't roam.

The Englishman, Simon, was a librarian at one of the prestigious colleges at the University of Cambridge. He was bookish in his choice of glasses but rebellious in his jeans. And decidedly dangerous with his walking stick.

Lathered and covered, Simon and I were ready to proceed. Karl waved us on, preferring to linger and enjoy a cigarette or two. Jasmine asked if she could join him. She had probably thought better than to walk another kilometer under the shadow of my judgment. Plus Karl's cigarette was probably free.

Without Karl to challenge him, Simon slowed his pace to match mine, which made for a still-hurried but more pleasant walk. We walked past dairy farms before briefly marching uphill to Villamayor de Monjardin, the highest point of our day. There were no more towns until Los Arcos and not many trees crossing our intended path. Our afternoon walk would be a hot and unforgiving one.

The early moments of our march were lovely enough, through vineyards and woodland, but two kilometers later, our trek became a rollicking romp through farmland and uninhabited grassland. Whenever anything crossed our path to offer a little shade, like a plot of trees or a string of bushes, we stopped to drink water and admire the landscape of majestic greens, yellows, and browns.

While we walked, we talked. Music, mostly. Britpop, mostly. To me, as a young man in the nineties, Britpop had seemed both exotic and attainable. American grunge was too angry, and urban hip-hop was too mystifying. Britpop was happy. It was swingin' London with a 1990s makeover starring lads in trainers and rock girls with guitars.

While I was scouring the indie stores and music mags for my Britpop fix, the older Simon was actually living the Britpop life in Camden Town. Before his bookish years in Cambridge, he had been a thirty-something street musician plying the pub circuit for lager and spending money.

"I once saw Noel Gallagher!"

"No waaaaaay! Where?"

"I think it was him. You know, before he started Oasis he loaded gear for The Inspiral Carpets—"

"I heard about that, yeah—"

"So I saw the roadies setting up the stage once. I think it was Noel…"

After we discussed the musical merits of Britpop bands such as Blur and Pulp, we turned to the nineties prog-rock pioneers like Marillion and IQ.

"I once saw Marillion perform at the Hammersmith Odeon! During their first album too—"

"No waaaaay—"

"I was right outside."

"Wait . . . what?"

"Yeah, I stood on the corner playing guitar outside the Hammersmith. And I kind of heard them through the side door…"

It was just a steady diet of rock 'n' roll talk, along with a few dubious claims of celebrity encounters. It was anything and everything about music and fame…just as long as we didn't talk about our personal lives and Pam's cancer.

Simon knew nothing about me, and I knew little about him apart from his early Camden days in the pubs. We were pop-music encyclopedias regaling each other with musical memories that never once scraped the surface of where we came from and what we were doing on the Camino—mission accomplished for my muddled mind.

And Pam would be relieved, too. I had stopped sulking—and as long as I didn't pick apart other pilgrims, I *could* make Camino friends. She was right (again). *Keeping* Camino friends, however, proved a bit more difficult for me . . .

10

HOSTILE LOS ARCOS

MY CONVERSATION WITH Simon ended only when we reached the dry riverbed of the Caudiel. The small hill range near the former stream was covered in replanted pine trees, providing us with the first significant shelter from the sun since we had left the main-street shadows of Villamayor de Monjardin.

We were only a few kilometers away from Los Arcos, but it was the perfect place to rest and re-apply the sunscreen. Not burning my skin was a priority, so I encouraged Simon to walk ahead without me.

"All right. See you in the square in Los Arcos around five, yeah? I'll tell you about the time I met Ringo."

"Ringo Starr? Where?"

"Outside the Enterprise in Camden. I think it was him . . ."

My rest was short. I carried no food and I was low on water. I left my shadowy sanctuary and plodded through more cereal fields and olive groves until I reached a fountain on the outskirts of town. Lapping up the fresh water, I was properly sated but still appreciably disturbed. Without Simon's contributions to my rock 'n' roll ramble, my mind wavered again and focused on my ailing wife. It made the walk sluggish and dreary—despite the promise of Pam's next letter and Brie's offer to help keep me company.

The dusty road soon bowed to the brick and stone buildings of bland and listless Los Arcos. Burnsley called the entrance into town "sleepy." He was being generous. It was comatose and depressing.

Just like Puente la Reina and Estella, Los Arcos had developed and thrived because of the path of the Camino. Unlike Puente la Reina and Estella, Los Arcos had never blossomed with its own artistic grace.

I passed by the first albergue, which offered "good facilities," for the second albergue farther down the street, which promised "excellent facilities." I don't know much about this world, but I do know that "excellent" always trumps "good."

I was too early. The congenial hospitalero was still brushing her wet hair. Could I return in fifteen minutes? Sure. Did I have a reservation? No. That was all right; just drop your bag behind the others. That would guarantee me a bed. I trusted her and complied. Who was I to argue with a foolproof system like that?

Outside the albergue, the street headed toward the banks of the Odrón River and the Plaza de Santa Maria. The Iglesia de Santa Maria inhabited one side of the square, its colonnade the only place in town offering shade and protection from the sun's penetrating rays—outside of the patio umbrellas sprinkled around the center of the square.

That's where I found Kate and Janet enjoying a late breakfast before their afternoon dash to Torres del Rio.

"Are you mad?" I asked, ordering a small beer from the restaurant waiter lingering beside me.

"There's nothing to do here," insisted Janet as she scrubbed more sunscreen on her neck and face in between taking bites of her crispy toast and bruised tomatoes.

"Did you hear the news?" asked Kate.

I braced myself for a pilgrim predicament. Perhaps New York Brian had run out of money. Perhaps Mississippi Holly had had her feet amputated. Perhaps Madrid Paola had lost her Wi-Fi signal!

"The king of Spain announced his abdication last night."

Oh, it was actual news . . . from the actual world.

"Spain still has a king?"

"You didn't know that? Don't you live here?"

"Well . . . not *exactly*. It's more like an extended holiday."

"It's all over the TV," added Janet.

"I guess it would help if I knew Spanish—"

"You don't know Spanish? Don't you teach English to Spanish students?" These were innocent enough questions, but, trickling off the tongue of sarcastic Kate, they came across as a light scolding.

"Yes, well . . . we don't *exactly* speak much Spanish during our lessons."

I was suddenly rescued by Brie. She had plopped down on the chair beside me, her sandy curls wet with perspiration, her cheeks a scalding red, her floppy hat the ugliest headgear in all of the Iberian Peninsula.

"Hiya!"

"Hello, Brie. Have you heard the news? The king of Spain announced his abdication last night." Kate was testing her.

"Spain still has a king?" asked Brie.

Kate and Janet, the two professors from Columbia University, hurriedly departed, failing to hide their disgust at the ignorant slobs they were leaving behind in Los Arcos.

The king's announcement was certainly historic news. The monarchy as a public institution was still popular in modern-day Spain; more than seventy percent of its citizens were in favor of a ruling monarch, frustrating the Basques and all the other regional separatists.

Several forms of absolute and limited monarchy have ruled the various territories of Spain as early as the eighth century. However, it was the Roman Catholic union of Ferdinand II of Aragon and Isabella I of Castile in 1469 that created the Spanish Empire which went on to explore (and exploit) the Americas. And it was Ferdinand and Isabella who funded (that Italian) Christopher Columbus and his initial colonization of the New World.

It was only in 1931 that the monarchy ended with the establishment of a short-lived republic. With King Alfonso XIII in exile, the Spanish Civil War broke out in 1936. Three years later, with backing from Nazi Germany and Fascist Italy, Francisco

Franco and his Nationalists won the war and ruled the country as a dictatorship until his death in 1975.

Back in 1969, Franco had already chosen Prince Juan Carlos, a grandson of Alfonso XIII, to be the next head of state. Two days after Franco's death, King Juan Carlos I became the first reigning monarch of Spain since 1931.

Franco had always assumed that the new king would simply carry on his established dictatorship. Juan Carlos I had other ideas. He dismantled Franco's regime and instituted democratic reforms that established a constitutional monarchy by 1978. And just like other royal houses throughout Europe, the king's role was now more ceremonial and symbolic rather than practical.

The king's popularity finally took a hit during the 2008 global financial crisis. Suddenly the wealthy king and his family seemed out of step with the rest of the suffering population. In 2012, the king was photographed during a hunting expedition in Botswana standing over a dead elephant; this despite the king's patronage of the World Wildlife Fund. The king's popularity dropped below fifty percent.

To his credit, Juan Carlos I did significant damage control: apologizing for his indiscretions, increasing his tax contributions, becoming more transparent with the monarchy's books, and brokering international investment deals for his country.

While the Spanish people generally forgave their king, other members of his royal family came under closer scrutiny. So, on June 2, 2014, in order to save the family reputation and instill goodwill toward his people, King Juan Carlos I stepped down from the throne and gave the keys to the kingdom to his diligent son, Felipe. Immediately, the retiring king's approval rating shot back up to seventy percent.

It was great to see Brie again, ugly floppy hat notwithstanding. Her mischievous hazel eyes were sparkling, and her thin lips curled into a wide grin that was a balm to my uneasy mind.

"So...ready to crack on? *Knock, knock, who's there? Landerrain on Saint Anthony.* Have you sorted it?"

She had memorized Pam's clue. I couldn't decide whether her concern was adorable or melodramatic.

"I just got here—"

"Well, stop arsin' about. What are you waiting for?"

Brie followed me back to my Los Arcos accommodation. She had registered in the first albergue, the one with the "good facilities." "Good enough for me," she chirped.

She paced the lobby while I registered and received my credencial stamp.

"Come on, come on . . ."

Brie was more anxious than I was to uncover Pam's next letter. She was right: I was "arsin' about." I was too anxious about its contents. Not knowing the extent to which Pam's health was compromised was hell. Knowing the full extent of its effects might be worse.

It was odd that you could readily meet fellow pilgrims on the road and outside the bars—but not inside the albergues. Despite the close sleeping quarters, pilgrims tended to keep to themselves, reading, napping, or silently executing their daily chores.

The Camino road was cooperative and convivial. The town square was communal and confessional. The albergue was an army barrack with rules and procedures and a sacrifice of one's liberties—which seemed to lead to self-reliance and disinterest.

My room in Los Arcos was filled with Frenchmen—cyclist Frenchmen, judging by their bike bags and frightening Lycra pants. And I spoke less French than I did Spanish.

They remained quiet too, wordlessly making their beds and retreating to the bathroom to continue their chores. Except for one fat Frenchman who mumbled to himself while he spread his extra-large sleeping bag over his bunk.

I could only imagine what he was muttering. "Tuck in the bed sheet, tuck in the bed sheet. Okay? Good. Now where's that pillowcase? There it is. Cover that pillow, cover that pillow. That's it. Good job . . ." Later in the bathroom, the fat Frenchman grunted as he washed himself behind the shower curtain. "Lather up that back, lather up that back. Okay? Good. Now where's that penis? There it is. Wash that penis, wash that penis. That's it. Good job . . ."

I came to understand the accepted aloofness of the albergue. On the path and inside the square, you have the option of engaging with or retreating from your new acquaintances. Inside the albergue, you can't play favorites. You're assigned your roommates, and, language barrier or not, you're stuck with them until the dawn of the morning.

The Los Arcos albergue offered its own laundry service, and I was glad to utilize it—at whatever the cost. There was no price too high to escape a grunting Frenchman washing himself.

Brie sprang to her feet when I returned to the lobby.

"So you're done, then? Yes?"

I nodded.

"Off we go, then." Brie grabbed my hand and yanked me outside.

"Wait . . ." I protested.

"No more arsin' about. I found it!"

"Found what?"

"*Landerrain on Saint Anthony.* I sorted it out with the hospitalero. Saint Anthony, we fancied, was Calle San Antón. You know . . . San Antón . . . Saint Anthony? Makes sense, yeah?"

We headed back to the square and snaked through the adjacent streets until we arrived on Calle San Antón. Unlike the dusty road leading into town, this avenue of brick and stone was clean and scrubbed for prosperity. Still deserted. Still sleepy.

"Now what?" I wondered

"*Landerrain on Saint Anthony.* There must be a Landerrain on this street."

We inspected every building until we discovered a stylized sign reading "Landerrain" on the wall of a residential building. Landerrain appeared to be the last name of a Los Arcos family. In keeping with the spirit of the street, it was a formidable brick dwelling with a solid oak door and one large window on the ground floor, shuttered and barred to strangers. Impervious rather than cozy. A sign posted on the mailbox seemed to confirm that. "*Por favor, no depositar propaganda en este buzón.* " ("Please do not place advertising in this mailbox.")

I searched for Pam's letter around that mailbox, along the edges of the door, above and below the windowsill, and behind the piping mounted on the wall. I found nothing.

"*Knock, knock, who's there?*"

I looked back at Brie, who was keeping a lookout in the street, her arms folded, her eyes twinkling with mischief.

"*Knock, knock, who's there? Landerrain on Saint Anthony.* It's a knock now, innit? Give it a go."

It was obvious now that I was meant to disturb the Landerrains in order to receive my next letter.

I knocked. No answer. Knocked again. No answer. Knocked loudly. No answer. Tried again. No answer.

"Nobody home," Brie affirmed, opting to sit down in the middle of the street.

"What are you doing?"

"Waiting."

"Are you sure?" I asked, inspecting both directions of Calle San Anton. Still deserted.

"Nothing else to do. This is the best thing going in Los Arcos."

I joined her on the street. The moments ticked by. Two tired tourists sitting in the middle of the road, staring at the Landerrain door, looking left and right for any sign of life.

"What am I going to say to them?"

"You're going to ask for your letter," said Brie matter-of-factly.

"Now would be a good time to know some Spanish."

"Don't you teach English to Spanish students?"

"We don't speak much Spanish during our lessons."

"Makes sense."

More time elapsed. No movement. No change.

"Do you think we should explore the town?" I wondered.

"You just wait, Jamie Draper."

Los Arcos was only worth a cup of coffee on the Camino. It was simply a pit-stop town that straddled the Odrón River. Its once-famous castle was destroyed and gone. Its mighty walls that had once surrounded the entire town were largely missing.

Even Burnsley had little to say about Los Arcos. He barely described the Santa Maria church. He casually name-dropped the town's Roman origins but then failed to point out any points of interest. The best he could do was brag about an eastern gate that no longer existed.

Kate and Janet might have been onto something. Eat a meal and leave. I'm sure that's what German Karl was going to do. And Poor Jasmine. (Although to be fair, she was content to eat in the woods and dine on supermarket bread.)

"What I could use is a phone," I mumbled to Brie. "Call my mother-in-law again. Ask about Pam. Maybe e-mail some friends and find out what they know."

Brie reached into her pocket and handed me her cell phone. "It's a load of shit. But have at it."

"Are you sure?"

Brie squeezed my arm and kept a lookout on the street while I busied myself with a phone call to my mother-in-law and e-mails to my friends. Adding to the agitation was the fact that Brie's phone screen periodically froze and her autocorrect function was out of control.

There were no immediate answers, but the word was finally out. My wife was sick and I needed to find her as soon as possible.

I returned Brie's phone and sighed. "If my mother-in-law calls back on your load-of-shit phone—"

"Say no more, Jamie."

We then noticed a woman lugging two bags of groceries heading toward the Landerrains' address. Was this the moment? Should I call out? I wasn't entirely sure. When the woman reached the front door, I finally sprang to my feet.

"Excuse me! Por favor! Por favor!"

My flailing limbs and my stressed Spanish only agitated the woman as she struggled with her keys.

The presumed Mrs. Landerrain was in her mid-fifties, her long black hair pulled tight into a ponytail. She was stocky and firm with massive arms peeping out of her white lace dress. Overdressed for shopping. And generally overly perturbed.

"Por favor. Landerrain. Sí?" I gasped.

The keys still in her hand, Mrs. Landerrain lowered her groceries to the ground and faced us. She didn't answer. She only scowled and waited for more information.

"Tell her about the letter."

"Sí. My wife. *Mi…* Pam. Pam Draper." Now I was gesturing in the air, handwriting a letter, folding it, slipping it into an envelope. Hey, it had worked at the Café Iruña.

"She's not getting it," said Brie. "Do it again."

But no, she understood me. Mrs. Landerrain's eyes suddenly narrowed and she lunged toward me, accidentally kicking aside her grocery bags. Vegetables and fruit spilled onto the street as the missus repeatedly hit me. Hit me! Pounding my shoulders and chest with her fist, her house keys jabbing my skin, her voice a torrent of enraged Spanish with choice words like *imbécil, estúpido*, and *esa pobre mujer* (jerk, asshole, that poor woman).

I covered myself as best as I could while Brie gathered the rolling apricots and oranges.

"Maybe she's got you confused with someone else?"

"Does she look confused?!" I cried, backing away from the abuse and covering my head.

"Careful. You're going to step on her groceries—"

"Could you leave the fruit alone and help me?!"

Brie finally dropped her load and approached the angry Mrs. Landerrain. "Hey. Hey. Stop that. Hey."

The angry missus finally stopped hitting me. But her torrent of heated Spanish was far from over.

"Now would be a good time to know some Spanish," offered Brie.

"I know enough."

I watched Mrs. Landerrain's gestures and listened intently while translating out loud whatever I could.

"She met Pam a while ago, apparently in the square," I said, while the missus pointed toward the Plaza de Santa Maria.

Mrs. Landerrain soon softened. She was talking about my wife and seemed quite fond of her, using the phrase *buena mujer* (nice woman) more than a few times.

Then she became quiet, almost whispering, even looking behind her to ensure that only Brie and I were entitled to her disclosure.

"She says Pam told her that she was sick."

Brie didn't need the translation for that. There was no mistaking what the missus meant by the word "*cáncer.*"

Mrs. Landerrain continued speaking for a few more moments and then suddenly stopped. Satisfied with her own explanation, she stooped to gather her scattered fruit and vegetables.

"What did she say?" asked Brie. "Jamie, what did she say?"

I sighed. "She doesn't have Pam's letter anymore."

With nothing left to say or explain, we helped her pick up her remaining groceries. The assault over, the confrontation diffused, we held her bags while she unlocked her door.

Brie asked one more time, "So no letter?" Then she turned to me. "What's the word for 'letter'?"

"*La carta*, I think."

Mrs. Landerrain made a ripping gesture and said something congenial that sounded like an apology.

"It was months ago," I muttered. "She didn't think I'd come."

We surrendered the bags, and Mrs. Landerrain looked me over one final time before she closed the door. "*Lo siento.*"

"She's sorry."

I didn't move. I focused on my feet and let my feelings of helplessness and frustration wash over me. Brie shuffled her feet and then hugged me from behind, her fingers clasped across my chest and her head resting between my shoulder blades. Neither of us stirred. We were just two tired tourists standing silently on Calle San Anton . . . for a very long time.

I woke up the following morning to a muttering fat Frenchman reorganizing his backpack at the foot of my bunk bed. "Good sleep on the mattress, good sleep on the mattress. Wide awake now? Good. Time to ride, time to ride. Let's go . . ."

Three of his Camino comrades burst into the room to retrieve their bags and urge their muttering friend to move it along.

"*Comment était le petit déjeuner?*"

The thundering Frenchmen declared their morning meal was delicious. "*Beaucoup de choix!*"

Well, at least there was some breakfast variety this time. That was encouraging.

I sat up and waited for the gabby Gauls to leave the room before I climbed down from my bunk. For once I wanted to savor a little privacy. Maybe scratch something without detection. Maybe stand completely naked for more than a shameful second.

I reached for my discarded Burnsley and peeked at the day ahead. It was my longest scheduled walk so far, with a 28.6-kilometer jaunt to the small city of Logroño. Little shade, lots of farmland, some early steep sections, plus dire warnings to pack water and wear a hat. I made one more prediction I could count on: there would be no letter until the following day.

After my morning routine, I settled in for the albergue's lauded breakfast inside its dining area. As advertised, there was indeed some variety, but it was part of the same old tired menu. It still consisted of coffee, orange juice, toast, and jam, except here there were three types of bread, two varieties of coffee, and tart marmalade to complement the sweet strawberry spread.

While I nibbled at my oversold and underwhelming morning meal, I considered the other Camino clientele.

Au naturel was the name of the glamor game on this Camino. Cosmetics were practically non-existent. The only creams and lotions seen were used to stave off injuries and prevent chafing. And while the women's makeup was minimal, the men rarely shaved. The rugged look was de rigueur. This meant the women were just as quick as the men in washing up and preparing for the day's wearying slog. Wake up, get ready, and go in less than ten minutes, and nobody gets left behind.

And forget about any fashion-forward statements in the clothing department. Everyone brought along their limited rotation of three shirts and the same old trusty pair of pants. After a week of walking, you could faithfully forecast what everyone would be wearing the next day. "I see you went with the blue T-shirt today. I guess tomorrow you'll be going with the green?"

Outside the albergue, Burnsley's warning of little shade was instantly muted. It was overcast and chilly, requiring me to wear my fleece pullover to start my day. If the entry into Los Arcos had been bland and listless, leaving it was an equally lackluster experience. Soon I was walking in a straight line behind dozens of other pilgrims, down a dirt and gravel track through scrubby brown farmland.

I pondered the previous night. After our confrontation with Mrs. Landerrain, Brie and I had wandered back to the town square to find Simon sitting alone at a patio table. He waved us over, and I made the introductions.

Brie and I tried our best to erase the recent unpleasantness. It wasn't easy. The only trick that worked was to encourage Simon to regale us with old stories from his Camden days.

"Simon says he once saw Noel Gallagher—"

"Well, I *think* it was him . . ."

Eventually Melbourne Colleen and Scottish Jock joined us. After introductions and the ordering of food and drink, it became easier to forget Mrs. Landerrain and Pam's missing letter as the two entertaining Brits loudly bonded over every London location they had ever lived in and loved.

"You were in Islington, then?" asked Scottish Jock. They had already thoroughly discussed the boroughs of Camden, Westminster, and Kensington/Chelsea.

"Three years."

"I was on Holloway Road until they broke the ground on Emirates—"

"Oh, bloody hell. I was there until 2007 or thereabouts."

"You don't say—"

"But never mind the Emirates. Give me Highbury any day—"

"I was at Highbury for Arsenal's final game against Wigan!"

"Thierry Henry—"

"Three goals!" they said in unison.

"Good old Highbury," said Scottish Jock with a chuckle.

"After Holloway, I actually moved to a basement flat near Highbury Hill."

"Lot of famous people in that area. I think George Martin has a place there—"

"I once met Ringo Starr in Camden."

"Bloody hell!"

Brie stood up to leave during Simon's spurious Ringo Starr story. (Spoiler alert: he didn't meet the actual Ringo Starr.) This time there were no hugs, photo requests, or e-mail exchanges. She simply slipped away quietly and waved back to me, mouthing the words "See you tomorrow."

No one noticed for a few moments. Simon was focused on his Ringo narrative. Scottish Jock was enraptured by Simon's story. Melbourne Colleen was enraptured by Scottish Jock.

I missed Brie the moment she left our table, and I tried to understand why she withdrew. Perhaps she was just tired. Perhaps Simon's stories bored her. I mean, she lived in London all her life and yet she had never once spoke up to offer any sort of opinion. I wasn't even sure in which part of London she lived. East London, I think. Hackney?

Perhaps the babbling Brits reminded Brie of her husband's drunken chats with his mates down at the local. Perhaps she was still hurting from her own breakup and needed time alone.

I made a pact with myself to be more of service to Brie… somehow. After all, she had ably supported me in every way; talking less, listening more, comforting me when I needed silence, and speaking up when I needed encouragement. It was my turn to help *her*. How, I didn't know. But I would try.

11

LOGROÑO BREAKUP

I SPED UP on the trail, passing other pilgrims, wishing my "Buen Caminos" while keeping my eye trained for a limping Brie somewhere along the rolling farmland. A few kilometers outside of Los Arcos, I crossed the San Pedro River, and the gravel path soon yielded to a quiet country road leading up to the sleepy hamlet of Sansol.

I considered Sansol for a brief inspection but pressed on to Torres Del Rio, one kilometer away, majestically perched on the adjacent hill. With the next major center more than ten kilometers away, now was the ideal time to rest and re-energize.

Torres Del Rio was fifty percent bigger than its hilly counterpart of Sansol, if only because its population of 150 souls was larger than Sansol's one hundred. Its sacred centerpiece was the twelfth-century church of the Holy Sepulchre, based on the church of the same name in Jerusalem. And like most religious relics on the Camino, it was ignored.

Outside the town square café, pilgrims stretched their legs and refueled with sugary snacks and café au lait. I searched the faces for someone I knew and found Amsterdam Sarah and Glum Linnea sitting on their packs and sharing a sandwich.

"Have you seen Brie today?"

Both shook their heads. Sarah smiled while Linnea looked more miserable than usual.

"Having a bad day, Linnea?"

She shook her head again but seemed on the verge of tears.

"Where's your friend? Paola?" I asked, changing the subject.

"She left the Camino and went back to Madrid," stated Sarah. "She dropped her phone and couldn't fix it."

I waited for the punch line. There was none.

"In the thousand-year history of the Camino, that may be the dumbest reason to give up the walk."

Sarah shrugged.

"People have died out here."

Sarah shrugged again.

"Holly lost the use of her feet, and she's still out here."

"Paola liked her phone," said Sarah matter-of-factly.

To many on the road, the mere presence of a smartphone showed disrespect for the authenticity of the experience. Yes, while the fine pilgrim tradition insists that you carry all your possessions on your back—and certainly a smartphone can fit inside your pocket—its temptation and application clashes with the theme of the intended journey: this was supposed to be about taking a break from our modern lives.

We were supposed to meditate on personal and spiritual change—not check out the latest baseball scores. The journey was about confronting our comfort zones—not seeking contentment from our friends' selfies.

Smartphone users also took advantage of the dishonorable technology to book choice hotels and busy albergues in advance. To many of us, this felt like cheating. And it felt like contempt for us hardworking peregrinos who had to scramble to find a suitable bed for the night without the luxury of a smartphone reservation.

This Camino contempt for smartphones wasn't universal. Many travelers had several valid reasons for keeping in touch with their loved ones back home. I mean, what was the alternative if you desperately needed to contact a non-pilgrim? An internet café? Because, let me inform you: inside today's Spain, the internet café is virtually dead.

When I'd ask to use the internet, the reply was always, "Señor, we have Wi-Fi." "But I don't have a phone." The sarcastic ones rolled their eyes; the polite ones were stunned into immobility.

Even if the town did have an internet café, it invariably wouldn't be open or would rely on computer software that hadn't been upgraded since 2005, making every document you saved on your USB key unreadable. The internet café was dead; long live the smartphone. Good job, Steve Jobs. You have conquered the Camino.

Fortified with caffeine, I left Amsterdam Sarah and Glum Linnea for the long walk to Viana. It was a 10.6-kilometer march on a dirt track up and down rolling hills, dipping sharply into ravines before immediately climbing cursory peaks, where Viana would inch closer along the horizon.

It was an ominous exercise. Rain clouds threatened to ruin the day, compelling many pilgrims to wear their brightly colored ponchos and cover their packs with their built-in rain liners. From a distance, the path looked like a broken gumball machine with red, blue, yellow, and green candies rolling down the scrubby hillsides. I resisted the extra layer and endured a five-minute sprinkle. It was the only rain I would see for weeks.

I thought more about the previous night in Los Arcos. Long after Brie had left our dinner table and shortly after Simon and Jock had argued about who was the greatest Scottish footballer of all time, Melbourne Colleen turned to me and asked, "So what bad news did you get?"

"If you don't mind her asking," interjected Jock.

"If you don't mind me asking," repeated Colleen.

"All right. So . . . my wife left me a few months ago. So, I . . . needed an adventure. That's why I'm here."

I sat back and forced a smile. I had finally shared some of my story. It was over.

It wasn't over.

Colleen and Jock gravely nodded. Then Colleen asked, "And the bad news?"

"My wife leaving me isn't bad news?"

"You just said that happened a few months ago. But the bad news came on the Camino…"

My three new pilgrim friends patiently waited for my reply.

"Well, she's sick, too. Apparently."

"Apparently?"

"Look, I don't know the details. I just know she's sick, okay? So, there's that. My wife left me and she's sick. How long has she been sick? I don't know—"

"How come you don't know—"

"See? This is why I don't want to talk about it! I know there's a lot of holes in my story. But I don't want to break it all down for everybody, okay? I just want to do my walk and do my thing. And I don't need the whole world knowing about my sad little life. If everybody else wants to share their *own* personal reasons for their walk, fine. *But I don't.* Why is that so hard to understand?"

"Okay, okay. Sorry," said Colleen quickly. "Just trying to help."

"Just trying to help," affirmed Jock. "That's all."

"I know, I know. But I don't need everybody asking me about how I'm coping or how I'm *feeling*—"

"Understood, mate, understood."

"We totally understand," nodded Colleen.

Jock added, "Although sometimes it's good to get things off your chest—"

"No, it isn't. Not this time. I don't want to be the Camino charity case."

"Oh, absolutely not. Understood, mate."

Just then the waiter returned to inquire about more drinks.

"I'll have one," said Jock. Then, ever so gently, "Jamie, how about you? Do *you* . . . fancy another?"

"See? You're already doing it."

"What?"

"You're talking to me like I'm the charity case."

"No, I'm not—"

"Yes, you are! It's all in your tone. It's like . . . full of pity, and sadness, and I'm hopeless now or something . . ."

Jock raised his hands in defense.

"Yes, we'll all have another drink!" I snapped to the poor waiter.

Simon and Colleen still had full glasses of wine, but they knew better than to argue with me in that moment. And the tension I had just created at our cozy Camino table was about to get worse . . .

The dirt-path approach to Viana ran parallel to the highway for quite some time before the Camino route suddenly merged with it. Then the hilltop town loomed straight ahead, the tower of its Church of Santa Maria poking its head above the brown shoe-box apartment buildings blotting its eastern suburb. Despite the tower's beckoning appearance, my eyes remained focused on my feet as I recalled the previous night's discomfort.

After I had accused Jock of taking pity on my problems, I continued to poison the evening with some pointed opinions of my own.

"Now let's talk about your bad news," I challenged Colleen.

"What bad news?"

"Well, you're walking with Jock. You're clearly in love with him. But he has a girlfriend waiting for him in Santiago!"

"I know."

"She knows."

"I didn't know," quipped Simon, attempting to lighten the mood.

"Doesn't that bother you? Eventually, he's going to have to choose."

"I know."

"She knows."

"This doesn't bother anyone?"

"Look," said Colleen. "I didn't know at the start, but I got over it and—"

"I told you at the start!" bellowed Jock.

"No, you didn't—"

"At Saint Jean, I told you—"

"After we slept together—"

"No, before—"

"No, after—"

The argument over the timeline of Jock's girlfriend confession continued for some time. I didn't feel particularly good about it. I had brought it up to take the heat off my misfortunes, but I soon realized I was being petty—and quite obnoxious.

Eventually Colleen wrapped her hands around Jock's clenched fist resting on the table and offered a resolution to their squabble.

"The point is: I got over it. And after a bad marriage with a bland husband, I just wanted a warm body in my bed again."

"There ya go!" exclaimed Jock. Then, after a quick sip from his beer, "Just a warm body, eh?"

"You know what I mean."

I turned to Jock. "Does your girlfriend back in Santiago know?"

"Hell, no! She'd kill me!"

"Show him the texts."

"She texts you?"

"All day long!"

Jock presented his smartphone and scrolled through some of his girlfriend's messages. There were numerous "I love you" sentiments and frequent "Why haven't you written me back?" appeals. However, Jock appeared to write back just once a day, citing poor smartphone reception and fictional Camino schedules.

"I might be cross at this tidy arrangement if I were the girlfriend," whispered Simon.

"I don't know what I'd do if I found out my wife was cheating on *me*," I added.

"Well, *you two* don't have to worry about it," said Colleen.

I ascended the road into the center of Viana, entering through the wall's eastern archway, where a 2007 banner still announced the five-hundredth anniversary of the death of Cesare Borgia, the town's most infamous houseguest.

He was the illegitimate son of Pope Alexander VI and his mistress, Vannozza, and was groomed for a career in the church, becoming a cardinal by the age of eighteen. After his younger brother, Giovanni, a commander of the papal army, was mysteriously assassinated (some say by Cesare himself), Cesare gave up the priesthood and was handed his brother's post.

He married the sister of the king of Navarre but remained a notorious womanizer, fathering at least eleven illegitimate children and eventually contracting syphilis, which allegedly disfigured his handsome face.

Cesare fought in various military campaigns and ruthlessly ruled over various territories in northern Italy under the patronage of his father the pope. So when Pope Alexander VI died of malaria in 1503, Cesare was left without a safety net.

Julius II, a sworn enemy of the Borgia family, soon confiscated Cesare's territories, arrested him, and sent him to a castle prison in Spain—which he eventually escaped.

Cesare's final sanctuary was in Navarre, where his brother-in-law, the king, appointed him commander of his army. There Cesare went to work recapturing Viana from rebel forces but failed to reclaim the town's castle.

Then during a severe storm on March 11, 1507, the besieged rebels fled the castle with Cesare in hot pursuit. However, he outraced his own men, exposing himself to his enemies in a nearby ravine, where they ambushed and killed him.

Cesare Borgia was interred in the Church of Santa Maria until a visiting bishop insisted they dig up his bones and rebury them under the street so the citizens could trample over his sinful past. After many years of petitions, his remains were once again moved back inside the church to mark the five-hundredth anniversary of his death, with the Archbishop of Pamplona proclaiming "Whatever he did in life, he deserves to be forgiven now."

I was looking for my own form of forgiveness from Scottish Jock and Melbourne Colleen as I darted through Viana. On one street corner, I spied Den Mother Betsy counseling some young pilgrims and making sure the girls were eating right. Inside a souvenir shop, I spotted German Lukas and Argentine Camila holding hands and admiring the St. James figurines while Grumpy Abram watched them through the window with disgust.

My only focus was on finding Brie or Jock and Colleen. With Brie, I wanted to follow through on my plan to be a better friend. With Jock and Colleen, I wanted to apologize for my previous night's rude behavior. None of them could be found.

I knew with some certainty where to find Jock and Colleen later that evening. After another round of drinks back in Los Arcos, Jock had turned to Simon, scribbled down an address, and invited him to his birthday "piss-up" at his hotel in Logroño. And after another round of drinks, a drunken Jock finally invited me as well.

I was still separated from Logroño by several hours as I followed the yellow arrows through Viana and exited, exactly as I had entered, through a medieval stone arch.

I descended through the suburbs as the path pivoted around sullen homes and abandoned warehouses until I reached the highway again. I crossed over it onto a quiet road that led me through unattended fields. I was completely alone, the only sounds coming from my feet grinding the gravel.

The path ran through more fields and occasional woodland until signs of industry returned in the form of a distant paper factory. It was significant because, after crossing the nearby footbridge, I was unofficially leaving the autonomous region of Navarre for the equally independent region of La Rioja.

Its name is derived from the Rio Oja (one of the seven tributaries from the mighty Ebro River). Fertile valleys dominate the north and mountain ranges sprawl across the south.

The region's claim to fame is its fine wine. And while its grapes were first planted by the Romans, it was the medieval pilgrims returning home from Santiago who advertised its superior quality throughout the rest of Europe.

Its capital, Logroño, was only three kilometers away as I

ducked under the ring road and walked alone up a paved asphalt track. Ever so gently the track rose along the base of a grassy hill while, ahead to my right, cable towers and unremarkable subdivisions announced that civilization was close at hand.

Within twenty minutes I had reached the Puente de Piedra, which crossed over the Ebro, Spain's greatest river. The name meant Bridge of Stone, which seemed redundant since most of the bridges I had crossed were made from stone.

Burnsley instructed me to turn right onto the cobbled Calle Ruavieja and head for the twelfth-century Santa Maria de Palacio church, whose pyramid tower remains the town's most distinctive landmark (lovingly called the Needle). The only landmark I was interested in, however, was the building *beside* the church, the first of the town's albergues.

Since it was only noon and I had not seen a single soul for almost two hours, I was fairly certain I would have the privilege of picking the building's best bed. I was wrong. The instant I entered the albergue's courtyard, I was met by a horrendous queue of eager pilgrims waiting to register inside the office. The lineup was so long it spilled out of the lobby and extended around all four edges of the courtyard. It was rather confusing, and I had to be told where to stand.

This meant that everyone who followed behind me also had to be told where to stand. It made sense when your first instinct was to head straight for the lobby. It always took a few seconds to wonder, "Why are all these pilgrims sitting around the patio with their backpacks?"

I lasted ten minutes. In that time, no one had moved an inch yet the lineup had extended farther out the courtyard door and into the street. I counted the pilgrims standing in front of me. There were fifty. Let's see, sixty-eight beds, fifty pilgrims waiting outside, many more waiting inside . . . this was a tremendous waste of time.

I left the lineup and marched toward the cathedral to Calle de los Portales, the city's main pedestrian promenade, and entered the first three-star hotel I saw: the Hostel Entresueños. There was no lineup and there was no hesitation. If they had a room, I was staying. How expensive could it be?

I didn't have to tell the clerk that I was walking the Camino. The other guests loitering in the lobby wore dresses and suits. No one carried a backpack.

I passed her my passport and my credit card. "No albergue tonight for me," I proudly announced.

"Too noisy," she agreed while typing furiously.

"It's going to be great to get my own bedroom."

"The bed is big and soft."

"No wait for the shower, either."

"It will be nice to be clean."

My small talk was merely an attempt to get some kind of pilgrim discount. Maybe there was a Camino coupon. Maybe there was a rewards program to encourage more pilgrims to abandon the albergues. I even slid across my credencial to seal the deal. The clerk simply stamped it and slid it back to me.

"It is sixty-three euros. You leave in the morning, yes?"

Sixty-three euros? An albergue costs ten. And that often included a meal.

"I guess there's no pilgrim discount?"

The clerk shook her head, and a wicked smile finally crawled across her face.

The six-hundred-percent mark-up aside, the hotel brought welcome modifications to my Camino routine. I showered without inspecting the floor for human hairs, and I walked around naked without covering my genitals in shame. Then I cleaned my clothes in the sink without freezing my fingers in cold water. And it remained hot during the entire washing process.

And then . . . I lay down naked on my bed . . . and napped. I hadn't been tired until that very moment—even after racing across Spain with Simon. But it had all caught up to me.

The stillness was deafening and glorious. When I woke up a few hours later, I was more than richly motivated to reunite with my wife and ease her suffering and distress—as well as find some missing friends.

Like many of the other towns on the Camino, Logroño was founded as a Roman settlement and then abandoned after the fall of the empire. By the tenth century, the town was equally valued and disputed by the kingdoms of Navarre and Castile until it was crowned the capital of its own territory.

It contained a charming mix of modern and medieval diversions but lacked the city spectacles that would necessitate a repeat visit. Sure, there was a Gothic cathedral with twin towers spiking over the heart of Old Town, and, yes, there were dozens of tapas restaurants bursting out of its central square, but there was nothing truly astonishing about its history.

However, its formidable size and modern methods meant it wasn't bewitched by the sleepy siesta, the horrendous time-waster that saps many of the charms from most of the smaller towns.

Walking the street I was immediately struck by the futility of trying to find Brie. When she had taken her leave in Los Arcos and mouthed the words, "See you tomorrow," we had both assumed we would spot each other in the town square. But Logroño had too many squares, and too many pubs and restaurants. Was she walking on this street? Or that one? This side of the river? Or that side?

On any other day, we would have begged for more entertainment choices. That day, it was our Camino comeuppance. Be careful what you wish for . . .

Since I was spoiled for choice for the first time since visiting Pamplona, I became rather picky as I perused the menus of the agreeable cafés on Calle de los Portales.

My hesitation seemed to confuse all the waiters. As soon as I crossed the threshold of an establishment, I was greeted with a boisterous "Hola!" and a sweeping gesture toward one of their unoccupied tables.

"No, no, no; I'm just looking."

The Spanish weren't aware of that concept. *Just looking? What the hell does that mean? You just walked through the door of my restaurant. What's the problem? Why do you disrespect me like that? Sit down, for crying out loud! Eat something!*

I picked the fifth restaurant on my stroll for snacks, if only to put an end to my mind games with the Logroño food industry.

I found Scottish Jock and Melbourne Colleen at our appointed time inside the lobby of Hotel FG Logroño, the elegant stone hotel opposite the Puente de Piedra.

They were sitting outside the lobby bar, nursing their cocktails, slouched in overstuffed chairs that were spaced several feet apart. Simon hadn't shown up, and the tension was palpable.

"All right, where are we going?" I innocently asked.

"I'm not going anywhere. *He* is, though," said Colleen.

"Better be getting on back to Santiago, mate," announced Jock.

"Shit, was it something I said?"

"Oh, no, no…"

"Something *she* said," said Colleen.

"It's not that—"

"Read the texts. 'Please come home, Jock. I thought I could handle this, Jock. I can't wait forever, Jock.'"

"You knew this at the start; I told you about her in Saint Jean!"

"Yeah, after we slept together—"

"Before—"

The old timeline argument continued unabated for a few more moments.

"You didn't say you were leaving the Camino once we reached Logroño!"

"Before Logroño, after Logroño—what difference does it make? I'm just a warm body anyway—"

"So Simon's not coming?" I asked.

The quarrelling couple continued their hostilities, oblivious to my presence.

"I'm getting a drink," Jock finally snapped as he pulled himself out of his chair.

Colleen just stared at her cocktail.

"Soooo . . . it wasn't anything I said?" I asked.

"This isn't about you."

"Okay. It's just that . . . back in Los Arcos . . . I was having a hard time . . . and then I was kind of rude—"

She repeated, "This isn't about you."

"Right. So let's leave it at that, then. Good."

Leaving the hotel after some rather awkward goodbyes, I spent the rest of the night walking around Logroño under the illusion I might find Brie. I strolled up and down Calle de los Portales, up and down Calle Ruavieja, through every square in Old Town, and through every lobby of every albergue listed in Burnsley. No luck.

After ten o'clock, when all the good little pilgrims were tucked inside their creaky bunk beds, I gnawed on dry chicken pieces and fries dripping in mayonnaise at a late-night shawarma joint. It was not late, but it felt late. And even though I was registered in a hotel, I felt surprisingly uncomfortable breaking Camino curfew.

I returned to my hotel before the hour struck eleven. Curfew or not, I still had to get up at dawn. And I still had to join my fellow pilgrims on the long and winding road toward Santiago.

Despite the absence of snorers, I still woke up every hour in my hotel bed unsure of the time, worried I had somehow slept through the Camino cavalcade. By the time my wakeup call came at six o'clock, I was already packed and ready for battle.

Just like the previous day, it was another long walk: 30.1 kilometers to the town of Nájera. Once out of hectic Logroño, it was supposed to be a peaceful jaunt through parklands and farmlands with little effort needed to reach the higher elevations.

The major difference in today's journey was that there would be a letter waiting for me.

A hearty breakfast was recommended before the 12.7-kilometer leg to the first town of Navarrete, but I paid more attention to Burnsley's other warning: the route out of Logroño was tricky, so extra care was needed to follow those yellow arrows. If Burnsley had been confused . . . God help us all!

I skipped my morning meal and latched onto two Italian pilgrims outside my hotel. They strode the streets with admirable confidence; they even whistled as they walked, as if the morning silence might lull them to sleep. I followed a few meters behind and never let them out of my sight. It was borderline stalking.

I followed them out of the city. I followed them through the suburban park. I followed them through the public parkland that led us to the Logroño reservoir. I then nodded my thanks and rushed ahead along the gravel pathway that encircled the lake.

By the time the gravel turned into asphalt and the trail climbed gently toward Navarrete, I was all alone. The Camino had returned to its familiar form, with acres of vineyards on either side of the track confirming that, yes, La Rioja was indeed the wine capital of Spain.

At the top of the hill, a chain-link fence separated us from the encroaching highway; hundreds of handcrafted crosses made from twigs and other scraps of wood had been affixed to the fence by previous pilgrims.

In my five days of wandering, it was the most overt expression of Christian faith on the Camino I had encountered. Despite the ancient road's religious origins, I had witnessed few travelers visiting the village churches. I also saw no one bow their head in prayer and heard no one speak about God in their lives in any meaningful way. And there wasn't much talk about vices, either, beyond a few sexual confessions and the occasional admission to the overconsumption of cocktails.

For the most part, walking the Camino was a clean-living experience, with only a naughty minority lurking in the margins.

Of course, that was about to change when I read Pam's next letters . . .

12

NÁJERA REUNION

AFTER MY CASUAL ENCOUNTER with the faith-based fence, the Camino landscape resumed with vineyards and farmers' fields, followed by a couple of crossings over the highway and the appearance of the sorry ruins of a twelfth-century pilgrim hospital, after which I finally plodded up the steep slope into Navarrete.

The historic town was built on the hill by an unnamed Castilian king who wanted to protect his nearby Castilian border. Today, Navarrete is under the protection of the Spanish crown as a *Conjunto Histórico* (a type of heritage designation). And not only is the town famous for its rosé and its sixteenth-century church, it's also home to many pottery factories thanks to the abundance of the dark red clay found in the surrounding countryside.

After such a long morning walk, most pilgrims stopped in town to rest and refuel at one of the streetside cafés. And I, like most of the other pilgrims, stopped at the first café that offered any type of nourishment. However, every table was occupied, and there was a long lineup forming at the bar.

I spotted a street sign advertising another café only one hundred meters away. When I arrived a minute later, it was empty. Huh? Was I the only one who had noticed the sign? Was I the only one who hated unnecessary queues? Or was I the only one who was patient enough to walk an extra hundred meters to order a coffee and sugar pastry?

On the way out of Navarrete the gravel track returned, and the next seven kilometers to Ventosa were disagreeably similar to my entry into Navarrete: a virtually solo trek running parallel to the highway through rolling hills covered in vineyards.

The uniformity (some might call it the "monotony") of the terrain made my mind wander. I continued to pine for Pam, of course, and I kept my eyes on the road for any sign of Brie, but I was mostly thinking about Scottish Jock's torrid affair with Melbourne Colleen. Clearly, Jock still adored his girlfriend back in Santiago. Why potentially throw it all away to sleep with Colleen? What was the appeal? Did she represent some naughty novelty that was too good to pass up? Or did she simply break up the boredom of his humdrum life? Whatever the reason, it certainly seemed like Jock's guilt and regret about the affair was growing.

This wasn't a moral dissection, mind you; this was a cause-and-effect exploration. And I couldn't work it out. Every affair is different, so I suppose that everyone's reason for having that affair is different as well. And while it was completely none of my business, I now wanted to know more than ever.

Since almost every pilgrim was in a sharing mood on most Camino nights, I was fairly certain that Scottish Jock would eventually confess his carnal justifications. In the meantime, I struggled to determine his motivations.

Melbourne Colleen's reason for the affair was more easily discerned. Sure, she said she just wanted a "warm body" in her bed again, but the tryst also seemed to signal the reawakening of her sexual desire after a bad marriage. Her undoing in this arrangement, it appeared, was putting too much emotional significance in her Camino encounter—at least in terms of the amount of heart and mind Jock was willing to invest.

This was all speculation, of course, and quite judgmental without the benefit of any facts or cross-examination of the two participating parties. But it kept my mind busy as I approached Ventosa.

It was as insignificant as any other village on the Camino, but the steeple of its sixteenth-century church was a welcome signpost among the repetitive vineyards. And just like Navarrete, Ventosa was a suitable spot to break for a snack.

I didn't even have to enter the village. A café was conveniently located only meters from the Camino path. Without even considering the posted menu, I ordered another coffee and ate another sugary pastry.

Back on the road, I bluntly asked myself, "Why am I eating so terribly? Am I really that uninspired?" I also noted I had yet to read my wife's next letter but was already acting depressed. Was it a subconscious sign of things to come?

My melancholy mood remained for the rest of the morning as I climbed the dirt track to the day's highest point, Alto De San Antón. Finally, the town of Nájera could be seen straddling the horizon. Now I had a focal point as I descended through more farmland, which was only occasionally peppered with ragged hills and tight clusters of trees. A mountain range was also looming behind my destination, but without snow or other identifiable marker the mountains soon faded from my mental picture like the forgotten edges of a painted canvas.

The red-dirt path soon widened to a gravel road as I overtook other plodding pilgrims heading into Nájera. "Buen Camino," I mumbled as I passed each group, never pausing to say anything more but always inspecting their faces to see if anyone looked familiar.

The vineyards and farmlands were eventually replaced with office buildings and factories as the path yielded to busy locals crossing the footbridge that spanned the Yalde River. This was now the Nájera suburbs. And if the entrance into Los Arcos had been bland and listless, Nájera's initial offerings were unsettling and repugnant. To say that the town lacked charm was far too generous. This was Los Arcos but on a grander and blander scale.

I didn't understand it. The earlier scan of my Burnsley had detected words like "historic," "magnificent," and "beautiful." Did my eyes deceive me, or was Burnsley completely misguided?

My attitude adjusted once I began to cross the bridge over the Najerilla River into the older part of town. Finally the Burnsley hype made sense.

The river itself was shallow and sparkling. Its banks were lush with green grass for play and leafy trees for shade. And along the shore was a pretty pedestrian boulevard with shops, restaurants, and all manner of tables and benches to rest and relax.

Even the bridge road was constructed in a slick cobblestone pattern, which led to rows of delightful buildings painted in hazy hues of yellow, brown, and red. Behind it all stood a majestic hill of trees (crowding the faint outline of a former castle), which abruptly ended in a dramatic wall of red rock stretching across the town like the sprawling curtain to a spectacular carnival show.

Burnsley was right. Here lay the "historic" Nájera, and it was indeed "magnificent" and "beautiful." And it was more than that. Small towns can be either charming or dreadful, and most can be commonly classified as dull. Old-town Nájera surpassed all those limitations. Within seconds of setting foot on that bridge, I had decided I could live here for an entire summer and be thoroughly content.

Despite my positive reaction, my desperation to read the next letter from Pam left me in no humor to enjoy the town or properly secure a bed for the night.

I carefully considered her earlier two-word clue, "Red Rock." The cliffs? The letter had to be located near those cliffs. But where?

I retrieved Pam's Clue Sheet and discovered the Nájera riddle was the longest one of the bunch, written as a tribute to her favorite movie, *The Shawshank Redemption*. *"There's a red rock bridge up near Nájera. At the base of that bridge, you'll find a cupboard that has no earthly business inside a Spanish bridge. There's something sitting in it I want you to have."*

If you remember the film, it was part of the message the escaping convict, Andy, gave to his old friend, Red. Andy directed him to find a soon-to-be buried box of money with instructions on where to find Andy in Mexico if Red ever got parole. Of course I saw the parallel to Pam, the escaping wife who directed me to find her letters of instructions on where to eventually find her in Spain if I ever got the courage to walk the Camino.

But I also conjured up other troubling images and themes

from the movie: finding your self worth while living inside a prison (like living inside our marriage); Andy not showing his wife love and driving her away into the arms of another man (like I had driven Pam away to Spain). And how would I analyze Andy having to "crawl through a river of shit" to come out "clean on the other side"?

Maybe I was overthinking it. Maybe Pam was simply playing around with a movie quote. Maybe. But I wouldn't know for sure until I found that next letter.

Was her note underneath the bridge I was standing on? Unlikely. *The Shawshank Redemption* reference suggested a remote location, and this bridge was heading into the heart of the old Nájera. Plus, it wasn't near the red rocks. There was another bridge located farther down the riverbank leading to the edge of town.

After crossing the bridge, I bounded down the steps to the pedestrian boulevard and marched directly toward the isolated overpass. Only when I got close, when the houses stopped, when the red rock cliff soared dramatically from the dusty street, did I finally remember a positive theme from Pam's favorite film: hope, even in the bleakest of situations, is always a good thing and should never die.

"*There's a red rock bridge up near Nájera.*" It was located less than four hundred meters from the town center, but it was isolated and forgotten. The red cliff rose close to the edge of the overpass, its smooth wall undulating across the town's border, as if hundreds of rock plates were stacked on top of each other to mark the eons of time that predated even the Roman settlers.

"*At the base of that bridge, you'll find a cupboard that has no earthly business inside a Spanish bridge.*" I snuck down to the bridge's foundation, tiptoeing across the strands of grass that separated the base from the babbling river. Sure enough, there were two cupboards cut into the support. If they had been designed with windows to protect them, the glass was long removed. One was completely empty, but the other had two thick electrical cords plugged into a duplex box with various unmarked buttons.

This cupboard was covered in cobwebs, littered with rocks and discarded pop cans, and looked like a terribly unsafe place to stick one's unprotected hands.

"*There's something sitting in it I want you to have.*" I would have to ignore the safety hazard, because I had also noticed a small letter strategically placed under some of those rocks.

Once again, the letter was wrapped in plastic. And once again, it was damaged—not by moisture, but by human hands!

The envelope was unsealed, and the letter itself was severely stained. By what, I didn't know. Coffee? Gravy? Someone had opened the envelope and read the letter—while eating the world's messiest sandwich? I mean, what was that? The perpetrator had then stuffed the letter back into the envelope and reburied it under the rocks.

On closer inspection, the letter also appeared to be missing the second page. Perhaps it was too damaged and the intruder had thrown it away. Perhaps it was salacious, and the intruder had wanted to keep it for himself. I'd never know.

I scampered up the slope to sit on the grass and read what was left, and legible, of Pam's letter.

> Dear Jamie,
>
> Welcome to Najera! How beautiful was that walk into town today? I mean, not at the beginning, of course. But once you crossed that bridge?! I just love that red cliff . . .

The first stain ruined the rest of the paragraph, but I don't think I missed anything. Pam was still effusive about her impressions of Nájera when her missive resumed a few sentences later . . .

> I want to stay an extra day, but I really don't want to fall behind my new friends. Hasn't everyone been so wonderful? Every night I learn something new from these people. The wine helps, doesn't it . . .

The next section was difficult to read, but she seemed to describe a nice couple from Seattle who had become her close companions. The humorous husband was knowledgeable about world events and even had a soft spot for Canada, while the bubbly wife was curious about Pam's job and asked a lot of questions about the ad business.

Pam also mentioned frequent encounters with a retired couple from Arizona who had once lived in International Falls, Minnesota, and listened to CBC Radio out of Winnipeg to get an outsider's perspective of the United States.

It was all very carefree and convivial, and despite my relief that my wife was having a good time on the Camino, it was also very frustrating under the decipherable constraints of this letter.

> *Look, I know I went on and on about how I was feeling in the last letter . . .*

Sadly, no, I didn't know. Mrs. Landerrain made sure of that . . .

> *And I hope you now understand why I had to leave you and Mom and my doctor to deal with this on my own . . .*

Sadly, no, I didn't. But I simply had to accept that decision. I had no other recourse now . . .

> *I don't want to repeat myself but trust me, every day is still hard. But every day I also don't regret my decision. This is still the best thing I could do for myself!*
>
> *So, thank God for days like today in beautiful Najera where I can just soak it all in and enjoy it. And thank God for people like Rick and Amy, who definitely help me when I'm not feeling well. AND when I am! And Joel and Diane, too . . .*

I could only assume she was referring to the couples from Seattle and Arizona. And I could only assume she was a fighter and getting some form of medication to help her cope.

The next section was so smudged I could identify only the words "drugs" and "*farmacia*." I could only imagine what drugs she was taking, but I had noticed there was a pharmacy with a qualified doctor in every sizeable town. Getting proper medical help every day was not an issue.

Flipping the page, I panicked to see so little left to read and so much damage done to the rest of the letter. In the next section, she appeared to be asking me a series of questions about my impressions of the Camino and whether I had met any people who were inspiring me. There were no legible paragraphs anymore—only sentences and phrases.

> Have you made any friends? I mean, 'close' friends . . .
>
> I hope you're not gloomy. You get so gloomy when you don't get your way . . .
>
> I can't believe how many people walk alone . . .
>
> They tell the most honest stories, don't you find? They never hold back . . .
>
> They even hook up! Isn't that a riot?! . . .

All that remained at the edge of the paper was an unfulfilled "*I wish* . . ." and a jab of "*Don't you dare* . . ." Then the letter abruptly ended. The second page of hope and warning was lost forever.

What did you wish, Pam? And what were you daring me not to do?

I sat on the bank of the Najerilla River for another hour at least. Rereading the parts I could decipher. Cursing the parts I could not. Tearing up a little. Daydreaming a lot.

Finally, I couldn't ignore the pilgrim's routine anymore. I had to secure my bed for the night. A hotel was a serious consideration, but they were located back in the boorish suburbs. According to Burnsley, all the available albergues were situated on *this* side of the Najerilla River.

My search was brief and initially disappointing. The first private albergue was fully reserved. The second private albergue no longer existed. The larger municipal albergue was crawling with traveling teenagers and was listed by Burnsley as "somewhat cramped."

Fortunately I stumbled upon a third private albergue near the first Old Town bridge (which was conveniently not listed in Burnsley). There were only two beds left. Would I mind paying a little extra for a smaller room with only three other roommates?

"A little extra? I'll pay you double and give you a big hug!"

Nájera was founded by the Romans. Its name, however, was an Arabic derivative meaning "between the cliffs" or "between the rocks" or "between two hills." Suffice it to say, it was between *something*.

After the Moors flattened Pamplona in 929, the kingdom of Navarre made Nájera its new capital, constructing a castle on the hill and reinforcing the town to be a strategic military base.

A century later, with Nájera safe from attack, King Sancho III modified the Camino route so that pilgrims could visit the town and bring along that valuable Camino commerce.

The story behind the town's most famous urban legend occurred in 1032 when Prince Garcia III (Sancho's heir) was hunting along the shores of the Najerilla River. After he spotted a peculiar dove overhead, he sent out his royal falcon in pursuit. The prince followed the flight of the birds into the trees, where he stumbled upon a hidden cave.

Inside the cave he discovered the falcon and the dove were resting in front of a statue of the Virgin Mary, alongside a jar of fresh lilies, a lamp, and a bell. The prince considered this a miracle (I would have assumed that a squatter had left it behind and was out for a stroll).

This discovery prompted the prince to form an order of knights called the *Caballeros de la Terraza* (Knights of the Jar). When he became king, Garcia III constructed a church on the site, which survives today with the cave (and a replica of the Virgin statue) still intact inside the crypt (along with the tombs of thirty medieval kings). After sustaining significant damage over the centuries because of regional clashes, the original church has since been refashioned into the impressive Monasterio de Santa Maria La Real.

I never did explore that monastery or its magical cave. Instead, I wandered aimlessly around Old Town, from the shopping spoils of Calle Mayor to the beaten-down bungalows on the rocky roads near the red-rock cliffs.

My mind was busy reviewing Pam's final clues in her first batch of letters *and* their vast distances—the "typewriter" letter was almost one hundred kilometers away in Burgos, while her "pilgrim" letter was 150 kilometers beyond *that* in León (straight through the heart of the dreaded Meseta). So, should I continue my woeful walk? Or should I pick up the pace by using more convenient transportation?

I contemplated all of this as I sat on a bench in the Plaza de España drinking a bottle of the local beer. The majestic monastery loomed large ahead of me. The castle ruins sat atop the cliffs overhead. The ladies gossiped around the patio tables while the men played cards. Then there were the small children kicking a soccer ball among the remains of a twelfth-century albergue. Medieval remnants mixed with modern-day élan—this town square was what every town square aspired to be—and I quickly decided that this magnificent town was worthy of a good, unapologetic night of drinking.

Only one person on the Camino had the power to save me from myself. "Hiya, Jamie!"

Brie plopped down beside me with her own bottle of beer. She had gone native, eschewing her pilgrim uniform for a cheap lace dress that exposed her slender shoulders. Her once-pale skin now was now freckled across her back, and her cheeks were pink and flushed. Only her sandy curls looked the same, falling down to her eyebrows and begging for a thick brush to comb away the mystery that crossed the top of her peculiar little face.

"I was standing right there admiring the church and the cliffs, and I was thinking, 'Is there a prettier sight on the whole Camino? I don't think so.' And then I saw you. And I thought, 'I can't join Jamie without a drink in my hand; it's been far too long.' So I marched right in there and ordered a beer. And the lady said, 'Which one?' And I didn't know; I don't drink beer. So, I said, 'I don't care.' And that didn't sit so well with her, because the Spanish don't know what it means when we say we 'don't care.' So I apologized about ten times and then finally pointed to one. So, here it is, and I hope it's a good one."

"It's great to see you too, Brie."

"She didn't call."

"Who?"

"Your mother-in-law."

Brie passed me her phone. "If you want to check on things . . ."

I checked my e-mail account. A few old friends had written me back. No one knew anything relevant and only expressed general concern about Pam. No one asked about me or wondered how I was.

"No one knows anything," I said as I returned her phone.

"That may be good news, Jamie."

I wasn't convinced.

"Everybody shares bad news. That's what gossip is all about, innit? So they don't know anything, yeah? That could only mean good news. No news . . . is good news."

"Maybe."

"So, dear Jamie, what happened after I left?"

Now I did all the talking. I detailed every minor moment from the Los Arcos roundtable to my culpability in the breakup of Scottish Jock and Melbourne Colleen.

"It was a mess from the start. Don't you worry," Brie assured me.

I then described my search for Pam's letter before I dropped it on her lap.

"Really?" Brie gasped and thanked me for my trust with a warm smile and a wink.

She read it in silence, not once commenting on the excessive stains or the missing page. She returned the letter and looked directly into my worried face.

"You do get gloomy when you don't get your way."

"Yes . . . *and*?"

"I really like Nájera too. It *would* be nice to stay another day."

"Brie . . ."

"Don't get wound up. It doesn't say much now, does it? We know why she left. We know she's sick and it's hard and all that. But she has some drugs and plenty of friends who take care of her. Sounds like she's having a lovely time, all considering."

"Well, what about the rest of it?"

"Don't know. It's all bunged up. Had you fancied a curry or something when you read it?"

"That's from somebody else! Somebody else read it before I did—!"

"Oh."

"See? That's important, isn't it?"

Brie thought for a moment but only offered another "Don't know."

"And did you notice there was a missing page?"

"I *did* notice."

"Right? The letter just ends, doesn't it? But she wrote more. Maybe much more! Either the rest got ruined, or the guy who read it earlier just took it. What do you think about *that*?"

"Don't know. It's gone, innit?"

"Fucking hell . . ."

"Well, I'm sorry, Jamie. I can only read what she told you."

"I need that next letter."

"Quite right."

"I need to go to Burgos as soon as possible. Will you come with me?"

Brie, of course, agreed to accompany me to Burgos. But she tempered my urgency and encouraged me to walk to Burgos rather than board a series of buses.

What validated Brie's argument was her identification of Pam's desperate desire that I experience the Camino the very same way she had experienced it. That meant walking it. And Pam, diagnosed with cancer, continued to carry on with the tiring task, even at an incredible disadvantage.

Some of Pam's more powerful phrases from her initial letters suddenly came burning back to life. *"You won't be able to completely understand me and everything I've been going through lately until you do this walk."* *"Once you've embraced the whole concept of the Camino and what it can do to your life, everything just becomes so clear and meaningful. It changed me completely for the better and gave me so much peace."*

Even her incomplete "Don't you dare" comment in her last letter became a little less mysterious. I could now envision her probable pleas. "Don't you dare . . . hop the bus to Burgos. Don't you dare . . . quit the Camino. Don't you dare . . . give up on *us!*"

"Plus, you don't want to be a tramposo, do you?" teased Brie.

Only after we dined and drank at the Plaza de España and I escorted Brie back to the "somewhat cramped" municipal albergue did I realize my nagging problems had once again dominated our discussion.

"I'm sorry, Brie. I forgot about everything that happened to you after Los Arcos."

Brie forgave me with a smile and a quick embrace. "Well, now we have something to talk about tomorrow, don't we?"

That does it! No more complaining about the Camino. No more outward pining for Pam. I once again committed to becoming a better pilgrim—and a better friend to Brie. I owed her that.

Of course, this proved more difficult than I thought. And I was severely tested the following day . . .

13

SANTO DOMINGO MIRACLES

WHEN I BOUNDED down the stairs of my albergue the following day, I found Brie waiting for me in the lobby. She was patiently sitting on a bench, all geared up and ready to go, contently watching the other pilgrims dart and dash through their morning preparations.

It was a short walk today, an exactly twenty-one-kilometer stretch, mostly uphill through farmland without any shade. Burnsley called it "wonderful" because the remote trail was located far away from the hectic highway.

"Buen Camino," Brie said cheerily.

"I thought we were meeting at your albergue."

"Couldn't sleep."

"Too many snorers?"

"Too many kids."

Declining an immediate breakfast, we left Old Town Nájera for a neighboring natural park that led us gently uphill on a soft dirt track through the pines. Although Brie huffed and puffed, her pace was equal to mine; clearly her wonky knee had sufficiently healed, and her lingering blisters were now under control.

We didn't speak much beyond our mutual "How are you doing?" checkups. Brie always said, "Fine." I always said, "I could slow down if you want."

No, Brie was quite content to walk directly behind me, her labored breathing masked by the clickety-click of her trekking poles.

Once the pines peeled away, the landscape returned to farmland as we approached our first town of the day, Azofra. We had already covered 5.8 kilometers, and our appetites called for coffee and something sweet.

It was puzzling to me why anyone would bypass Nájera for this dilapidated dustbin, but the sleepy village still accommodated an exclusive hotel and two mid-sized albergues. Even its holy house, the Church of Our Lady of the Angels, looked like hell.

It was equally puzzling to me why all the famished pilgrims crammed into the first available café, while a spectacularly similar one remained free of customers a few meters away.

We opted for the empty café. And soon, with coffee steaming from our cups and strawberry jam spread liberally across our toast, Brie briefed me about her own Camino adventures. Leaving Los Arcos by herself, she had run into Amsterdam Sarah and Glum Linnea in Torres Del Rio and accompanied them all the way to Logroño.

"Sarah says you were looking for me. I'm not so bad, am I, Jamie?"

"Well . . ."

"No need to explain," Brie said with a laugh.

Was she just flirting with me? Was I blushing?

However, the three Camino companions split up when Sarah and Linnea opted for a Logroño hotel while Brie patiently waited in that dreadfully long albergue line.

"Logroño was nice enough. I finally got my hair cut."

I studied Brie's face closely. Her hair length looked the same. Her curls still crested her eyebrows. Was she kidding?

"You did?"

"Yes, Jamie, I did," Brie sighed. "Blokes never notice."

"It's hanging in your eyes."

"It's the style, if you must know!"

Much like mine, her walk from Logroño to Nájera had been largely on her own. She saw no one from our group and acquainted herself with no one new.

"It's hard to believe," I remarked.

"Is it?"

"Everywhere we go, people know you. Almost everyone I met on the Camino is because of you."

"I'm not so bad, am I, Jamie?"

"Why do you keep saying that? Who says you're bad?"

"You were just asking about me in Torres Del Rio. It was rather sweet, that's all."

"I didn't mean anything by it—"

Brie laughed again. Was she just flirting with me again? Was I blushing? And why didn't I mind?

Brie's sudden playfulness was muted once we left Azorfa and made the slow and steady climb toward the next village of Cirueña. Burnsley called it a "delightful track," but it was a mind-numbing slog. The vineyards, which offered growth and greenery, were replaced by vast fields of wheat and hay, which presented a tedious blur of beige and rusty gold.

The only thing colorful in this section of the Camino came from the bubbly personality of Alison, the long-legged postgrad from Kansas City. We could hear her gaining on us outside Azorfa, because she was whistling an indeterminate tune that gained in strength until she stopped to wish us a "Buen Camino."

"What song were you whistling?" I asked.

"Oh, I don't know. I made it up! I kinda lost track of what I was whistling, so I just whistled louder, you know?"

Obviously.

"Are you walking alone?" asked Brie.

"Oh, no. My friends are back there eating breakfast," she said, pointing back to Azorfa with her trekking pole. "I always walk ahead and wait for them. It's like I'm walking two Caminos!"

I'm sorry, what?

"So, how did you even choose the Camino?" asked Brie.

"I don't know. My friends wanted to go to Europe and stare at paintings and buildings. But I'd rather see stuff I like, like fields and stuff. It reminds me of home. Well, except for the Spanish stuff. I don't know why people here don't speak more English."

You don't?! Suddenly, I missed Jasmine, the sandwich-eating Australian who slept outdoors. She had more sense.

This odd conversation continued all the way to Cirueña, with Brie peppering her with questions and Alison answering with her wobbly logic.

"You see all these vineyards, but where are all the grapes? I keep seeing 'em, but I don't see anything purple . . ." "Sometimes I see, like, ten yellow markers on the street? And I still get lost! Isn't that crazy?" "My friends hate all the albergues, but I don't mind them. The snoring totally puts me to sleep . . ."

Eventually I slowed down to walk behind Brie and Alison to drop out of earshot and nurse my jaw back to health after having clenched it for several straining kilometers. The effort to become a better pilgrim and keeping my thoughts to myself were becoming a strain.

The yellow markers Alison found so confusing led us past a golf club complex outside the village of Cirueña, followed by a series of empty apartment blocks. It seems the Cirueña suburbs were for sale. They offered leisure living under the Spanish sun, but nobody was buying. It was only when we reached Cirueña proper that the town came to life.

At the first available restaurant, Alison announced, "Well, I think I'll wait here for my friends." Noticing the pilgrim lineup at the counter, she said, "They're always full, aren't they?"

When Brie considered joining her for a mid-morning snack, I whispered, "Santo Domingo is less than six kilometers away. We'll get there early and get a good bed for once."

Brie nodded, and we wished Alison well. We managed only a few steps before Brie began giggling, "Snoring puts her to sleep? Why do they speak so much Spanish *in Spain*? How did you not lose your mind? I mean, I know I rabbit on and on, but I thought she was just winding us up, you know? And you were so quiet!"

"I'm a new man, Brie," I replied with a grin.

"Obviously! Well done, you—well done!"

Brie's delight and my relief at passing a critical pilgrim test lifted our spirits through the otherwise-dismal community of Cirueña. The village had absolutely no appreciation for growing grass or nourishing trees and made sure that every one of its buildings was painted the same dreary brown.

The ensuing 5.9-kilometer plod to Santo Domingo de la Calzado was even worse: a gradual hill up and then a slow descent down. Straight as an arrow, through tall grass and mangy hay without shade or any memorable distractions.

Then the outline of Santo Domingo appeared on the horizon. Instead of offering us enchantment, it offered us dread. The uniformity of its skyline signaled lackluster compartmentalization. There were boxy factories on the right, identical suburban apartment buildings on the left, and a humdrum historical core surrounding its lofty cathedral.

Since the entry into Nájera had eventually unveiled a scenic surprise, however, I held out some hope for Santo Domingo de la Calzada. But as we entered the unsightly suburbs, my hope soon withered. The town had started off as an ugly suburb, and it remained that way right up to the door of the small albergue centrally located on Calle Mayor.

The welcoming hospitalero was pleasant, of course, but his crooked teeth and odd 1960s haircut were unsettling. He looked like an unattractive version of Peter Sellers. He assigned me a top bunk and slipped a small photo into my credencial.

"What's this?"

"My saint," Peter Sellers answered.

The pride in his saint, Santo Domingo, or Saint Dominic, was understandable. Born in 1019 in a nearby village, Dominic was a humble shepherd who aspired to become a monk but was rejected by the Benedictine bullies for being illiterate. So Dominic hid himself in the forest and built his own hermitage. Soon he met the bishop of Ostia, who ordained him as a priest, and the pair got to work on building a wooden bridge across the Oja River to help out the pilgrims (later rebuilt by Dominic as a sturdier stone structure).

This became Dominic's life work: to improve the Camino conditions for the traveling pilgrims in La Rioja.

Fair enough. However, this is where the supernatural shenanigans start. The story goes that Dominic hacked his way through thirty-seven kilometers of forest . . . alone . . . using nothing but his magical sickle to clear the way. Some say he also rid the forest of bandits. Sure, why not?

Eventually Dominic's more direct Camino route replaced the Roman road that had wound its way between Nájera and Redecilla del Camino. He also established the seeds of the town that would later bear his name by building a hospital, a pilgrim shelter, a church, and his own tomb. The legend suggests he did this all alone. In reality, Dominic's solo efforts were widely supported by King Alfonso VI of Castile, who wanted Catholic settlers in the area to supplant the local Muslims.

After a life of Camino service, Dominic died in 1109 at the age of ninety. In 1334, King Alfonso XI named the town after him (with *de la calzada* meaning "of the causeway").

This all played a part in my overall disappointment with Dominic's hometown. After such high praise for the saint with the supernatural sickle, I was expecting something much more magical. Whatever he accomplished, he should be applauded. Whatever the city fathers did after his demise, they should be ashamed.

I was also a little disenchanted with my albergue arrangement. It was allegedly run by (unseen) nuns, so the sexes were separated, with Brie bunking in a different room. When I approached my assigned bed, I was disappointed to find a fat Spaniard sitting on the lower bunk pointing and laughing at me. He then gestured with grunts and groans that he snored.

Of course, I didn't find his announcement remotely funny. "Then you should sleep in a private room! Why do the rest of us have to listen to your snoring? It's rude!"

Of course, he didn't understand me and kept right on chuckling and grunting.

When I joined Brie in the lobby after our chores, she was perfectly content to lie on one of the albergue's leather couches and read her guidebook for the rest of the afternoon. That meant she wanted to nap. It was understandable. For the first time on our trek, an albergue provided tempting seats on which to relax and unwind. Nobody wanted to lie in bed like a child, but everybody wanted to stretch out on a leather couch and close their eyes.

I was too hungry, and I elected to explore the town instead. I walked toward Avenue Juan Carlos I, the main business street bordering the historical core, for a late but proper breakfast. The eggs were undercooked, but there was plenty of toast and bacon to line my stomach.

Next, I headed for the Oja River to inspect the 148-meter-long Puente del Santo, the Saint's Bridge, the stone crossing that Saint Dominic had built.

It did its job with its sixteen arches straddling the seeping stream, but it lacked any . . . flair. Just like Dominic's Camino trail, it was completely straight and unimaginative. And unlike the Najerilla's riverbanks, which were lush with green grass for play and leafy trees for shade, the Oja riverbanks were neglected and overgrown with weeds and inconvenient shrubbery.

I continued exploring the historical core with little enthusiasm. It was dull and drab around every corner. Where was the town's pretty pedestrian boulevard with its enticing shops and restaurants? It didn't exist. Never trust a hermit to construct anything fun.

I returned to my albergue and searched for an available couch. No luck. The best I could do was sit next to Brie, who was fast asleep with her open guidebook spread across her chest and her sock feet propped up on the coffee table. I pulled off my shoes. With nothing to read and no one to distract me, I closed my eyes for a potential nap—and slept peacefully for hours.

"Jamie, wake up. Jamie, wake up."

I opened my eyes to a beaming Brie hovering over me.

"Wake up, sleepyhead. It's time to nosh up."

Lacking imagination, I led a famished Brie back to Avenue Juan Carlos I, where several restaurants had set up sidewalk patios. We inspected a few posted menus before choosing the one with the most photos of food. Neither of our meals matched up to their flattering snapshots.

It was only after we ordered our second bottle of wine that Brie elevated our dinner prattle into something significant.

"When you were away, I got some Martin news."

"Really?"

All day long I had resisted any questions about her ex-husband and their relationship. I endured Happy Alison, I agreed to share a bunk with a snoring Spaniard, and I toured the town alone while Brie napped. Not once did I pry about her personal life. Not once did I push her into discussing anything she wasn't willing to freely share. Now was my chance to finally give her some support. This was finally going to be about her—and only her.

"He's getting it on with one of my mates."

"Getting it on? How do you know?"

"My neighbor texted me."

"The one with the lung cancer?"

"No, she's dead."

"Right. Sorry."

"No, my next-*door* neighbor. She's seen everything. Me and Martin and our fights at home, me and Martin at the pub, Martin and his mates at the pub, Martin all alone at the pub; nothing got past this one, that's the truth."

"I get it. So—" Why was I so impatient? Let her talk at her own pace. Relax . . .

"Right. So, she sees Martin at the pub the other day, playing the video slot machines like he does. But get this: he's not alone this time. And he's not with his mates. He's with this slag."

"What is that? A slut?"

"No, she's not a slut! She's one of my mates!"

"I'm confused. So, she doesn't want to have sex with him?"

"Oh, she wants to shag him. But she's not a slut!"

I could only assume that referring to her promiscuous friend as a slut somehow reflected poorly on Brie. "So, she's a slag?"

"Exactly!"

"And she's one of your friends?"

"Yeah. Mabel."

"You have a friend named Mabel?"

"Ahhh, she looks nothing like a Mabel, that's for sure. More like one of them French-type girls I was never keen on—"

"Hellooooooo!"

We were suddenly interrupted by the Camino's impossibly cute couple, Argentine Camila and German Lukas.

"Sorry," said Camila. "Do you two want privacy?"

Yes! We were talking about her husband having sex with one of her friends; I was politely listening; I was finally being a good friend. Go away!

"No, not at all," said the ever-gracious Brie. "Have a seat."

Lukas hesitated. "If you're having a bad moment…"

"Nahhh. Sit, sit. It's over."

"We were just leaving, weren't we?" I asked, hoping Brie would join me in my escape. It didn't matter. The waiter innocently exposed my lie by bringing over the second bottle of wine.

Lukas pulled over a chair for Camila and guided her to her seat before gallantly tucking her under the table. They even made sitting down on a patio disgustingly cute.

"So, you were saying?" I asked Brie.

She shot me a withering look. Sex talk about Mabel was over.

"We should warn you. The food doesn't exactly match the photos," offered Brie.

"That's okay," said Lukas, reaching across the table to hold Camila's tiny hand. "Our appetite never matches the photos, either."

Was that a joke? It didn't even make any sense. No matter; the two women giggled anyway.

Camila turned to the waiter and ordered another bottle of wine in Spanish. He nodded and clipped his heels and ran off like his house was on fire. When Brie and I had ordered, he was distracted by the pretty girls walking the sidewalk and went for an extended smoke break.

"Did you see the cathedral?" asked Camila.

"Not yet," said Brie.

"No? You didn't see the chickens?"

Camila was referring to one of the most famous miracle stories about the Camino—albeit a story that's been amended several times over the centuries.

Back in the fourteenth century, a German family of three traveled the Camino and came to rest in a Santo Domingo inn. During the night, the innkeeper's barmaid or servant or beautiful daughter—of course she was beautiful; is there any other kind in these stories?—tried to slip into bed with the German teen and seduce him. However, the virtuous lad rebuffed her advances and said he was seeking salvation on this trip, not sex with a beautiful barmaid/servant/daughter.

This didn't sit too well with the embarrassed barmaid/servant/daughter. In fact, the jilted girl sought her revenge by planting one of the inn's silver goblets inside the boy's bag. The next morning, she reported the goblet missing. A search was made, the goblet was found, and the boy was brought before the town's judge or mayor and immediately found guilty.

His punishment? Death by hanging. (That seems rather excessive, doesn't it?) Did the jilted girl speak up after the sentencing? Nope. Did the lad's parents appeal? Nope. They simply carried on with their trip . . . as you do.

One month later, after reaching Santiago de Compostela and then returning through Santo Domingo, the parents decided to pay respects to their dead boy . . . who was still hanging from the gallows! That's right. He was left hanging for a month. How lazy was this town?

Then the lad cried out to his parents. He wasn't dead, after all! He was being held up by an invisible St. Dominic or St. James or the Virgin Mary!

The parents ran to that same judge/mayor, who was now just sitting down to a meal with his friends, and told him their boy was still alive. The judge/mayor laughed at them and said, "Your son is no more alive than these chickens we're about to eat!"

At which point, the cooked birds (which still had their heads attached) either stirred on his plate and clucked, or grew feathers and crowed, or grew feathers and flew away.

(And, yes, the boy was then set free.)

Today, the town's motto remains, "*Santo Domingo de la Calzada, donde cantó la gallina después de asada.*" ("Saint Dominic of the Causeway, where the chicken sang after being roasted.") And the cathedral pays tribute to that miracle of miracles by housing a caged rooster and hen for all to see.

"Nope, didn't see the chickens," I replied.

"Should have eaten the chicken, really. That pasta wasn't very good," mused Brie.

Brie and I shared a smile, and I suppose we looked rather comfortable with each other, because Camila then asked, "Are you two a couple now?"

"Noooo!" I thundered, perhaps a little too quickly and a little too emphatically.

"Rather loud," Brie commented, looking rather hurt.

"No, I'm just . . . You know. We're not, right? That's all. And you know why I'm here on this Camino." Turning to Camila, I said, "Brie and I are just friends, that's all—"

But Brie wasn't letting it go. "You don't have to explain."

"No, but it feels like I have to—"

"No, it's okay. 'We are just friends, that's all.'"

"Did I say something bad?" Then, pleading to Lukas, "Did I say something bad?"

"No, it's not bad," interjected Brie. "But last night you asked me to come along with you to Burgos, that's all—"

"Yeah, but you know why." Then, to Camila, "It's all innocent, I swear." Then back to Brie, "Did you think it was something more?"

Brie started to smile—she just loved making me squirm—but it was too late for me to recover. I completely missed her joke and blurted out, "I'm looking for my wife!"

"Maybe you already found her," giggled Camila.

"No, I didn't!"

"Rather loud again," teased Brie.

"Listen, my wife's missing, okay?" I raised my voice with every sentence. "She's missing. And she's sick. And she wrote me all these letters and left them all over the Camino, and I'm following all those letters and learning why she left me. And, oh shit, here we go! Now I'm everybody's charity case again and everyone wants to know how I'm doing and how I'm coping. Look, I just want to walk this stupid thing and get to the bottom of everything, that's all!"

Well, that pretty much shattered my model pilgrim motto. And, once again, according to Brie, I had had a shit-fit in front of the peregrinos.

Brie calmed me down and assured me she was just "taking the piss." She filled in the holes of my long, sad story and explained that she was a naturally curious person who was accompanying me only to provide sympathetic support.

Camila and Lukas agreed it was all rather romantic. That this sentimental statement came from the most incredibly cute couple on the Camino made me slightly nauseated.

I drank the rest of my wine and said nothing of significance for the rest of the evening, until Camila and Lukas bid us good night outside our albergue.

Brie turned to me. "So, you're a new man, are ya?"

"Oh, shut up."

"Oh, so what? So they know too. They called you a 'romantic.'"

I sighed. "I guess it makes no sense to you, does it?"

"What's that?"

"That I just want to mind my own business while I walk the Camino? And deal with my doubt and grief all by myself?"

"I'm the same as you, Jamie. Really, I am."

I paused to consider if we could return to that Martin and Mabel sex story. No; I resisted addressing that question again. It seemed better to end the night on the best of terms.

However, I did want to make a small point of clarification. "So you were just 'taking the piss' out of me back there? You weren't hurt when I said this was all innocent?"

"You called me 'friend.' How could I be hurt about that?"

Brie forced a grin and turned for the lobby door. If she was disappointed . . . it was only a little.

14

BELORADO SCARS

I SLEPT very poorly that night, and not because of my latest out-burst, or because of Brie's possibly hurt feelings, or because of my ongoing private doubt and grief about my wife, or because of the snorting Spaniard lying below me. The earplugs actually fulfilled their promise and blocked out his nasally roars. Unfortunately, he was also a tosser and a turner, and he ferociously shook that creaky bunk until the crack of dawn.

When some sleepers rose from their beds in the morning, I instinctively climbed down from my bunk too.

It was so dark. Why was it so dark? In the men's bathroom, I discovered the time was only four forty-five. Where was everyone going? What was the point? They'd reach the day's destination far too early; no albergue would be ready for them!

I went back to bed desperate for a few more restful minutes.

When I arose with the remaining pilgrims at the proper hour of six o'clock, I consulted my Burnsley for a preview. The book warned that the day's 22.9-kilometer walk was "dangerous," if only because the track would run parallel to the highway in some sections. Note to Burnsley: just because you can sometimes hear the cars, it doesn't mean they careen off the road and run you over.

Later, when I was pulling on my walking shoes, a folded note dropped out of one of them to the lobby floor. It was from Brie, complaining about her lack of sleep and telling me of her sudden decision for a premature start. She was confident I would catch up to her on the road and promised to wait for me in Belorado inside the town's largest albergue if I did not.

I wasn't surprised by her predawn decision. I was surprised she had picked out the correct shoes, though—until I noticed similar folded notes landing at the feet of other male pilgrims in the lobby. Brie must have hedged her bets and left notes in a dozen pairs of shoes.

It was soon a blur of bewildered exchanges. "Brie? Who is Brie?" "Who the hell is Brie? I don't know a Brie." "This must be a mistake." "You get the same note? Is this a joke?"

I laughed and held up my own personal note. "Brie is a friend of mine! She was just trying to leave me a message."

I departed without further explanation. Who knows how many more shoes contained her note? Who knows how many more men would travel to Belorado with the intention of meeting their new mystery admirer named Brie?

Crossing the Oja River over Saint Dominic's bridge was my last point of interest for several hours. The ensuing walk toward the first village, Grañón, brought nothing new. It was a lonely gravel path up an unassuming slope draped with unattended fields, where one wondered, "When did the weeds end and the hay begin?"

And, yes, Burnsley was right: the Camino path was separated from the highway by a few insignificant meters, so when a car roared by you were left thinking, "I suppose a reckless driver *could* careen off the road and run me over . . ."

I reached Grañón after 7.2 kilometers but declined to explore the village for any sign of food. It was several minutes after seven o'clock but, honestly, who would be awake this early on a Saturday morning to serve me breakfast?

The scenery improved after Grañón. The hay was replaced by wheat. The seedy browns gave way to vibrant greens. And the path was now peppered with clusters of trees while the distant hillocks punctured the horizon. The variety was welcome.

I soon passed a road sign that announced I was leaving the

La Rioja region for the autonomous community of Castile and León. (Is there any other kind in Spain?)

Both León and Castile (Land of Castles) first appeared as independent kingdoms in the tenth and eleventh centuries, leading the way in purging the region of its medieval Muslim rulers, before permanently merging in 1301. Alternating between various configurations and associations over the ensuing years, the territory became recognized as an official autonomous community only in 1983. A small faction in León continues to demand further autonomy and a split from Castile with their rallying cry of "*León solo!* " ("León alone!")

With mountain ranges in the north and east, much of the terrain consists of one large plateau, the infamous Meseta, with the entire territory representing twenty percent of Spain's total area but only five percent of its population.

Its Castilian language is also the dominant dialect of Spain and represents the language the English-speaking world generally refers to as "Spanish."

With few large towns, the region of Castile and León is nicknamed "the granary of Spain," with wheat still regarded as the area's most traditional crop followed by barley, rye, and oats. Only in the heavily irrigated zones near the mountains (far away from the Camino) does the fertile land grow vegetables and support livestock.

During the Middle Ages, the land was densely forested, until the trees were cut down to cultivate cereals (and provide easier access to the Camino). This explains the small clusters of juniper, pine, and oak that appear as arboreal aberrations on the monotonous grainy landscape.

Approximately four kilometers after Grañón, the Camino led me to the one-street village of Redecilla del Camino. With its population of 150 souls, it was hard to imagine this outpost once housed three pilgrim hospitals and almost a dozen hermitages. I was just hoping for an open restaurant with a pot of coffee. But I was denied.

More villages were close at hand, so I remained hopeful I would soon get fed. However, Castildelgado and Viloria de la Rioja remained closed. All these villages remain alive because of the Camino, yet no one could be bothered to get out of bed to serve the pilgrims any food.

Viloria de la Rioja had more explaining to do. This village was the birthplace of Saint Dominic. Remember him? The holy man who single-handedly upgraded the local Camino path? Well, this village apparently forgot that. The house in which he was born had been recently dismantled, and the baptismal font inside the church where he was baptized had been removed. *What is wrong with you people? The man's your saint, and you can't be bothered to keep a few historical souvenirs?*

By the time I reached the next town of Villamayor del Rio, 3.4 kilometers later, I was famished. Villamayor del Rio was known as "the town of the three lies" because it was not a "large town on the river," as the name suggests, but rather a tiny village over a stream. I didn't care about its deception; its one expansive restaurant was open.

It was the first time all day I saw more than a handful of pilgrims *anywhere*. The nature of the day's more-or-less straight path through ghost towns without any landmarks meant the pilgrims walked single-file, either far ahead or far behind me.

I looked for Brie among the dining tables but found neither her nor anyone else I recognized from the Camino. No matter. I devoured my sandwich and my coffee and was out the door before the next wave of hungry customers crammed the café.

Less than five kilometers away, through more of the same monotonous landscape, was Belorado. It was a sizeable town of two thousand people in the valley of the Tirón River, lying in the shadow of a mountain that had once boasted a castle and a fortress to protect it from Castile invaders. The Romans had been here, of course, but it later evolved into a divided community with distinct districts based on race and religion. It didn't last. In the thirteenth century, the town was home to eight churches. They're all gone now, replaced by two "new" churches. The town was also home to a large Jewish community. They're virtually all gone now too, no thanks to King Ferdinand's Jewish Expulsion in the fifteenth century.

Belorado eventually became known for its leather industry. As the demand for leather diminished, so did its once-thriving trade. The best description you can find in research on the town is that it's "peaceful" or "relaxed." You might as well call it unlucky and depressed.

That was the mood outside the large private albergue where I found Brie waiting in line with fifteen others for the albergue to complete its cleaning and open its doors.

Brie welcomed me with a hearty laugh and a mischievous smile. "Got my note, did ya?"

"Half the albergue got your note."

"Couldn't take any chances, you know?"

One hour later, Brie and I stood outside the albergue, clean, serene, shielding our eyes from the sunshine, eager for any endeavor. Pam's next letter was still more than a day away. I knew *I* needed something to occupy my mind.

"Tour of the town? Give it a go?" suggested Brie.

"You want to walk down to the river?"

Brie shrugged.

"You want to see a church?"

"Which one?"

"The one against the cliff?" That would be the sixteenth-century Church of Santa Maria built against the limestone cliffs full of ancient caves where hermits once dwelled.

Brie shrugged.

"I thought you wanted a tour of the town?"

"Lied."

Minutes later, we were sitting at a patio table in the very pleasant Plaza Mayor, dining on a variety of tapas and drinking ice-cold pints of beer. The cafés on this side of the square were open for business and offered a colonnade of shelter. The uncovered restaurants beside the Church of San Pedro, with its handsome clock tower, were closed until dinner.

"Can I ask you something?" I mumbled between bites of my grilled sardines and blue-cheese croquettes.

"I been waiting for this. Off you go."

"Waiting for what?"

"It's been killing you all day, innit? Off you go, Jamie. Say the words—"

"I don't know what you do," I said forcefully.

That caught Brie by surprise. "What?"

"All this time together, I don't know what you do for a living."

That opened the verbal floodgates as Brie regaled me with stories about her unsatisfactory career as an East London waitress at various bars, pubs, restaurants, diners, and High Street tea shops. She never lasted more than a year at any one location. There was always a moment where she would hand in her uniform and swear she would never return to the task of serving ungrateful customers and enduring long hours, poor tips, and spiteful managers.

"But I'm back in uni now."

"Oh, yeah?" I roused myself from the frozen expression of interest I had established long after I had thoroughly understood what she did for a living.

"Martin didn't like it much when we were together."

"Studying what?"

"It cost money rather than made money; so there was that—"

"What are you studying?"

"Plus he was only doing odd jobs, so times were tight—"

"Brie!"

"Yes?"

"Studying what?"

"You'll have a go at me."

"No, I won't."

"Martin always had a go. Waste of time, he said—"

"Brie!"

"Yes?"

"I'm not Martin."

Brie looked me over and smiled. "Spot on, Jamie."

"Look, I taught history to teenagers who didn't respect me and didn't give a shit about what I had to say. Then I sat at home at night writing terrible detective novels with plots that my dumbest students could easily figure out. *That* was a waste of time—"

"Art therapy!" blurted Brie.

"What?"

"I'm studying art therapy."

The verbal floodgates opened once again as Brie explained her promising career as an art therapist. She hoped to help couples who couldn't communicate without arguing, families where the children couldn't express their feelings without frustration, or inside classrooms where the students couldn't concentrate because of learning disabilities.

Art therapy could also be used, Brie told me, in aiding combat veterans, sexual-abuse survivors, natural-disaster victims, prison inmates, and lonely senior citizens.

"How come you don't want to visit churches then and check out all the artwork?" I asked.

"I'm on holiday, ain't I?"

"But, still, you must be curious?"

"Not really. The people who made it are all dead."

Brie told me the purpose of art therapy was essentially to heal the client in some way by giving them a new outlet to express themselves. It's through engaging their minds in the creation of this art—whether through drawing, painting, sculpting, or taking photographs—and then later reflecting upon it. The hope was that clients could unlock their inhibitions to better cope with the more detrimental issues in their lives such as crippling stress or trauma.

"So, patients paint dead people and blood and murder scenes and things like that?"

"If only it was so simple," Brie said rather seriously.

In each and every case, she explained, it was about tapping into their feelings and perceptions of the world, examining the finished product and finding its symbolism, and, further to that, contrasting what was on the page and what was sometimes missing.

Then she talked about how art could simply be soothing. It's been proven, she said, that landscape paintings in a hospital room can subconsciously reduce the need for minor painkillers and markedly reduce recovery time.

Painting the soothing scene yourself is even better. Then you have a distraction from your debilitating illness and a mental escape from your pain.

"It's a good crack for people who are really sick. If they think about the sickness all the time, they feel small and knackered. Making art gives them a bit of a pick-me-up."

"Maybe Pam should have taken an art class instead of coming on the Camino." Now I was the serious one at the table.

Brie apologized for forgetting herself. "Loads of lovely landscapes here, though. That'll make her feel better, don't you worry." She extended her hand and rubbed mine in silence. "It's all about trust, this art-therapy business, Jamie. Same trouble I have in my own life, I guess."

"How about me? Do you trust me yet?"

Brie withdrew her hand. "Here it comes!"

"What now?"

"'Do you trust me yet?' Here comes what you really want to ask me."

"What?"

"About Martin and Mabel again."

"The slut?"

"She's not a slut; she's my mate!"

"Ooh, I hope we're talking about someone from the Camino!" With little grace and a lot of bluster, Marge and Bill, a heavyset couple from Texas, interrupted us and promptly announced they were both fifty years old, recently married (her second and his third), and currently on their honeymoon on the Camino.

"Not the whole thing, mind you," bellowed Bill. "Just a week to walk off the wedding cake and then we're off to Barcelona!"

"You don't mind if we join you, do ya?"

They sat down without waiting for our answer.

"How about you two?" asked Nosy Marge. "You two lovebirds? I can spot 'em a mile away."

"She really can! You should see her on the Camino. 'Bet that one's married. Bet that one's not.' She's always right!"

"Well, sorry; not this time," I said as gently as I could, careful not to agitate Brie. "Just really good friends on our way to Burgos."

"You sure?" asked Nosy Marge.

"She's always right!" added Bellowing Bill.

"Yup, pretty sure." I turned meekly to Brie. "Right?"

Brie chuckled and tapped my hand. "Relax, Jamie. Cheers."

"Oh, you hear that, Bill? She's English!"

"Fancy!"

Thankfully, we weren't alone with Nosy Marge and Bellowing Bill for long. As the only table in the plaza still occupied by pilgrims, we were soon joined by all the other weary travelers.

Lawyer Wendy from San Francisco sat down with us after Bill noticed her creeping along the cloister on her way to the grocery store. "San Francisky! Grab a drink with us! San Francisky, over here!"

Lawyer Wendy gave me a dirty look once she noticed me sitting at the end of the table.

"Oh, you again. Still fighting with the snorers?" she sneered.

"No complaints," I said in the sweetest voice I could muster.

"Oh, you want to hear some snoring? You should hear old Bill over here!"

"Guilty as charged!"

Next came German Karl and Aussie Jasmine, still joined at the hip as I had left them back in Azqueta. Karl only wanted to get a light for his next cigarette, but Bill and Marge insisted they sit down at our table.

"An Australian and a German, could you imagine that? Where else but the Camino could they meet?" gushed Marge.

Jasmine also gave me a dirty look once she noticed me sitting at the end of the table.

"You're looking well," I offered.

"Why wouldn't I be?"

"No reason. Let me buy you a beer."

"I'll take you up on that one!" interjected Bill.

"Me too!" chirped Marge.

Now I was buying everyone a round of drinks. That included one for Max, the Munich chemical engineer who recognized Karl from a previous Camino stop and plopped down beside him.

"I never take a vacation," Munich Max soon confided in me. "I'm the boss. Now they make me take a vacation. My wife says, 'Go. Walk the Camino.' Now I sleep in a dormitory like a child."

I liked Munich Max immensely. I could count on him to add some misery to the otherwise perky hysteria.

We really hit the depths of despair when Grumpy Abram suddenly approached our gathering group. He was the only one who didn't give me a dirty look once he noticed me sitting at the end of the table. He gave *everyone* a dirty look.

"I missed you, Abram!" I confessed.

"Why? Why would you do that?" spat out the Dutchman.

Now that we had a table full of fresh drinks, we methodically went through all the traditional talking points. We discussed the status of our feet, our diets, the starting points in our pilgrimage, and the reasons why we would ever wander across Spain.

Rewriting my previous history, I gamely contributed to every tired topic. Lawyer Wendy and Aussie Jasmine were certainly confused. Who was this gregarious peregrino? Brie approved of my conduct and kept flashing me winks and nods, while my stomach twisted itself into uneasy knots.

Then the collective concern turned to the next day's recommended destination, San Juan de Ortega. With a reported population of only twenty people and only one albergue, one hotel, and one bar to show for the entire village, we were all rather worried. Burnsley praised the town's "slower pace," but none of us were buying it. "What would we do all day?" "Is there really nothing else to see?" "And isn't tomorrow Sunday? What if the bar is closed?"

It didn't take long for everyone to start rationalizing the guidebook's recommendation.

"Well, maybe it's not as bad as we think," suggested Wendy.

"It could be rather cozy. All sleeping under one roof!" blurted Marge.

"I'd still like to look at that hotel, though. Could be fun in a big bed!" bellowed Bill.

"If it's so bad, why would they advise it in the book?" reasoned Max.

I ignored them all and focused on Grumpy Abram. He was the only pilgrim at the table who had seen the actual village, having walked the Camino two years ago.

"Keep going! Don't stop there! It's a waste of time!"

Oh, I sure did miss Grumpy Abram.

The afternoon drinks eventually dissolved into a boozy blur with Bellowing Bill kindly opening up his fat wallet to keep the pilgrim party going. This included a free meal across the square in one of the second-floor restaurants.

What we discussed I couldn't say, but I swear I remained pleasant throughout the entire evening, gratefully allowing Munich Max and Grumpy Abram to carry the cross of misery. It even earned me a good-night hug from Lawyer Wendy and Aussie Jasmine.

After our late dinner, we noticed the square was free of pilgrims and reclaimed by the locals. The benches were occupied, the tables were filled, and the square pulsated with energetic families and strolling sweethearts.

Walking back home to the albergue, Brie and I had to dodge the surly teenagers scattered in the street, clutching their bottles of beer and eyeing each other with lascivious intentions, like they must do every Saturday night in Belorado.

Back in our room, we were the drunken calm in the nightly curfew storm. While the other pilgrims scrambled to retrieve laundry, organize backpacks, and clean up for bed, we stood in the middle of the floor, tightly grasping the wooden frame of our bunk bed, quoting Nosy Marge and Bellowing Bill.

"Just a week to walk off the wedding cake and then we're off to Barcelona."

"Bet that one's married. Bet that one's not!"

"Oh, she's English! Fancy!"

Two uptight pilgrims hissed and told us to shut up.

This made Brie laugh even louder as she jammed her tiny fist over her mouth.

"San Francisky! Grab a drink with us! San Francisky!"

Brie beat me on the chest with her other tiny fist and shook her head. When she finally gained enough control to keep the peace, she removed her hand from her mouth and purred, "You two lovebirds? I can spot 'em a mile away."

Suddenly, her impersonation wasn't so funny anymore. "Too much? Was my friendship explanation too much?"

Brie shook her head and gazed down at the floor. When she looked up at my face again, she had tears in her eyes.

"It was fair play. You're a good friend. I mean that."

"Thanks," I mumbled. I could think of nothing else to add.

"Mabel was a good friend, too."

"Yeah. Her and Martin. That must suck." We had finally gotten back to that heartbreaking piece of gossip, but I was now too drunk and couldn't appreciate her vulnerability.

"But I'm not gutted."

"Not gutted? I'd be furious."

"Fact is: I'm more worried about poor Mabel."

"Worried? Worried about what?"

Her tears now streaming down her cheeks, Brie gathered the mess of sandy curls that always crested her thick eyebrows and lifted up her hair, for the first time exposing her pale forehead where two scars, one long and ugly, the other short and deep, snaked across her brow.

And then the albergue lights went out and plunged us into darkness.

Without further explanation as to her previously hidden scars, Brie slipped into the lower bunk, crawled under her sleeping bag, and pulled the fabric up to her chin. Her clothes remained on.

It took me a full minute to recover from Brie's revelation. Cloaked in darkness and drunk enough to disregard propriety, I peeled off my shirt, my shorts, and my socks in the middle of the room—leaving them in a tidy pile on the floor—and considered my awkward climb into my bed.

Nope. Not good enough, not ready; my need to know more information trumped the sleeping needs of my fellow pilgrims.

I dropped down to my knees with a thud and leaned in as close to Brie as I dared. "Martin did that? Tell me! That fucking animal! How did this even happen? Why didn't you tell me earlier?"

"Not exactly Camino talk, Jamie," Brie whispered calmly.

"It is exactly Camino talk! It's exactly what people talk about!"

"Shhhhhh!" hissed several pilgrims.

"They're such nice days on the road," Brie cooed dreamily. "Why ruin it with my sobby mess?"

"Because we're friends, Brie. Better than friends. You're my only friend in Spain . . . and I need you."

"That's sweet, Jamie," she yawned. "We'll crack on tomorrow, I promise."

With that, Brie rolled over and turned her back to me.

Deep inside my malaise, my memory re-ignited. I recalled the breezy afternoon Brie and I had first descended down Alto del Perdón.

Less than a week ago, I had easily dismissed the chattering Brit who seemed to fill the silences with innocuous rants. Now she was an emotionally integral part of my fumbling attempt at reconciliation with my own shattered life. She was damaged and brave at the same time—and all I wanted to do was reach out and hold her.

I inched in closer and quoted her own words from when we first met on the mountain. "'You're in love and everything's fine one minute and then suddenly it's not fine and you're not in love anymore.'"

"That's right," she peeped.

"He *hurt* you!"

"Shhhhh!" hissed several pilgrims again.

"Oh, piss off!" I roared. "Where the hell are you when the snorers take over?!"

Brie turned to me and touched my face with her soft, tiny hand to quiet me down. "Don't have a go with the other pilgrims, Jamie. Go to bed. We'll have a proper chat tomorrow."

Once again, Brie rolled over and turned her back to me.

I reluctantly climbed into bed and fell asleep without much resistance. I was freed from my troubling theories about Martin's cruelty thanks to the charity of Bellowing Bill's fat wallet. An alcohol-soaked bloodstream trumps a crowded mind every time.

15

AGÉS INSIGHT

MY PREVIOUS NIGHT's insistence to know all the details about Martin's perceived attack was greatly reduced by the time my roommates shook the room with their predawn preparations.

Oh, I still wanted to know everything. However, I was reminded of Pam's recollection about the day I gave her flowers and held her hand while she was upset about something that had happened at the Smart Set store. Sometimes it was better to be quiet. Maybe this was one of those times. Maybe I should be patient and attentive rather than urgent and inquisitive.

It was odd, I thought, as I slid my feet over the bed frame and unsteadily leaped down to the floor . . . that while my wife was pouring out her heart in her Camino pages she was also unintentionally giving me solid advice for future relationships.

Or was it unintentional? And, wait a minute, *what relationship*? Friendship! Future friendship, that's what I meant . . .

My discarded clothes were still in their forgotten pile in the middle of the floor. The morning hangover made picking them up more difficult. The realization that Brie was sitting up in bed and watching me made it more awkward.

I waved. She smiled. I nodded. She nodded back. Neither of us was willing to break the tension with any troublesome words that might be misconstrued or lead to any ill feelings.

Our accepted silence now settled; we carried on with our duties like nothing was amiss or pending. We cleaned up, we dressed, and we began the day's journey amid the usual exodus of Camino civility and kindness and the reestablishment of the undercurrent of competition to get to our destination ahead of everyone else.

If we followed Burnsley's guideline, our walk would lead us through shaded woodland, up and down mountains covered in oak and pine, before it dropped us into San Juan de Ortega 24.3 kilometers away.

We would likely travel farther than that, however. Grumpy Abram's conviction about the hamlet's bleak isolation had convinced us of that. But how far we didn't yet know. Brie was blissfully quiet as I waited for my headache to subside.

We passed through the Plaza Mayor one last time, half expecting Bellowing Bill to pounce on us and buy us another round of drinks.

We slid through the hushed suburbs, crossed the Tirón River, and strolled through farmland for 4.8 kilometers to reach our first town of the day, Tostantos. Breakfast was, of course, a distant hope. The hamlet had only a population of eighty, and it was a Sunday morning in Catholic Spain.

The next two haunted hamlets of Villambistia and Espinosa del Camino continued the trend of shuttered access and shattered dreams of caffeine and toast.

We had been climbing a subtle incline since Tosantos, but now the gentle hills were more pronounced as the farmland thinned out between tight thickets of trees and wide swaths of wild grass.

After crossing the Oca River, we entered the village of Villafranca de Montes de Oca which, thankfully, was awake enough to the possibilities of feeding us. In fact, its entire reputation was based on that assumption.

Like many Camino towns, Villafranca de Montes de Oca contained one main street, one dominant church (this one was from the eighteenth century), and one secular landmark (the San Anton Abad hotel/hostel complex, which was partially constructed out of a thirteenth-century hospital).

It was also one of the designated *Villafranca* towns that lie scattered along the route, previously populated by French artisans whose residence was encouraged to boost business and local infrastructure.

Brie and I entered the first bar without a lineup and readily accepted the humble offering of café au lait, orange juice, and a buttered croissant.

We hadn't talked all morning. We also hadn't gazed at each other since we left Belorado. I waited. I smiled. I slowly ate. And I sipped my coffee with enthusiasm, pretending that everything about our breakfast was exemplary.

Brie didn't touch her food and stared back at me, unimpressed with my cheery charade.

"I suppose you want to know," Brie sighed.

"You did say 'tomorrow,'" I whispered, as if I was still surrounded by hissing pilgrims in their Belorado beds.

"I just feel so daft," Brie sulked, tearing her croissant into tiny morsels that she popped into her mouth like a kid munching on movie popcorn.

"We always do *after*, never during," I said. It sounded hollow. What did I know about spousal abuse? What did I even know about failing marriages? I was walking across Spain in complete bewilderment while my mysterious wife spelled it out for me.

"It just got so buggered after he fell off the ladder. Him at the local doing nothing but spending money. Me at school sussing out art therapy and spending more money—"

"I thought he did odd jobs around the neighborhood."

Brie gave me a doubtful look. "What was odd is he got any jobs at all. He painted a fence once for old Mrs. Roberts. So drunk he missed a few spots. But old Mrs. Roberts was too much of a dear to say something. I finished the job myself—"

"Okay."

"He watched Mrs. Duncan's terrier loads of times, because she was always on a package holiday. Why she even had a dog I don't know. And then him carrying on and barking all the time and pissing on the rug. 'Course, Martin didn't do nothing about that. I had to clean it and feed it because Martin was always out—"

"Right . . . So how did you get those scars?" I was worried that Brie might recall every single odd job Martin was alleged to have done.

"One night he just came home from the local. Pissed like always, still carrying a bottle. I'm knackered in bed, but Mrs. Duncan's dog was up and barking at him. Martin starts yelling. I go up and tell him to leave the dog alone and then start rabbiting on about how dogs take on the personalities of their owner. Something I heard at school, I guess. If you're yelling all the time, the dog goes mental. Martin didn't want to hear it."

Brie stopped talking for a moment and took her first sip from her morning coffee. "Not exactly hot, is it?"

"So Martin's yelling at the dog—"

"He *was*, but now he's yelling at me! Saying how I was too good for him now because I was working and going to school. He even knew about old Mrs. Roberts' fence because the old dear brings over a cake with my name on it. A vanilla one, too, just like the color of her fence! She was clever, that one. You wouldn't know it, because she always shuffled about like a broken old lady, but she was quick as a whip if you took the time to talk to her—"

"So Martin's yelling at you—" Now I knew why Brie didn't tell me this story back in the albergue. We'd be up half the night with all the hysterical pilgrims trying to sleep.

"Martin's yelling, the dog's barking, and all I want to do is nip back to bed. And then I say, and I don't see this coming, I say, 'I can't do this anymore.' Martin, he don't know *what* I'm on about, but I don't explain anything. I'm just so knackered, you know?"

I reached out and held her hand as tears formed in her eyes. She was speaking slowly and quietly, no longer embarrassed about her previous pain but somehow reliving it, allowing every weighted word to fall gently from her lips. It somehow released her from the burden she had been carrying in her heart. I couldn't be sure if this was the first time Brie had ever explained the end of her marriage to anyone, but I was certain she was somehow healed by it. I guess Scottish Jock was right. Maybe it was good to simply get things off your chest.

"Then just like that . . . Martin belts me with the bottle. On my cheek . . ."

I gripped her hand tighter.

". . . and I fall back, you know, out of shock and because of the wallop, and I fall . . . and bang my head on the coffee table. The dog's going mental, Martin's yelling at me to make it stop, and all I can think about is the blood on the floor. *My* blood. Of course, I start crying. But Martin . . . he doesn't see the blood, he never saw me hit the table. He's yelling, 'Get up, get up, don't be so dramatic.' So I . . . get up."

"Oh, shit—"

"'Oh, shit' is right! Martin then sees the blood on my forehead and he freaks right the fuck out! 'I hit you on the cheek! Why are you bleeding? How did this happen?' Then before I say anything, he drops the bottle...and belts me again! This time with the back of his hand. I don't know if it was out of reflex or something, but his ring cuts me on the forehead just below the other one . . ."

"His *ring*?"

"Yeah, he had this flash ring. It had a skull on it and he thought it looked posh . . . anyway, it was sharp in places, and it cut me."

"I'm so sorry."

"Yeah, well, I'm sorry I stayed there. Martin, he says 'Sorry' and he runs off and goes to bed and leaves me there. I even have to clean up the broken bottle and take the dog for a walk!"

"Fuck me. And then . . .?"

"And then what?"

"What did you do?"

"Nothing. What could I do? Martin didn't remember what happened the next morning and I just got patched up. I didn't tell anybody and just combed down my bangs and said I fell. It took me months just to get the guts to leave him. I can't sort it out, why it took so long. It just did. Now I just feel so stupid."

"It was brave of you to leave. Really. Not everybody leaves."

I let go of her hand and wiped away the tears from her cheek. Instinctively, without thinking and without permission, my hand lifted off her cheek and reached for her forehead.

There was nothing to be gained by examining Brie's scars, but that didn't stop my wandering hand. I guess I just wanted to somehow make a tactile connection—to let Brie know she didn't need to hide anything behind her curls. Those scars marked the end of her horrible marriage and the beginning of her freedom.

Whether those intentions carried across the table in that Camino café was unclear. As my hand reached her forehead, Brie's fingers met mine and entwined with them. Together we slowly traced the length of the longest scar.

That accomplished, Brie dropped my hand and reached for a napkin to dab away her remaining tears.

"So, that's the end of that, Jamie Draper," Brie said, quickly regaining her composure. "I won't be a victim anymore. And not on this trip, neither! I'm not your charity case, you understand? And you're not going to ask me every five minutes how I'm doing. I don't want to talk about any of this anymore. You know now, and that's good enough."

It was odd to hear myself quoted back to me. And I agreed. "Fair enough, Brie Bletcher."

The rest of the morning was a steep ascent up the Montes de Oca, a series of hills that represented the highest climb on the Camino since the Pyrenees. The name translated to Goose Mountains, which probably had less to do with roaming wild geese and more to do with "Oca," a word that evolved from the earlier Roman settlement of Auca.

In medieval times, the hilly area was covered in dense forests and teeming with bandits. Brie and I witnessed neither. We did run afoul, however, of a new scourge infecting the trail: the true tramposos, the most wicked and vile walkers to ever cross the Camino. Not only did they not walk the walk with their possessions on their back, they were also serviced by cooks and a wait staff.

Up ahead, a panel van was parked on the side of the path, and a temporary picnic area had been erected. A barbecue grill blotted the horizon. A chef flipped burgers, a waitress uncorked wine, and several clean and dust-free "pilgrims" sampled beef, beer, salads, and desserts while sitting on folding chairs and eating off ceramic plates.

"I wish Jock could see this," I uttered dramatically. "He wasn't the worst pilgrim, after all. *These people* are the worst."

"They disgust me."

"I now know what hate truly means."

It felt good to display some faux outrage and lighten the mood so soon after Brie's marriage-meltdown revelations. Committing to the joke, Brie and I passed the heinous exhibition without issuing our customary "Buen Camino" greetings. Those were reserved for proper pilgrims. Proper walking pilgrims with backpacks on their backs, who ate Spanish food purchased and cooked in Camino towns by cranky locals.

But, boy, did that barbecued beef smell good . . .

San Juan de Ortega was 12.4 kilometers away through a wide path lined by stately pines and majestic oaks, up and down arduous hills, sporadically interrupted by a stream and a footbridge—all under the shade of the woodland canopy, and all without a café in sight.

For the first time, however, we were prepared. Our water bottles were full and our pockets were packed with snacks. Only our conversation was empty and without heft. We said little. We commented sparingly.

I tried to keep things light with innocuous questions. What was her favorite movie? (*Love Actually*.) What was her favorite TV show? (*Downton Abbey*.) Who was her favorite singer? (Adele.)

But mostly we walked in silence—apart from our "Buen Caminos" to passing pilgrims. Brie had spoken enough that morning. The only thing that required a discussion was whether to spend the night in San Juan de Ortega. I rejected it—sight unseen—and Brie agreed. That settled, we marched up and down those grueling hills. True to my word, I never did bring up "the Martin incident" ever again.

Three hours after we left Villafranca de Montes de Oca, with the trees even more towering and aged and the path now as wide as a country road, we began our easy ascent into San Juan de Ortega.

Saint John of the Nettles (or San Juan de Ortega) was a twelfth-century disciple of Saint Dominic who, just like his mentor, cleared the Camino path of trees and built bridges, hotels, hospices, and churches.

His sacred sanctuary in San Juan de Ortega (restored much later in the fifteenth century) became a pilgrimage in its own right as a last hope for women who couldn't bear children. The legend goes that the white bees that often buzzed around John's tomb were actually the souls of unborn children just waiting for good Christian women to visit. Or . . . they were just bees.

Either way, Queen Isabel, who was desperate to have more children, visited the hamlet in 1477. She became pregnant within the year, and the legend took on a life of its own—until the bees eventually flew away and died.

Soon the forest ended and the horizon opened to pastures of wild heather stretching as far as the eye could see. Exposed to the full force of the sun, we picked up the pace to get to the infamous hamlet that Burnsley painted as romantic and Grumpy Abram dismissed as a "waste of time."

Grumpy Abram was right.

The thirty-person outpost consisted of a few modern homes, a hotel, and a Romanesque church with an attached albergue and bar. That was it.

Optimists could call it quaint or charming all they like, but San Juan de Ortega looked dismal. I would also add the word "mean." After our long march from Belorado, Brie and I were keen to rest and refuel, if only for a few minutes. Asking for food at the bar, I was rebuffed and encouraged to sample the vending machine until the appointed lunchtime a few hours later.

"But I'm not staying here."

"Then you can wait outside."

There were a few available plastic chairs scattered alongside the building. But when I moved two of them into the shade for Brie and I to sit on, I was scolded for placing them inside a potential parking space. (The lot was empty.)

"But there aren't any cars."

"The cars will come! You can sit over there."

"We're not sitting in the sun."

"Then you cannot use the chairs!"

Okay. So, we sat on the ground and drank sodas from the vending machine. *Not* very romantic, *Burnsley*!

Brie and I discussed our overnight plans and decided on Agés, 3.6 kilometers farther down the Camino path. Its population was only sixty (still, twice that of San Juan de Ortega) but it somehow hosted four albergues.

"If it looks anything like this, we'll move on," I suggested.

Turning our backs on Burnsley's recommendation, the next leg of our journey was a gentle walk through pinewood until the trees gave way to the uninspiring scrubland that led us to Agés.

Our first impression of the new town? We weren't impressed. It was a brown blot nestled in the grass with nary a stream or a mountain to soothe the senses. We were so unimpressed we immediately dropped our bag to consult our Burnsleys. The next village, Atapuerca, was just 2.5 kilometers away. But it was hot. And we were hungry. And we had already walked 27.9 kilometers that day. Did we really want to apply more sunscreen? Did we really want to forfeit guaranteed food and drink?

Plus, in my approach to Agés, my left ankle had suddenly . . . "popped." No, it didn't make a sound. It just . . . felt like something snapped, like an elastic band that was stretched too far. Like a fishing line that suddenly ripped apart thanks to the weight and fight of the fish. It neither hurt me nor affected my gait, but something down *there* didn't feel right. What it was, I couldn't be sure. I wasn't overly concerned about it, but it gave me enough pause to suggest an end to our strenuous day.

We examined our albergue options in our guidebooks. Our recent experience had proven the wisdom of always ignoring the first option (it would be too full). The second option mentioned mattresses (too destitute). The third one advertised a hay loft (too rustic). The fourth albergue featured a bar. We chose the fourth one. Of course.

Following our usual rituals, Brie declined lunch in favor of a nap.

"Sure, sure. Take as long as you like," I cooed.

"I'm not your charity case, Jamie Draper," Brie said as she laid her head on her pillow.

"No, no; of course not."

Was every proposal and gesture going to be challenged now? Was I doomed to tiptoe the fine line between unwanted goodwill and proper decency?

Lunch in the albergue was chaos unbefitting the usually calm Camino. Twenty locals (a third of the village?) scrambled to get a drink before . . . well, who knows? At three o'clock, the bar was humming with hysterics. By three forty-five, when my cheese croquettes finally arrived, the cantina was empty.

With Brie in bed and no one to entertain me, what to do, what to do? There were no landmarks or monuments; only a humble church, the sixteenth-century Iglesia of Santa Eulalia, with its Baroque bell tower advertised as its most impressive feature.

As far as the histories of holy houses go, the Agés church was not one for the ages. Its only claim to fame was that it very briefly held the remains of King Garcia III of Navarre after he was killed by his own brother, King Ferdinand I of León, in the Battle of Atapuerca in 1054. (Remember Garcia III? When he was a prince he was featured in that legend about the dove and the falcon in the cave.)

The history of the church's namesake was much more upsetting. Eulalia was a pious thirteen-year-old virgin who entered the courts of the local governor in the year 304 to protest the worship of the Roman Empire's pagan gods. She even dared the governor to make her a martyr.

He obliged by subjecting the outspoken girl to thirteen different tortures—one for each of her years. Sources vary on what they were, exactly, but you can imagine a lot of horrid little devices wounding her in disgusting little ways.

When she was either crucified or decapitated (no one can agree on her fate), a dove flew out of her mouth and a snow shower appeared above her to cloak her naked, dead body.

Today in Spain, Eulalia is the patron saint of Snow Days. (Yes, there is a patron saint of Snow Days.)

With nothing to do, I visited the church that had once housed a dead king's body and was named after a virgin martyr. I was disappointed. The gold-leaf altar didn't capture the eye. The small statues of Jesus didn't inspire. The chandelier hanging above the pews suggested a nightclub setting more than a house of prayer.

After some quiet contemplation, I walked over to the only other major street in the village to the only bar that wasn't attached to an albergue. Once again, I sat alone. I missed Brie's company. I missed my wife's embrace. I missed the comfort of my shitty Toronto apartment with the TV that was too big for the living room.

However, I didn't miss *me*. The old me. The defeated high school teacher who couldn't write a murder mystery. I didn't miss the miserable man, lost in Palma, teaching English lessons to Spanish students who were more ambitious than he was and deserved far better instruction and guidance.

Upon even *further* reflection, I finally gave myself a break. I might not have been a model pilgrim, but I was evolving into a more model *me*. I was still too frustrated far too easily, but I was making slow and sizeable strides toward being the supportive and dependable husband my wife needed. I felt it. I was getting closer; I was closing the gap from self-imposed misery to having a stable heart that could freely and properly give and receive love.

*"Listen, only by walking this Camino will you understand—
maybe—what I was going through. So, yes, you really do have to
walk a mile in my shoes to understand me better."*

I had made the commitment. I had walked some miles, and I
was willing to walk many more. This gradual understanding of my
wife's feelings and intentions were much more challenging than
any physical journey—but I was doing my absolute best. I was
actively absorbing the Camino experience, passionately learning
from every available message from my wife, and slowly changing my perspective after years of living under a heavy, dispiriting
cloud that had mercilessly crept into our circumspect marriage.

"Hiya!"

Brie playfully brushed her fingers across my back and ducked
under the protective awning of my patio umbrella.

"Hang about, no drink? Gaaah, it's so hot!"

She darted inside the bar to remedy the problem. Blame the
heat, credit the nap; Brie was certainly more nimble than when
I had met her a week ago on Alto del Perdón. Had it really only
been a week? Now I couldn't imagine the Camino without her.

I thought of my own ankle and reached down to massage it.
It was tender but gave me no distress. It was probably best not
to walk on it much more that evening. It was probably best that
there was nowhere else to go in tiny Agés.

"How's your leg?" I asked Brie as she sat down with two sparkling pints of beer.

"Can't complain."

"You walk as fast as me now."

"Yeah, about that—"

"It's not much of a town, huh? Burgos should be better."

It was a familiar trend on the Camino. Party nights in towns
like Los Arcos and Nájera were always followed by quiet nights
in towns like Logroño and Santo Domingo de la Calzado. That
meant things were already looking up for our next night in Burgos.

"About Burgos," Brie mused. "I was having a bit of a think—"

"I've been thinking too. You were too good for Martin—"

"We weren't going to talk about that—"

"No, listen. My point is you're too good for me, too. All my moping and complaining—"

"Oh, shut it. Honestly—"

"But you know what? I've been doing a lot of thinking today. And I think I've changed since I've been on this Camino. Seriously. I mean, nothing earth-shattering or anything like that. But I have changed in little ways—"

"Jamie, I—"

"No, seriously, Brie. I can totally feel it. Before this walk, my head was so wrapped up in all my melancholy bullshit. You know, back in Mallorca? But it's all gone now. I mean, I'm not *happy* yet. And I won't be until I find my wife. But I'm in a much better place right now. I'm a little less miserable, less angry, less irritated—"

"That's brilliant—"

"I mean, don't get me wrong: I'm not about to high-five a bunch of snorers or anything—"

"Jamie—"

"But I am just *less*. You know what I mean? One word: *less*. I don't know how else to explain it. Before I was more . . . of everything, and now, I'm . . . less. Listen, I can handle things better; I want to try new things—"

"Jamie, you should dash off to Burgos without me!"

16

BURGOS BREAK-IN

BRIE LEANED ACROSS the table as if she were going to tell me a disturbing secret, although we were the only people on the patio, not to mention on the street, or outside in Agés.

"You're so close to your wife's next letter. You should just get up early, shove off, and walk as fast as you can."

"But—"

"Get to Burgos! I don't want to hold you back anymore."

"You don't hold me back—"

"How many letters do you have left?"

"Two . . . in the first batch."

"So go get them!"

Brie had been awfully quiet since her painful Martin revelation. Her confession had clearly opened old wounds and crushed her otherwise unflappable spirit. It was all understandable. And I didn't want to get in the way of whatever introspective time she now required. Still…I liked walking with bubbly Brie. I even liked walking with the less bubbly Brie.

"So, you want me to walk alone?"

"Yes. This is for you, Jamie."

"Right."

"And Pam."

"Okay."

"She wanted you to walk the Camino just like *she* did, and you're doing it. I just think you have to do the last bit on your own as quickly as you can, yeah? You still have massive questions to answer."

"You're right—"

"I'll meet you there, yeah? Tomorrow night in Burgos? I looked it up in Burnsley. The square on the south side of the cathedral looks wicked, okay?"

"The south side of the cathedral. All right."

We decided on seven o'clock and shook hands like we were sealing a friendly business agreement. Brie talked very little after that. She finished her beer, patted me on the shoulder, and wandered off, presumably to eat alone at our albergue bar.

I noticed she was walking again with a slight limp. Perhaps to prove her point that she couldn't keep up? Maybe Brie had inadvertently aggravated it . . . but I was suspicious. And a little sad.

I ate alone and drank alone and pondered alone the significance of the next two letters and the meaning behind Pam's next two clues: "typewriter" for Burgos and "pilgrim" for León. They were still separated by eight long days through the menacing Meseta. Did that mean something? Why the generous gap?

And then what? I had insisted there had to be another batch of letters, but I couldn't be sure. What was Pam's plan after León? And when was I going to reunite with her?

The next morning, I rose at the first sound of bunk beds rattling and bounded for the bathroom.

I considered my feet and noticed the left one was swollen and marginally bigger than the right one. Had it always been bigger? Was I just noticing it now? Standing on it revealed nothing, but pacing around the bathroom floor indicated a minute but noticeable pain—a minute but noticeable pain I could potentially ignore.

Besides, what could I do about it? Hitch a ride like some tramposo?! Pam would be too disappointed. I would be too disappointed. All I could do was rub my anti-blister stick around my foot and hope that whatever magic had prevented any blisters would now work to heal a swollen ankle.

Now, because I didn't begin my Monday trek from the Burnsley-recommended San Juan de Ortega, the walk would be reduced to a more manageable 21.8 kilometers. The guidebook also insisted that the hustle and bustle of Burgos would shock the senses of any pilgrim who had been lulled into tranquility by the calm of the countryside. *Oh, Burnsley, relax. It's a temporary playground, not eternal damnation.*

My first stop was the village of Atapuerca, where I held out some hope for an early breakfast. But Atapuerca was much too busy with much more important tasks—like contributing to history.

In 1994, during the construction of a railway link to the nearby mines, caves were discovered that contained ancient human remains, such as a jawbone and some teeth, which were calculated to be one million years old (give or take a few hundred thousand years). They were the oldest ever found in Western Europe, and the celebrated caves became a UNESCO heritage site.

It was a pretty impressive stroke of luck for old Atapuerca. But the village still didn't serve even a rudimentary pilgrim breakfast. Shameful. Old bones or a soft-boiled egg? Give me the egg.

From sleepy Atapuerca, the path gracefully climbed in elevation, leading me past a military site protected by a barbed-wire fence (because nothing suggests indomitable strength like prickly barbed wire). From there the trail was steep and rocky until I reached Punto de Vista, a sizeable summit, where the city of Burgos could be seen in the distant west, along with a string of villages sprinkled within the wide blanket of domesticated farmland.

Making my way down an equally rocky path, I soon reached a fork in the road and had to consult my Burnsley. If I continued straight, I could stroll down a poorly marked pasture. If I turned left, I could zigzag toward the hamlet of Villaval. I chose to zigzag.

Breakfast wasn't served in Villaval, either. Everyone was safely tucked in their beds, save for one lone construction worker who was fixing the back of his otherwise sturdy stone house. Perhaps when he was done, he could take a crack at mending the collapsed bell tower afflicting the abandoned church that greeted visitors when they entered the town.

Fifteen minutes later, in the village of Cardeñuela Riopico, at the very first open roadside café, I was finally rewarded with coffee, orange juice…and a clubhouse sandwich! Glorious chicken, crispy bacon, tangy mayonnaise, and perfectly toasted bread. Premade, still warm, orgasmic with every bite. I wanted to kiss the proprietor. I wanted to return to every eating establishment along the Camino and conduct a seminar entitled, "*This* is How You Prepare Breakfast!"

Suddenly, it was "What wobbly ankle?" My breakfast euphoria lasted straight through the next town of Orbaneja (the last parcel of civilization I would see before the Burgos suburbs) until the trail once again forced me to make a decision.

First, there was the historic route through an industrialized area to the busy Burgos streets. The second was a newer, longer trail along the river that promised a more pastoral setting. Because of the stress of the ankle, I chose the stress of the streets.

Soon I was surrounded by others, silent and serious, several meters apart, plodding along as one toward the city. Our chosen route pointed us to a housing estate, where Burnsley urged travelers not to miss the sharp left turn off the main road. He even pointed out that it was not well-marked. And yet…we all missed it.

And we knew we all missed it, because the yellow arrows stopped. Then one of the trailing pilgrims—an Italian—yelped that he had just spotted the mysterious sign. So we shuffled back and examined it for ourselves. Yup, it appeared to be the missing marker. It pointed left, and it pointed dramatically *down*. After a seemingly infinite number of arrows and shells cluttering the course, the Camino was suddenly cute and coy about the signage.

What proceeded was a lengthy farm track that poked through the wheat fields and wild grass with little to shelter us from the sun apart from the occasional cluster of stubborn bushes that sprouted along the path. At the first sign of shade, I stopped to apply sunscreen, and I fell far behind the others.

Soon I walked alone alongside the sinister security fence outside the Burgos airport. Burnsley said it was only a 1.2-kilometer stretch, but it felt significantly longer than that—perhaps due to the lack of shade or perhaps just because it was so dreadfully dull. There were certainly no planes taking off or landing to entertain me. In fact, I knew it was an airport fence only because my guidebook told me so.

Adding to my misery was the nagging limp hampering my left leg. It now hurt to walk. I was used to feeling tired after a long day's journey or feeling achy in my legs and feet in the evenings, but this was no ordinary ache. I needed medical attention.

With seven kilometers to go, the airport fence ended and I reached the main road that would take me directly to town. I thought about finding a taxi. I thought about hitchhiking. But, no; I marched on.

While Burnsley would likely have a series of strokes over the cacophonous vehicles honking and streaming down the causeway, I embraced them as a sign I was heading toward a civilized society that employed doctors and supplied drugs. I embraced the throbbing engine of commerce that would relieve me from my pain. Soon I didn't even need Burnsley anymore. The distant spires of the Burgos cathedral became my guideposts.

The blur and blast of the urban sprawl methodically fell away until I spotted an open *farmacia* on Calle de las Calzadas. The sign in the window read, "We speak English." As I limped across the floor, the pretty pharmacist behind the counter looked up from her medical journal and grimly nodded. "Camino?"

I explained my approach into Agés, the mysterious "pop," the elastic-band sensation, the pain of walking around the dreadfully dull Burgos airport. She didn't need to hear any of it. She rolled up my pants, quickly inspected the swelling, and scurried behind her counter to find a solution.

That was it? Maybe my story wasn't compelling enough. "Touch it," I suggested.

"I see, I see," she said matter-of-factly and handed me a tube of ointment. The photo on the plastic container portrayed a smiling soccer player. It conjured up images of footballers flailing on the pitch after being nudged off the ball by their opponents. Those bogus injuries were meant to draw penalties. This was real.

"That's it? It really hurts."

"Yes, I know." She explained that it was a heat ointment that needed to be applied two or three times a day. But only after I iced the ankle.

"Do you have any ice?"

"No."

"That's it? It really hurts."

"Yes, I know." She further noted that I should probably rest in Burgos for a few days.

"But I'm on the Camino."

"Yes, I know."

"I'm on a mission."

"Yes, I know. All the peregrinos have a mission."

The name of Burgos likely comes from the Visigoths who resided in the Iberian Peninsula before the medieval Moors swept through the region in the eighth century. By then it was already a military post, and the Visigoth word for walled village was *baurgs*.

In 884, Alfonso III, the King of León, conquered the area and officially founded Burgos as part of his ever-expanding Christian empire, which was incessantly battling the Muslim Moors.

The battle for control over Burgos continued throughout the centuries between various kingdoms. Even during the Spanish Civil War, Francisco Franco used the city as his military headquarters as he directed his campaigns in the Spanish north.

No historical figure symbolized the military mettle of Burgos more than Rodrigo Diaz de Vivar, known by the Moors as El Cid (the Lord).

He was born in 1040 and was brought up in the court of King Ferdinand the Great while serving under the king's son, Sancho. When Sancho II ascended to the throne, Rodrigo was named the commander of his Castilian army. Then in 1072, with Rodrigo by his side, Sancho II defeated his brother, Alfonso VI of León, resulting in Sancho combining their two kingdoms and sending his brother to exile. His dual reign was short-lived. Nine months later, Sancho II was mysteriously assassinated—and because he had no wife or heir, his combined kingdom reverted back to his exiled brother.

Now while Rodrigo faithfully served his new king, Alfonso VI, he did so only after forcing Alfonso to repeatedly publicly swear that he had had nothing to do with Sancho's death. The seeds of doubt had been sown, however, and Alfonso, jealous of Rodrigo's popularity and angry with his disloyal independence in his military campaigns, exiled him from his court in 1081.

Rodrigo, the career soldier, was suddenly out of a job. He offered his fighting services to other Spanish territories, but nobody trusted him. No matter. Rodrigo, the medieval free agent, went to work for the Muslim rulers of Zaragoza, leading several successful military campaigns against the armies of Aragon and Barcelona, as well as the other Muslim fiefdoms (the Moors, like the Christians, were never united in their rule, often warring with each other as much as with their Christian counterparts).

Then in 1086, after Alfonso VI was soundly defeated by the pesky Almoravids, a militant tribe of Berbers from North Africa, the king begged Rodrigo to return and fight for his kingdom again.

Rodrigo (now called El Cid) agreed and set his sights on Valencia, a choice Mediterranean city that he desired for himself. He first captured smaller cities and territories surrounding the city and then, with a combined force of both Christians and Moors, he laid siege to it in 1093. Captured the following year, the city became an independent principality that was essentially ruled by El Cid under the domain of King Alfonso VI.

However, the Almoravid army laid siege to Valencia themselves in 1099. During that siege, El Cid died, either by Almoravid arrow or by natural causes due to famine and dwindling natural resources. With his honorable death, his allies lost all hope. In

1102, his wife and followers finally handed the city over to the Almoravids and fled back to Burgos.

Today, a statue of El Cid in full armor, his sword drawn, cape flapping in the wind, stallion perched forward, defends the San Pablo Bridge, one of the many crossings over the Arlanzón River, which separates the Old Town of Burgos from its modern urban spread.

The Camino route led me to a different river crossing. The Arco de San Juan was a thirteenth-century pedestrian entrance inside the old city wall, long ago converted into the apartment housing that rimmed the edge of the river.

Pam's next letter was several blocks away, but I was desperate to shed my backpack and spare my ankle from the unnecessary weight. I ignored Burnsley's roll call of albergues and limped down Calle de la Puebla. Any private bed would do, and I booked myself into the Hotel Cordón, which boasted a rather exact nine-minute walk to the cathedral and another nine-minute stroll to the bus station.

The well-coiffed clerk behind the desk was equally exacting—and rather unimpressed with my unkempt appearance and lifeless small talk.

When I pointed out I was walking the Camino, he sniffed and said he had already concluded that. Why else would I be carrying a backpack?

When I asked if he could stamp my credencial, he licked his teeth and frowned. The Hotel Cordón was a fully functioning modern hotel for business travelers, not an albergue play center for pilgrims. "Try the cathedral," he suggested with a sneer.

When I mentioned that his English was impeccable, he snorted that he had perfected a wide range of languages from around the globe. After all, the Hotel Cordón was a fully functioning modern hotel for business travelers . . .

He further boasted that the city of Burgos was also home to the purest form of the Castilian dialect in the world. After all, it was first developed in this very region back in the tenth century.

I then reached into my backpack and retrieved Pam's Clue Sheet. The clerk's rudeness didn't deter me. He could still be useful in helping me pinpoint the location of her next letter.

"I need to find this place."

"Yes?" he sighed.

"*You can't write a Book without a Typewriter. You can't drink without a Pub. You can't grow without a Garden.*"

"That is not a place."

"No, it's a clue. But she's capitalized some of the words, so they must be important: 'Book, Typewriter, Pub, Garden.'"

"I am not interested in your game. I have other guests to attend to—"

I looked around. The hotel lobby was completely empty.

"It's not a game. My wife has cancer, and she left behind a letter. This is her message to take me there."

The sneer left his face, and he turned the sheet of paper toward him. "If she is so sick, why didn't she just tell you, hmm?"

"Would you like me to tell you the story?" I teased. "It's very long—"

He shook his head and turned the sheet back to me.

"There is a Book Pub in Plaza del Huerto del Rey. She means King's *Garden* Square. I do not know about this typewriter."

I inspected Pam's clue again and nodded. "That sounds about right. Okay, thanks. Now—"

"Yes?" he sighed.

"I just need to know how to get there."

A few minutes later, I was outside the hotel and heading farther down Calle de la Puebla, clutching the clerk's instructions hurriedly scribbled on the hotel stationery. No cleanup, no change of clothes, no backpack. Still no relief, still limping like a wounded soldier.

I harbored no resentment toward the rude clerk. After all, he had guided me, potentially, one step closer to my wife's mysterious whereabouts. He was simply a shining example of how a town the size of Burgos didn't need the Camino to survive, nor did it need to cater to the maddening pilgrims.

Much of the city's early wealth came from wool exports—and many of those exports helped finance the construction of many of the medieval masterpieces spread across Burgos. Today, the city's economic engine is driven by large-scale manufacturing in tandem with wheat farming and tourism. Tourism also plays a part. While Burgos is a significant Camino stop before the start of the Meseta, tourists are also drawn to the town all by itself.

The clerk's complicated route led me through three plazas and two retail streets before it deposited me in front of the now-notorious Book Pub.

"How far is this place?" I had asked him.

"It is nothing. Seven minutes."

"I have a bad ankle."

"What do I know of bad ankles? It is seven minutes for a Spaniard."

"What if the Spaniard has a bad ankle?"

"I have other guests to attend to!"

Fifteen minutes later, I was inside the deserted Plaza del Huerto del Rey. The large fountain with the stately queen astride a cartoon-ish fish nourished no one. The two taverns were neglected. Only the spires from the nearby cathedral peeking behind the brightly colored apartments offered any sense of pending adventure.

The apartment building housing the pub was a bright yellow, while the pub itself was dark and uninviting. It was an Irish pub, the first I'd seen on the entire Camino; another sure sign I was no longer on a pilgrim path of local curiosities.

I entered the pub to find it just as deserted as the plaza. The stacked books on the shelves nourished no one. The drab oak tables were neglected. Only the drowsy bartender who looked up from his book of crosswords offered any prospect of camaraderie.

He reluctantly mumbled "Hola." Sidling up to the bar, I could see he was making good progress on his puzzle, suggesting a quiet afternoon of peace and application ruined by a pesky pilgrim with a limp.

I inquired if he spoke any English and he shook his head. This made requesting a pot filled with ice much more difficult. Soon I was rolling up my pants, taking off my shoe, removing my sock, ordering a rum and coke, scooping the ice cubes out with my fingers, and then dropping them into another empty glass.

"Ice?" he yawned.

"Sí."

The drowsy bartender slipped past me and disappeared into the kitchen. While pans and pots clattered behind the wall, I further inspected the pub.

The typewriter was easy to find. It sat inside a glass case across from the bar. It appeared to be a cabinet devoted to world exploration, with a large globe and several dusty travel guides piled on the lower shelves.

Where was her message? Bending down, I noticed an envelope poking underneath the base of the typewriter.

I pulled the door. Locked.

The drowsy bartender wasn't as drowsy when he reappeared and placed a pot of ice near my foot, and I was no longer interested in tending to my limp. I gestured toward the locked door. Did he have a key?

He shrugged.

"Listen, I'm a pilgrim standing inside your pub without a sock standing next to a big pot of ice. Do you know any English or not?"

Now he smiled. The bastard.

"I need to see that typewriter."

"You can see through the glass, no?"

"But there's a letter underneath it. See? I know who wrote it."

He bent down to inspect it.

"I know it sounds strange, but my wife left it there months ago for me to find. She's playing a game, but it's all rather important."

"Is impossible."

"How is it impossible? We both see the letter; we just need the key."

"The owner not here," he shrugged. "Not in Spain. He has key."

"There's not a spare one? Nobody else has keys?"

"For case? Why do we need open case?"

"Well, when is the owner back?"

The bartender clapped his hands and shrugged.

Okay, so the owner wasn't coming back soon. We were at an impasse. I looked down at the pot of ice, and a desperate new scheme popped into my head.

"Thanks, anyway. And thanks so much for the pot of ice."

I plunged my left foot into the pot. My toes struck the ice and my heel dangled over the rim.

"I'm sorry, but do you have a bigger pot? It's the back of the ankle that needs the ice. I'm really sorry."

The bartender pouted and led out a sigh of disgust. "Wait."

He once again disappeared into the kitchen. I waited for the sound of clattering pots and pans behind the wall, but instead I heard his feet bounding down a creaky flight of stairs.

I had my moment.

I bent down and dumped the ice onto the floor—and then smashed the glass case with the empty pot.

Had the bartender heard? Was he bounding back up the stairs? I heard nothing but the sound of my own breathing.

There was no time to be cautious and careful. I lifted the type-writer and ripped the letter off the shelf. There was no envelope, just a sheet of paper.

I gathered my letter, my sock, my shoe and hurried out of the Book Pub. It was a painful blend of limping and running. Strong strides from my right leg followed by weak hops with my left. And it hurt like hell.

I didn't want to face the bartender. Would he care? Would he demand some form of payment? Would he call the police?

I "ran-hopped" back to Plaza Mayor, a bustling square I had

passed in my walk from the hotel, hoping to get lost in the crowd. No one was giving chase, but I still didn't feel safe. I was too close to the scene of the crime. I was too exposed in the open-air square.

So I ran-hopped farther toward the river, finally resting a few blocks away on the leafy Paseo del Espolón, the pedestrian promenade along the banks of the Arlanzón River. The trees provided a form of cover, the locals were cooling in the shade, there were benches on which to shrink and hide.

And no one cared that I was a barefoot pilgrim holding my shoe. Breathing hard, my ankle throbbing, I sat down on a bench and pulled on my sock. It was when I bent down to tie my shoe when I heard my name.

"Jamie!"

The jig was up! I was caught!

17

MESETA MADNESS

OF COURSE, I assumed I was in serious trouble for my destruction and desperate escape—until I wondered how my pursuer knew my name. Was it the bartender? And why did he suddenly sound so feminine? Oh! It was Kate and Janet, my original pilgrim friends from Pamplona, who had called me.

I hadn't seen them since their breakfast feast in Los Arcos. It had only been six days, but it actually represented dozens of towns, hundreds of new pilgrims, and several lifetimes of exploration, soul-searching, and painful conclusions.

My current pain soon dominated our discussion. After all, first in the Camino canon of topics was "How are your feet?"

"Is it tendonitis?" Kate asked.

"I don't think so," I said.

"What did the pharmacist say?"

"She didn't say anything; she gave me a cream."

"You should probably ice it first."

"I did."

"How long?"

"Not long."

"It might be tendonitis."

"I don't think it's tendonitis."

"I once had tendonitis. I would stretch it out and ice it first."

"I don't think it's tendonitis; the pharmacist gave me this cream."

"What kind of cream?"

"I don't know."

"You don't know what kind of cream the pharmacist gave you?"

"There was picture of a happy soccer player on the tube."

"Is that how you judge your drugs?"

Kate and Janet meant well. They just had bad timing. Pam's unread letter was tucked under my leg . . .

However, my Camino companions wouldn't budge from my bench until I promised to stretch my leg, ice my foot, and limp over to another doctor to get a second opinion about my injury.

Once I swore I would do all those things *before* I even entertained the *thought* of visiting the Burgos Cathedral, Kate and Janet stood up and gave me a hug. They were meeting friends for an early dinner and discussing their plans for Hornillos del Camino, the first recommended stop in the Meseta.

"You know the Meseta isn't easy, right?" asked Kate.

"It's not physically exhausting, exactly, but you really shouldn't walk the Meseta with tendonitis," agreed Janet.

Then I had to swear I would properly heal my foot *before* I even entertained the *thought* of entering the Meseta. Another promise, another hug, and Kate and Janet finally scampered off to their early dinner.

I looked around me. Was I really alone? Was I finally able to read Pam's letter without interruption?

I trembled a little as I lifted the sheet of paper. What was next? How was she feeling? Was she still with friends? Did she have any second thoughts about our marriage? And . . . when would we meet?

It was just one sheet of paper. Just one. Both sides filled. But just one sheet of paper. There might have been more pages at one time. But today, there was just one. Fortunately, Pam was concise. And I ached.

Dear Jamie,

I am so sorry for the long delay. Obviously I appreciate that you made it this far. If I'm being honest, I'll say it's been a rough couple of days. I get tired a lot and I stop a lot. Even when there's no one around and there's nothing to look at, I still stop in every town and sit down somewhere and take a breath.

I probably should take those opportunities to write you more, but I just don't feel like it, you know? It's me being selfish, I know, but I'm so out of breath and sore. I'd just write complaints anyway and I've said enough about that in the past couple of letters.

Of course, my frequent stops mean not many people want to walk with me anymore. To be fair, Rick and Amy and Joel and Diane are still around me all the time, but that's more in the evening in the squares and the albergues. But on the trail, I'm too slow for everybody and I stop too much. I don't blame them. Every time they get some momentum or something, I have to take a break.

Still no regrets, though! I told you I'm making peace with myself and I still mean that. This is hard but this is ALSO the best – if that makes any sense . . .

So DON'T feel sorry for me!! Seriously, don't pity me! I'm much tougher than I ever thought I was, Jamie. And I'm getting tougher every day.

I just get sad sometimes. Not a lot but a little. It's just sad that I couldn't do this walk feeling any better. And I'm sad that I couldn't do this walk with YOU! I mean that. But you're in school with the kids and I'm over here.

That's why Ronald has been such a help. Remember, Ronald? I mentioned him a bit in my last letter. Anyway, we've become closer, since he's now hurt too and walks at the same speed as me. He's about the only one who doesn't mind stopping in every town. It gives him a chance to have a smoke and find a cup of tea.

I wish you could meet him. I know I said that in the last letter. But it's still true. I bet you two would become great friends. He's funny and sarcastic and gets annoyed about the dumbest things – just like you!

And I don't want to say that I'm glad he's hurt with a bad knee, but I'm glad he's here. He's making this a lot easier.

It ended abruptly. There must have been another page. Maybe it was missing? Maybe I left it under the typewriter? Maybe I dropped it at the bar? Maybe?

The Burgos Cathedral, otherwise known as the Cathedral of Santa Maria, is arguably the finest Gothic cathedral in Spain, even though it is smaller than the one in Seville (the third largest church in the world). The Burgos building itself is a UNESCO World Heritage site.

Construction began in 1221, and various masters, both French and German, Renaissance and Baroque, have expanded and embellished the building with unique carvings, tombs, and tapestries over the centuries.

Today, there are twenty-one chapels, with fifteen encircling the naves, and it would take several hours to comb through them all with proper respect and decorum. Meanwhile, I barely stepped inside the building, entering briefly only to get my credencial stamped.

My priority was meeting with Brie, so I stood outside the grand southside door, the Puerta Alta de la Coroneria, which was dedicated to the Last Judgment of Christ with Jesus displaying his wounds to his penitent mother, Mary, and a pleading John the Baptist.

Locals and tourists queued up beside me to inspect the cathedral. Occasionally I would recognize a pilgrim from the road. We never talked; we never waved; we never even smiled. There was only a small rise of the eyebrows and the slightest of nods. It was our tiny point of recognition: "Hey, I know you." You're that Italian with the purple backpack; you're that German girl who never lets go of her boyfriend; you're that American who yells out "Tennessee" every time you drink a shot of whiskey.

It's like we were part of a privileged secret society blending in with the oblivious public. I steadied myself on my one good foot and peered at the faces parading past me. I thought I saw Den Mother Betsy. Was that Mississippi Holly? I swear I spotted New

York Brian. And if that wasn't Munich Max, then he had a doppelganger deep inside the Burgos Cathedral.

There was no mistaking Brie as she approached the church. It was a few minutes past our meeting time, and she looked rather distressed. But when she saw me, her face lit up and she smiled.

"Hiya!"

She embraced me so tightly I had to hop on my right leg and lean against her shoulder to stay upright.

"Careful—"

"What's wrong? You banged up? Did this happen today?"

"I hurt myself yesterday; it just got worse today."

"I didn't see you hurt yourself yesterday."

"I didn't tell you about it; I thought it was nothing."

"Nothing? I touch you and you almost fall over."

"I thought it was nothing; now it's something."

"Did you see a doctor?"

"I saw a pharmacist."

"Are they a doctor?"

"I think so . . . "

"Where does it hurt?"

"My ankle. Something popped."

"Is it tendonitis?"

"I don't think so."

"You should ice it. Did you ice it?"

"I iced it."

"When I hurt my knee, they told me to ice it."

"I iced it, I saw a doctor posing as a pharmacist, I don't think it's tendonitis. Can we sit down?"

We retreated from the Plaza de Santa Maria, and minutes later we were seated at an alleyway patio with a bottle of wine on the checkerboard tablecloth and my left foot in a bucket of ice.

"I had a sarnie just now," Brie announced. "Are you hungry?"

"Not really." I shrugged as I slid Pam's letter across the table.

Brie read it. I watched her. She sipped. I gulped. She exhibited tremendous concentration. I exhibited tremendous patience. Until she smiled…

"Why are you smiling? There's nothing to smile about."

"She says she's in a right state wanting to walk with you. That's smashing, innit?"

"She's not that sad about it. She's walking with someone named Ronald!"

"Seems like a nice bloke. Likes tea. Could be English."

"'We've become *closer*.' You read that? 'I wish you *could meet him*.' Did you read that?"

"I'm sure she means well—"

"Oh, really? Does she? 'I *really* wish you could meet *Ronald*. I bet you'd two become *great friends*.'"

"He's funny, sarcastic, gets annoyed about dumb things. Just like you, Jamie! That's crackin'."

"Is it? Is it *really*? Is it *really crackin*?"

"What you on about? Oh, no; hold on. You don't think . . .?"

"*Yes, I do think*. In the last letter, Pam kept telling me to make friends and not be gloomy."

"That was good advice—"

"Why was she suddenly soooo concerned about me making friends?"

"She cares about you—"

"Because she's feeling *guilty*! If I get close to someone, she can get close to someone! 'I wish you could meet him.' That was 'the wish' she had from the last letter. I wish . . . you could meet him. I'm right, aren't I?"

"But you did make friends, Jamie."

"You don't count."

"I'm going to ignore that right now—"

"What about Martin and that . . . Mabel? Right? They were just friends. She was *your* friend. Then look what happened."

"She's sick, you know. Your wife? The woman who separated from *you*? In case you forgot, she has cancer!" That last word came out rather loud. Brie looked around to see if anyone had been rattled by her outburst. Nope. We were still alone.

"Your wife has cancer," she whispered. "You hear how shattered she is about the whole thing. You should focus on that. Never mind this Ronald bloke."

I wasn't listening. I was too busy forging accusations in my head. There was no room for focus and insight.

"And it just ended, too. There must have been another page, but I don't know what it says. All I know is: Pam didn't write another letter for eight whole days. That next letter's hiding in León. That's eight days from here!"

"She *left* the next letter in León eight days from here. Maybe she did write sooner than all that—"

"Eight long days walking in the Meseta with Ronald's bad leg—"

"She's not alone, Jamie!" blurted out Brie, trying desperately to be supportive. "She says she chats up Nick and Amy and Joel and Debbie—"

"Rick and Amy and Joel and Diane—"

"Sound like solid mates for a woman in need. She said so herself. Stop worrying."

Brie finished her wine and poured another glass. It bought her more time to think of another helpful observation. But those extra seconds yielded nothing.

"What do you reckon?" she finally asked.

"There's no choice. I'm heading straight to León."

"Quite right."

Brie sipped her wine and watched me closely. "I suppose now I need a good hard think."

"About what?"

"About heading straight to León."

"I only bought one ticket."

It was true. After reading Pam's letter several more times and obsessing about its contents until my brain ached more than my throbbing ankle, I had limped across the Santa Maria bridge to the bus station to buy myself a one-way ticket out of Burgos for the following morning.

"Oh," Brie murmured when I revealed my bus ticket.

"You told me yourself to get those letters as fast as I can."

"Now more than ever it seems—" she mumbled.

"So, you think I'm right?! There *could* be something going between Pam and Ronald with the fucked-up leg!"

"Could! Of course, there *could*! But Pam is lovely and sick and I don't think so."

"You don't even know her."

"Of course I know her, Jamie! I read her letters. I know what it's like to have a husband who doesn't care much about you. I know what it feels like to be trapped so badly you just want to shove off straight away and never come back!"

It was one second. One second after her outburst, Brie launched her body across the table and grabbed my face with her hands and then spat out an apology.

"I didn't mean that. You care about her, I know. I didn't mean that. You are nothing like Martin. You are lush and brilliant and I didn't mean that. You just didn't know how she was feeling. You didn't know about all the pain in her heart before the cancer. You didn't know. How could you know? You two never had a proper chat. You didn't know. You are nothing like Martin. *Nothing* like him. You care; I know you do. And you care right now and you're walking across Spain for her. You care, I know; you really care. Please don't get wound up . . . please!"

It was difficult to speak with Brie's hands gripping my face. "I won't," I sputtered.

She finally let go and fell back into her chair.

"It's just that . . . I don't fancy walking by myself anymore."

Brie looked miserable. Whether it was her remorse from her slip of the tongue or her realization that I was leaving her behind in Burgos, it was my turn to reassure her.

"Brie, you have friends everywhere. Almost everyone I met on this trip is because of you. *I'm* the one who'll be alone."

"Not for long. You'll find her, Jamie. I know it. You'll find your Pam soon."

"Well, first stop's León. Then . . . hopefully there'll be another batch of letters. Or . . . maybe she's there in León. I don't know."

"You're going to miss the Meseta." Brie said it so softly I thought for a moment she was on the verge of tears.

"I'll see it from the bus. If it's as miserable as they say, I won't miss much."

"Maybe that's the way to go, innit?"

"You're not going on that bus. You're not going on any bus."

Brie was staring intently into the checkerboard pattern on the table. Now she looked up at me and raised her eyebrows. No?

"You're walking this Camino. All of it. You're going to fucking earn your compostela."

"But—"

"Don't argue with me. You know I'm right. The new Brie Bletcher—the new born again Brie Bletcher—needs to do this. She owes it to Missus Brie Baxter."

"After Alto del Perdón, you said not everybody makes it."

"Don't listen to Jamie Draper from Alto del Perdón—"

"You said some get too hurt. You said some just bottle it."

"You won't. You're too tough."

Brie smiled. It was the first time she had truly smiled since we reunited outside the Burgos Cathedral. I had missed it immensely.

"No one's ever called me tough before."

"No one's ever seen you walk the Camino before. And now you're going to finish it."

The ten-thirty bus to León the next morning was late. Many passengers remained lined up at the assigned stop while others paced and predictably checked their watches. It was a typical Tuesday and time was wasting. Appointments were made. Business arrangements had to be followed. Where was that bus?

I didn't stir from my seat on the crowded bench. I was wedged between an old lady with far too many bags to carry and three fidgety children who refused to appease their wailing mother and sit still for a single second—but I wasn't budging.

My ankle was feeling a little better, but I was seizing every opportunity to rest it. I had walked 219.7 kilometers so far, and I intended to walk many more. My miraculous cream wasn't going to fix me in a day, but my limp was already less pronounced.

I kept daydreaming about the previous night with Brie: our quiet dinner on the hushed patio; our slow walk back to my hotel; and, especially, Brie's sudden agitation when we entered the lobby.

"I gave you my home e-mail?" asked Brie.

"Yes. I'll borrow someone's phone and e-mail you tomorrow."

"You can't."

"What?"

"Well, you *can*. But I can't read anything until I get home."

"Wha—?"

"I threw away my shit phone. I dropped it on the street, everything got worse, I didn't care anymore. I was getting too many texts from my neighbor about Mabel and Martin . . . And I got so cross I just threw it away."

"I understand—"

"I didn't tell you earlier, because we were talking about you and Pam. Didn't think it was appro. So . . ."

"I threw my phone away in Pamplona. It's fine."

"Sorry. Were you expecting any e-mails from your friends?"

"No, I guess not."

"What are you going to do if you don't like what you find in León?"

"You sound worried—"

"What if you get bad news?"

"You think I'm going to get bad news?"

"No!" Then Brie took a breath and calmly repeated, "No. Pam met a nice bloke on the trail who smokes and drinks tea. That's all. Don't do anything horrible."

"Like murder him?"

"Don't be funny."

"Beat him up? Get revenge?"

"No." Then after pondering my jokes, she whispered, "Yes."

"I'm a high school teacher who writes bad novels. The worst I can do is make Ronald read one of them."

Brie playfully punched me in the chest. "Such an idiot."

Without warning, she hugged me quickly and kissed my lips. It wasn't romantic. And it wasn't familiar, like a brother and a sister. It was something in between, although there was no time to react to it. Brie was leaving, and I had to appreciate every moment.

"Be careful, Jamie Draper."

She then hurried for the door. Brie never looked back and she never slowed her pace, but I swear she wiped away a few tears from her cheek.

The bus arrived and the passengers impatiently piled on. By ten-forty, every seat was occupied. By ten-fifty, the aisle was filling up as the driver returned to his seat. Schedule? What schedule?

I had secured a spot by the window and was ready to settle the debate. Was the Meseta impressive and romantic? Or oppressive and sinister? Was that arid plain something to cherish? Or loathe?

I had already dismissed the popular contention that the monotonous landscape inspired deeper thought and insight. Self-revelations can just as easily be triggered by lush green hills and babbling brooks. All you had to do was turn off your smartphone and look around.

The myth remained, however, that the role of the first section of the Camino was to test you physically while the Meseta (the middle section) was to challenge you mentally. It wasn't physically strenuous; it only dulled your mind and lulled you to sleep.

The Meseta officially began approximately thirteen kilometers outside Burgos. Burnsley called the change in landscape "sublime" and praised the first day's journey into Hornillos del Camino as a "welcome respite" from city consumerism. With a population of seventy and a town with nothing to do but sit in the square, this welcome respite sounded rather horrific to me.

Because of the village's tiny size, my bus bypassed the Hornillos del Camino turnoff to pause at the second recommended pilgrim stop in the Meseta, Castrojeriz.

Through my dusty window I was now getting the lay of the land: it was flat and brown with endless fields of wheat, barley, and oats. If there were no crops, there was wild grass. If there were no wild grass, there was dirt. And if there were any trees, there would be only a handful, and they would be far away and unattainable. And the pilgrim path, if it could be seen from the highway at all, looked awfully straight.

Castrojeriz, at least, was a sizeable village. It even featured the ruins of a ninth-century castle standing on the nearby hill. Founded by the Visigoths, it was the site of various battles between the Moors and the Christians and once boasted eight hospitals, nine churches, and a royal residence. At least you could revel in the town's colorful past as you sipped your *cerveza*.

The bus left Castrojeriz for its forty-minute drive west to the next stop of Carrión de los Condes. This bypassed Frómista (the third recommended stop on the Meseta), which once was an important supplier of wheat to the Roman Empire (its name was derived from the Latin word for cereal, *frumentum*).

The area also marked the beginning of the notorious *senda*, a gravel footpath, pitched precariously close to the highway that was solely intended for the use of pilgrims. This footpath now dominated much of the remaining march in the Meseta.

Carrión de los Condes marked the halfway point in the Meseta section. Its substantial size—it had more than two thousand citizens—would be a boon to any weary pilgrim. Its history was even more impressive. During medieval times, it was home to ten thousand inhabitants and had more than a dozen hospitals caring for passing pilgrims.

It was named after its savior, Alonso Carreño, who had adopted the nickname Carrión after routing the ruling Moors in the ninth century and thus ending the alleged annual practice of surrendering one hundred local virgins to their Moorish masters.

Today, we picked up several pilgrims at the crossroads outside Carrión de los Condes. Perhaps they were tired of the Meseta. Perhaps they were now in a hurry for León. I contemplated inquiring as to their reasons for boarding, but my lazy gaze out the window at the tedious landscape lulled me into a catatonic doze.

I awoke when my bus turned for Sahagún, a town similar in size to Carrión de los Condes, which represented the halfway point of the Meseta's recommended sixth day and the overall halfway point of the entire Camino Francés.

The name Sahagún is a bastardization of "Saint Facundo." Facundo was martyred here with his brother, Saint Primitivo, after the pair refused to sacrifice to the local Roman gods in either the second or third century. In the ninth century, a monastery was finally built in his honor. In the twelfth century, the monastery was thoroughly enriched by Alfonso VI after monks helped him escape when he was held captive there by his warring brother, Sancho III.

It then became the most powerful fourteenth-century monastery in Spain; Sahagún was the medieval version of Las Vegas, a wealthy city in the middle of the desert with ten thousand citizens and its own university.

Today, it's a dull and drab town after two eighteenth-century fires devastated the monastery and much of the local area. Sahagún never recovered.

Our final station was León; we were bypassing the seventh recommended resting spot, Mansilla de las Mulas, which piqued my lagging interest in the Meseta because of its twelfth-century walls. Roman in origin, the name comes from "*man de silla*" (hand on the saddle) and "*de las mulas*" (of the mules), likely in reference to its previous prominence as a market town for livestock.

Two hours after leaving Burgos, we arrived in León. Two hours on an air-conditioned motor coach replaced eight days of walking without shade and eight quiet nights in tiny prairie towns with little to do but eat and drink (*after* the siesta, of course).

I felt no guilt departing the bus—only relief. Relief that I hadn't further aggravated my ankle. Relief that I hadn't had to endure the lifeless and mundane Meseta.

The bus station was a convenient ten-minute walk from the Old City Center; a convenient ten-minute walk to more amenities, comforts, and marvelous monuments. And ten minutes away from my wife's next letter.

18

SARRIA SANCTUARY

THE CITY OF LEÓN, rising off the banks of the Bernesga River, was founded as a Roman military encampment as early as 29 BC under Caesar Augustus. By 68 AD, the Roman Seventh Legion was stationed here to protect the roads leading to and from the nearby gold mines. And while the city symbol remains a lion, its city name is actually derived from the Latin word for legion, *Legio*.

In the tenth century it was known as the Christian capital of Spain. Three hundred years later, its luster and spiritual influence faded with the 1301 union of the León and Castile crowns.

A fine example of the city's decline in national affairs was that it once possessed its own language, Leonese, based on the Latin spoken by its Roman forebears. Developed in the Middle Ages, it is now almost extinct, spoken only by some of the elderly living in the northern mountains. However, the separatists want to revive it, and a few language courses have sprouted throughout the province.

León's remaining glory is its French Gothic cathedral, the Santa Maria de León. The site once housed Roman baths, which were converted into a royal palace during the Christian reconquest. Once the Moors were defeated, a grateful Ordoño II abandoned his regal home and began to rebuild it as a house of God.

The cathedral's impressive exterior is even more striking from the inside, where parishioners can sit in awe of its 125 stained-glass windows devoutly covering over eighteen thousand square feet of the church's walls.

While León deserves its own pilgrimage just to see the cathedral, it also represents the last major city before the final march into Santiago de Compostela. And it remains a favorite among the pilgrims, not only for its boundless beauty and urban sophistication, but because it also means that in less than two days, one would be clear of the Meseta. (The finish line was in Astorga, a mere fifty-three kilometers away, where the landscape's gray grain is finally replaced by grass, trees, and livestock.)

Not that the Meseta marginalized *me* in any way. I bypassed most of the menacing mess with a two-hour bus ride. I was a tourist with a backpack. And I was only here for one reason: to find my wife's next letter.

Pam's clue was straightforward enough: "*I admire the Camino. The tired pilgrim admires San Marcos.*"

San Marcos was nearby. I didn't even have to cross the river to enter the original Old Town. I simply had to limp north along its western bank and cross the Puente Rio Bernesga, the sixteenth-century stone bridge that connects to the Plaza de San Marcos.

Much like León's cathedral, the Hospital (alternatively called the Monastery or the Convent) de San Marcos has served many purposes over the centuries.

It began its life in 1173 as a modest pilgrim hospital and monastery dedicated to Saint Mark under the protection of the Knights of the Order of Santiago. In 1515, thanks to a large donation by King Ferdinand II, the building was expanded and featured a one-hundred-meter-long plateresque façade. It was then repurposed as a palatial headquarters for the naughty knights who now approached their honorable duties as though they were members of a drunken men's club.

By 1837, the building was falling into ruin and used as an army barracks. During the Spanish Civil War, it served as the local jail, which imprisoned thousands of Republicans.

Following the war, it was repeatedly condemned by the city until it was finally purchased by the government in 1961 and reconstructed, at great cost, as a luxurious inn called the Parador, which offered a fifteen-percent discount to pilgrims.

As I entered Plaza de San Marcos I scanned the square for any faces I might recognize. It was pointless, of course. I was separated from my friends by more than 180 kilometers. I had left them all behind in Burgos.

"*I admire the Camino. The tired pilgrim admires San Marcos.*"

I searched for Pam's tired pilgrim. It was, thankfully, simple. There he sat at the base of the stone cross facing the façade.

He was a modest man made of stone, his head and back against the column, his beard full, his eyes closed, his sandals discarded beside him. No possessions, no staff. Peaceful and noble. In front of him, a yellow arrow and a Camino shell stenciled in the pavement, pointing to the Puente Rio Bernesga, led him toward the edge of the Meseta.

I sat down beside him and stared at the elegant and solemn surroundings. My eyes crisscrossed the façade while others tried to capture the length and breadth of the building with their cameras.

Good. Everyone was busy. Too busy to notice my eager hands fondling the weary warrior from top to bottom looking for any crevice where I might locate my letter.

I finally found it between the pilgrim's legs, where his robe hung across his ankles. Bending down and stretched across the steps, my fingers worked as quickly as they could to rip apart the tape that was holding it in place. Once I retrieved the letter, I sat down with my back against the column, just like the weary pilgrim.

Pam's letter was once again protected by a plastic bag that had completely failed to do its job. It was wet inside and severely damaged, so the paper fell apart when I pulled away the plastic.

Trying to dry the pieces on my lap did little to improve their condition. The letter was just too damaged. The few legible words flickered down the pages like bullet points in a PowerPoint presentation.

It was virtually hopeless. The only words and phrases I could decipher formed an incomplete narrative, seemingly hiding the truth within their unknown context. But they would have to do. And, upon later reflection, they were enough.

Dear Jamie,

I couldn't read the "dear." But I knew it existed. Much like the rest of the following phrases I discovered inside the letter . . .

> *I wrote to you in Castrojeriz and Carrión and Sahagún. I wrote to you twice in Sahagún. But I ripped those letters up . . .*
>
> *If you walked, I'm sorry. I can only imagine what the Meseta was like for you . . .*
>
> *They say it gives you time to think . . .*
>
> *But I had more than enough time to think . . . and forgive . . .*
>
> *And I need you to forgive me now . . .*
>
> *Ronald was a help . . .*
>
> *Town after town, he was always a help to me . . .*
>
> *He may have loved me, I don't know . . .*
>
> *I didn't love him back . . .*
>
> *I couldn't . . .*
>
> *I was so strong at the beginning . . .*
>
> *I did not give him my heart . . .*
>
> *It was one time . . .*
>
> *I don't know, I was feeling vulnerable and sorry for myself . . .*
>
> *I'm sorry, Jamie . . .*
>
> *Our marriage was over, but that's no excuse . . .*
>
> *I didn't lose you as a husband. That already happened . . .*
>
> *See it from my perspective; you don't know the pain . . .*
>
> *I'm giving you a gift now. The Camino is giving you a gift . . .*
>
> *I hope you can see that . . .*
>
> *Get out of that apartment, move on . . .*
>
> *The Camino is just the start . . .*
>
> *Love your Pam, always*

It was all I could read. Pam had composed three pages from her heart but the ink was smudged into oblivion and her full intentions were now erased. There were no legible sentences, only scattered phrases. And even inside those fragments, there was always a word or two missing, which forced my mind to fill in the blanks and pick words that made the most sense. The rest of the lengthy message was a disaster.

My earlier concerns about Ronald had proven to be more accurate. Now the usual hopelessness I felt about Pam's painful Camino was instantly replaced by a seething rage. Brie was right. I wanted to do something horrible.

So now what? Was this it? Were there more letters? Where was Pam now? Was she still with Ronald?!

I had no answers, of course. I needed more information. And I suddenly knew just where to find it.

It was when I recalled that day in Palma, sitting on the bench inside the Plaça de Santa Eulàlia, conducting my English lesson with Luis—with that large envelope from my mother-in-law on my lap, and that smaller package tucked inside of it with that strange return address . . .

Digging deep to the bottom of my backpack, choking on my tears, I pulled out the envelope—the small one I had received back in Palma—and spit out, "Looks like I now know someone in Gibraltar!"

Sixteen Days Later

It had been sixteen days since I last saw Brie. It had been sixteen days since she kissed me on the lips and hurried away, wiping the tears off her cheek. It was now Thursday, June 26.

The World Cup had been raging for days, and it was the last day of the group-stage competition. In pubs and restaurants across Spain—and across Europe—locals and tourists gathered to watch the world's best compete in Brazil. It had been so important to me when I discussed it with English Simon and German Karl outside Estella. Now I didn't even notice.

It was hard not to notice Brie, though. I was standing outside my Sarria hotel in my customary spot on the pedestrian bridge overlooking the babbling Sarria River.

She screamed, "Hiya!" and ran across the parking lot as fast her bulky backpack would allow.

I lifted my head and smiled. I was happy to see her, but I couldn't muster much more of a reaction than that. Not in my current condition.

It had only been sixteen days, but Brie's appearance was different by degrees. The Camino walking had certainly agreed with her. She was still thin but much more toned. She was still uniquely pretty but now confident about it, rather than uncomfortably quirky.

Perhaps it all came down to her haircut. The bangs were gone. The sandy curls were tamed. I could now see her entire face . . . which meant I could see her forehead. The scars were still there, of course, but Brie had applied a little makeup to cover them up the best she could. It was effective enough, I suppose. Now the scars were a minimal mention rather than a major distraction. Perhaps other people wouldn't notice them at all.

It had been sixteen days since that kiss; 386 kilometers since those tears . . .

Thanks to my two-hour bus ride, I was familiar with Brie's first eight days traveling through that dust and drudgery between Burgos and León.

A browse through my Burnsley provided the itinerary of her next eight days. Once she left the comfort of León, Brie's next stop was likely the humble village of Villar de Mazarife. This was followed by the former Roman stronghold of Astorga, which also brought a much-welcomed end to the menace of the Meseta.

Then came the ominous approach to the hamlet Rabanal del Camino before the strenuous climb up and down the Montes de León into the town of Ponferrada, the former headquarters of the notorious Knights Templar.

Brie then bedded down in Villafranca del Bierzo, a town built on the slopes of two steep valleys, once populated by medieval French pilgrims who elected to remain in Spain after their pilgrimages.

Then came the notorious ascent to O Cebreiro. Outside of the rough road up the Pyrenees, this was the steepest climb of the entire Camino, ending at a misty mountaintop village consisting of quaint stone houses with conical thatched roofs (called *pallozas*).

Lastly, Brie rested her head in one of the worst burgs of the Camino, Triacastela. It was a tiny town that had once boasted three worthy castles but now had nothing left of note and didn't seem to be in much of a hurry to replace its missing history with something remarkable and beautiful.

Sarria wasn't as guilty of such impassivity. The tower of its ruined castle, the Fortaleza de Sarria, was preserved. Its thirteenth-century monastery still had a fine plateresque façade and an order of monks residing there. Its main street, Rúa Maior, was still lined with splendid eighteenth-century houses (along with most of the town's albergues and restaurants).

I was probably dwelling in the finest house of them all, the four-star Hotel Alfonso IX, named after the last king of León and Galicia and the town's official founder (following its Celtic formations and Roman roots).

His nickname was the Slobberer because he foamed at the mouth whenever he was enraged. A better nickname might have been the Fornicator because of his proclivity to marry his cousins and produce numerous children. His two wives bore him eight children, while one of his mistresses bore him six more and another delivered four.

Then in 1230, at the age of forty-two, while on his own pilgrimage to Santiago, Alfonso IX died in Sarria, the town he had founded. His son, Ferdinand III, already the king of Castile, soon inherited his father's kingdom of León and Galicia, which merged León with Castile for the rest of Spanish history.

Today, his town, Sarria, 115 kilometers east of Santiago de Compostela, is popularly credited as the starting point for any pilgrim short on time and light on ambition who wants to complete the Camino and receive the official compostela.

And that's where I was reunited with Brie: in the town Alfonso IX founded, not far from the hotel named after him, on the pedestrian bridge leading to the string of bars and restaurants along the river, below the hill that led to Rúa Maior and the rest of the town's treasures and pleasures.

Brie talked and I listened. I got lost in her exhaustive narrative, piecing together what was important and discarding the rest. She had grown weary of the lack of privacy in the albergues and was now exclusively bunking in budget hotels. Tonight, she was treating herself to a nice bed in a four-star hotel; the only four-star left in the foreseeable future on the Camino.

She was touchy at first, stroking my arm, rubbing my shoulder, even picking at my unruly hair. She finally retreated when I gave her nothing back. I couldn't. A smile was painful. My aching eyes were too tired to focus on her beaming face.

She cleared her throat and whispered in my ear. "I'm sorry, love. What about you? You've lost weight. You let your hair grow. You could use a trim here and there. So . . . tell me . . . "

"I've been here for days."

"Here? You've been staying at this hotel? How long?"

I struggled to come up with an answer and then dismissed the calculation with a shrug.

"Why?" she asked.

I again struggled to come up with an answer, finally blurting, "Can I show you?"

We walked back to the Alfonso IX, and Brie clasped my hand. The hotel was a cream-colored box that suggested a mental-health facility rather than the luxurious lodge offering pampering and refreshment it was.

The hotel interior seemed to fulfill that promise with its leather chairs, a grand piano, and a superlative restaurant beckoning guests to sample its cuisine. But the chairs remained empty, the piano keys were gathering dust, and the restaurant was never open to the public.

"Do you want to check in first?" I asked.

"Show me what you want to show me first."

I led her toward the elevator. We could hear the hotel cafeteria now, the only section of the cream-colored box that ever hummed with activity.

We said nothing in the elevator, but I could feel Brie's eyes peering up at me. Perhaps worried by my silence. Perhaps concerned by my despair. I glared ahead at the elevator door and felt her tiny hand grip mine tighter.

I led her down the hallway, tugging my hand free so I could pull out the key card from my pocket.

"The maid hasn't been in here for a while," I droned as I slid the plastic pass across the lock.

The latch was in my hand, but I hesitated to push through the door. Brie brushed aside the obvious delay and took her backpack off her shoulders. Tossing it aside, she straightened up and smiled. Any further hesitation would just increase the tension.

I opened the door and followed her in.

I couldn't see her face, but I could hear the gasp as she scanned my room. The double beds were stripped of their pillows and sheets. My clothes were left in tiny piles across the floor like landmines. The curtains were closed to embrace the darkness. The TV was left on, and left silent, in order to manufacture a pocket of light to fight back the gloom.

However, I don't think my unruly mess produced Brie's gasp. Nor was it my small pile of notebooks strewn across the floor filled with my steams of consciousness that pivoted between sadness and anger . . . and hopelessness.

No, it was my artwork: the pencil drawings discarded on the floor, some accented in pen, some crumpled in despair, some as pristine as an exhibit masterpiece. All created by my shaky hands when writing down my feelings and my morbid thoughts became too much to bear.

All of the sketches were manipulated memories of my Camino. The dirt and grime among the magnificent landscapes. The pockets of trees amid the endless wheat. The never-ending road. The pilgrims at the edge of the sheet, dotted like insignificant ants. Once in a while, a lone figure in the center of the page. A woman with chestnut hair and pale skin and tiny feet, walking away from me. Not ignoring me, but imploring me to follow her. Urging me to move on.

Brie looked back at me, tears already welling up in her eyes.

"She's dead, Brie. Pam's dead."

Brie and I sat silently for a long time in that room. I was slouched against the wall, staring vacantly at the closed curtain while the glow from the television set irritated my teary eyes.

I couldn't move— not my legs to cross the room to turn off the TV, not my hands to wipe away the tears. Not even my eyes to relieve the irritation. I was hopeless and defeated . . . and not for the first time that week.

Brie slouched against the wall beside me; her head resting on my shoulder, both her hands gripping my left in some pious gesture of prayer.

It was a pure drain of emotion, similar to what I had experienced when I found out Pam was dead. Brie was reacting to the news that I had been living with for days, so of course, it triggered the same old emotions in me. I had honestly thought I was done with crying. I had thought I was done with feeling numb. Not yet. I was close . . . but not yet. I needed Brie to snap me out of my helplessness.

Suddenly, Brie let go of my hand and with tremendous effort pushed her body off the floor. She then wiped away any lingering tears and sternly surveyed the room.

"Right. Usually it takes me a couple of sessions to figure out what's been going on. Think I got it sorted here."

"I was just tired of thinking and writing all the time."

"Quite right."

Brie lifted a drawing off the floor. "Quite good, actually. I think I remember that road."

"I can't give you any details about Pam. Not yet."

"No need. There's more important things to do now. First off, you need to nip out of the room straight away."

"I was out of this room when you met me—"

Brie crossed the room to open the curtain. *That* made me move with a jolt, if only to cover my eyes and turn my head.

"I leave this room all the time," I said, cringing at the light.

Brie crossed her arms and looked skeptical.

"I tour the hotel, I tour the town—"

"Tomorrow we're leaving and walking to Portomarín."

She went on to make a compelling argument for the therapy of exercise and the great outdoors. My lingering anguish and stress had internalized and disconnected me from the world. I needed external challenges in a supportive environment to re-energize my mind and feed my soul.

I didn't argue. She talked and talked, but I had already agreed in principle. She only clinched it with my own words: "You're walking this Camino. Maybe not all of it, but the rest of it. You're going to fucking earn your compostela."

I nodded and pulled myself up off the floor. I tried to smile back, but I'm fairly certain it came across as a pained grimace.

"I have to say goodbye."

"To who?"

"To this place."

My suffering in Sarria had mirrored my earlier misery in Palma. When I wasn't climbing the walls of my room, I barely summoned the strength to get off the floor and leave the hotel.

I first would cross that pedestrian bridge over the Sarria River and join the locals and tourists in search of a meal and a drink on Rúa Malecón.

Reminders that this was still a Camino town were everywhere. Some of the steel bars along the fencing were in the shape of shells. So were the ashtray bins. Even the mural painted on the wall depicted a young pilgrim following the yellow arrows of the Camino.

Since I had already made the effort to leave my hotel, I would often follow the actual yellow arrows of the Camino and climb the staircase of Rúa Maior, where the ancient cobblestones mixed with sheets of cement, where the remaining eighteenth-century walls blended with the twentieth-century apartments.

I ignored the albergues. I ignored the restaurants. I ignored the views of the countryside that presented themselves whenever a Sarria sidestreet collided with Rúa Maior.

From here, Rúa Maior was less of a staircase and more of a modern ramp. I acknowledged the thirteenth-century San Salvador church, but only as a marker to turn for Rúa da Mercede.

At this point of my uphill climb, I was all alone. Few locals lived here, and few tourists ventured this far from the menus and monuments of Main Street.

The final frontier of my Sarria wanderings was next. While the monastery at the end of the road pointed pilgrims westward toward Santiago, it also pointed to the cemetery across the street, with its abundant aisles of memorials to the city's dead. Many of them small and insignificant, piled high as compartments in a filing cabinet. Many of them above-ground tombs. Some of them as big as toolsheds. Some rustic and humble. Some grand and garish. All of them providing me with some small degree of comfort.

I would wander aimlessly for an hour or more until I picked a random tomb—it didn't matter which one—and pretend I was paying proper respects to my wife.

I somehow found it cathartic to have a stranger's tomb stand in for my wife's missing grave. It didn't matter who they were, or what they were named, or at what age they had passed away. They had lived on this planet, on the same stretch of earth my wife had once walked. And they had been loved. Just like my Pam.

19

CAMINO COMEBACK

AFTER MY FINAL TOUR of the tombs, I returned to the hotel to find Brie waiting for me in my room. She had showered, she had changed her clothes, her hair was wet, and the room smelled . . . fresh.

She had also tidied up, made the beds, folded my discarded clothes, and arranged my Camino notebooks and artwork pages into neat little stacks on the desk.

"The hotel was full; I hope you don't mind."

I shrugged and noticed that the double beds were pulled apart. Far apart.

"That's all right, isn't it?" Brie asked.

"I don't mind."

I kicked off my shoes and flopped onto the bed nearest to me, silently staking my claim. I should have thanked her for her efforts, but I was too intent on taking a nap.

That was how I had coped the previous few days: long walks to the city of the dead followed by long naps in my dirty room. Okay, so the room wasn't dirty anymore, but I could still sleep away my sorrow.

Wait a minute. The sheets smelled odd. What was it? Oh, they were clean. Brie must have cornered a maid in the hallway. I didn't ask.

Just as I closed my eyes to kill the rest of the evening, her voice rose up from the floor.

"Jamie, I'm hungry."

I assented to Brie's implied request, and we joined the locals and tourists in search of a meal and a drink on Rúa Malecón. We settled for the Next Pool Bar in the quietest section of the dining lounge next to the forgotten pool tables.

Brie did all the talking. There was a time when her one-sided conversation would require plenty of nods and meaningless phrases like "I see" and "I guess so" to prove I was listening. But that night in Sarria, I was free from having to make any affirming gestures.

Brie said little about the uninspiring towns of the Meseta except that it was all a dreadful mess where the never-ending horizon played tricks with your brain and the walk through the monotonous landscape lulled you into mournful memories.

"Some people say it's beautiful," I finally offered.

"Those people should holiday more."

"They say it gives you time to think."

"You know what I thought about? The flies. Nobody ever mentions the bloody flies."

Brie talked a lot more about the people she had met on the Camino since we parted. There was Harriet and Naomi, whom she encountered in the early days of the Meseta in Castrojeriz. Harriet was sixty years old, from Australia, and loved the wide-open skies and the colorful details of the land. Naomi was fifty years old from London and hated the monotony of the Meseta and the nagging blisters on her feet that just wouldn't go away.

"They were opposites, but they were mates. But they walked too slow, and I had to leave them."

Then there was Raisa from the Netherlands and her German boyfriend, Aldo, whom Brie joined in Astorga. The young college couple had met on the Camino two years ago in Sarria and fallen in love. Now they had returned to walk the entire French Way together while they contemplated their futures. She wanted to become a painter but worried about making a living. He wanted to become a doctor but entered nursing to improve his training. Both were delaying their stressful entries into the real world.

"But they were too happy. I had to give them up."

"Too happy?"

"All that young love. Wait till he falls off a ladder and hurts his back and collects disability pay and gets drunk every day at the local. Then let's see how happy they are."

Brie talked about many more Camino characters, like Kyle the Englishman with ADD who scoured every town looking for the best TV screen to watch the World Cup matches. And Hendrik, the retired Dutchman who liked red wine and Cuban cigars and had a strict itinerary organized by a tour company that arranged all his hotel stays.

There were many more mentions and many more characters, but I was fading fast under the moonlight and dreaming about my bed. During my troubled time in Sarria, sleep had been my only comfort and silence was my only friend. There was a routine to it. As soon as darkness enveloped the town, I ached to shut off my mind and drift into the abyss; for a few short hours I could stop my merry-go-round of emotions.

Brie was determined to change all that and reintroduce me to the land of the living . . . and the walking.

"You're knackered. We can go. We'll have a good and proper chat tomorrow."

I didn't mind the implication that I would tell her everything that happened after León—because I knew that I would. I wanted to tell her everything. Just not that night.

After paying our bill, we walked back slowly to the Hotel Alfonso IX. I did everything slowly now. There was no urgency for anything. Except sleep.

Brie even held my hand, although I suspect it was less of a romantic gesture and more of a firm intent to keep me upright and steady, fearing I might bolt for one more melancholy tour of the town.

"The last time I saw you, you were limping."

"Magic cream from one pharmacist, ibuprofen from another," I said matter-of-factly. "I was fine in a few days."

Brie said nothing more as we crossed the parking lot and plodded up the entrance stairs. She also remained silent in the hotel lobby and during our brief ride in the elevator. By the time we approached our room, however, she was staring me down and ready to burst.

"You want to know what I found in León, don't you?"

"*Just* give me that! Damn it, Jamie—I won't be able to sleep."

"Pam's letter," I confirmed as I again tugged my hand free to retrieve my key card from my pocket.

"That's all I'm keen on. I swear. Nothing else tonight, I promise."

All this time, our entire night together, story after story, listing one new Camino friend after another: Brie had been killing time. She just wanted to know what happened to Pam. And what I had done.

"Her letter was taped under a statue and completely ruined; I could barely read it."

I opened the door and followed her in. And just like before, I kicked off my shoes and flopped onto the bed closest to me.

"But you could read some of it?"

Having read Pam's ruined letter dozens of times, I was able to summarize it without much trouble. I could even quote most of it.

"Dear Jamie, I wrote to you a few times but I ripped them all up. I'm sorry if you walked the Meseta. They say it gives you time to think. I need you to forgive me now. Town after town, Ronald was always a help to me. He may have loved me, I don't know. I didn't love him back. I did not give him my heart. I was feeling vulnerable and sorry for myself. Our marriage was over, but that's no excuse. See it from my perspective; you don't know my pain. The Camino and I are giving you a gift now. I hope you can see that. Move on. The Camino is just the start."

"Holy shit."

"Yes," I yawned. "All kinds of holy shit."

"You were right about that bugger, Ronald."

"I was right about that bugger Ronald," I yawned again and closed my eyes. "There's still no joy in it. But I was right."

"Jamie, this is massive."

"No, it was massive sixteen days ago, but not anymore."

"What did you do? Seriously, Jamie, what did you do?"

"I went to Gibraltar."

"Gibraltar? Why the bloody hell do you go to Gibraltar?"

"It had all the answers."

"What did you do? Jamie? What did you do?"

I didn't reply. I couldn't reply. I had already shut off my brain and drifted into the abyss.

"Jamie. Jamie. Jamie, it's time to go."

My eyes fluttered open. I hadn't moved from my Sarria bed since I had drifted away. I only knew time had passed because the open window revealed a pale blue sky basking in the dawn.

It was time to go—to reconquer the Camino.

Once awake, Brie didn't say another word, urging me through my morning routine simply by sitting on her bed, fully dressed, with her backpack already strapped over her slender shoulders.

I filled my backpack for the first time in several days, quickly cleaned up, and changed into my pilgrim clothes.

Once again slathering my feet with my anti-blister stick, I stared at my artwork still stacked in mysterious piles on the desk. *Do I take them? Do I leave them?* I looked to Brie, but she only shrugged in response.

Tying up my shoes, I finally made a decision. *Nope. Not taking them. It's a present for the maid. Keep them, burn them; they served their purpose.*

I looked to Brie and attempted a smile, still fairly certain it came across as a pained grimace.

"You up for it?" she whispered.

I nodded.

"Brilliant. Let's go fucking earn your compostela."

Moments later in the hotel lobby, I paid my bill while Brie picked up sandwiches and takeaway coffee from the cafeteria. I was already over the limit on one credit card and approaching the ceiling on the other. I hadn't made a payment to either card in weeks. I was probably late on both. I didn't care.

The friendly hotel clerk printed off my receipt and wished me a "Buen Camino." Pointing at my backpack, he noted, "You here so long, I did not know you were peregrino."

"I took a break."

"Yes, very tiring."

"Sure, let's go with that." Tucking the receipt into my bag, I asked, "So, you guys were full last night?"

"Full, señor? No. Many beds open."

"Is that so?"

Brie arrived with the sandwiches and coffee.

"My man here says the hotel wasn't full last night."

"Is that right?"

"Many beds open," the hotel clerk confirmed.

"I was told it was packed out. Shall we . . . ?"

If Brie was embarrassed about her lie, I couldn't tell; she quickly turned her back to me and headed for the door.

The Camino path out of Sarria matched my usual tour of the town. We crossed the pedestrian bridge over the Sarria River and strolled along the fencing of Rúa Malecón before climbing Rúa Maior. At the thirteenth-century San Salvador church, I once again turned for Rúa da Mercede. This time, I disregarded the cemetery gates and walked along its outer stone wall for the westward road to Santiago de Compostela.

We were in Galicia now, the final territory of the Camino journey, with over a thousand kilometers of coastline kissing the Atlantic Ocean while bordering Portugal in the south.

Its name comes from the Gallaeci, the Celtic tribe that once lived here. The Romans, under Caesar Augustus, later exploited the area for its gold and other valuable minerals. It was subsequently conquered by the Visigoths, the Moors, and even raided by the Vikings, before being aligned to the various configurations of the former kingdoms of León and Castile.

Through it all, despite its various captors, Galicia remained isolated from the rest of Spain, utilizing its wet and mild climate and forested landscapes for farming, raising livestock, and forestry, along with fishing. While Galicia is referred to as the country of a thousand rivers, it is equally derided as the land of a million cows.

It also prospered and developed its own language, Galician, a Romance language closer to Portuguese than the Castilian Spanish. Surprisingly, it was Francisco Franco, a Galician from Ferrol, who suppressed the official use of his native tongue. Only after his death did the Galician language make a comeback, along with a new sense of Galician nationalism.

Today, the region is another one of Spain's autonomous communities that focus more on self-government issues rather than on national affairs.

My biggest issue with Galicia was the ferocious return of allergies that had been dormant since my teenage years. All that greenery, all that wet and mild air. Once we passed the Sarria cemetery I couldn't stop sneezing. My eyes became teary and puffy, and my nose ran like a faucet.

The only thing worse was Brie's constant concern. "Are you okay? Are you crying? You're all bunged up. Is this too much? I'm so sorry; I thought this would help. You had to leave that room, Jamie; it was the only way you could get better."

"It's my bloody allergies."

"Are you sure? Because if you need to stop for a minute and let it all out, let me know—"

"It's my bloody allergies!"

We turned off the country road for the medieval stone bridge, the Ponte Aspera (Rough Bridge), over the trickling Celeiro River. The path gently climbed and wound its way through ancient woodland for the rest of the morning.

It should have been a pleasant walk. Mighty oaks and gnarled chestnuts provided a cozy canopy under the searing sun. Tiny hamlets popped up without warning along the road. Unseen birds provided a natural symphony of chirps and tweets. The only obstruction to enjoying all this beauty and wonder were my leaky eyes and insistent sneezing . . . and the flies.

Oh, those fucking flies! I didn't need to read Burnsley to get an indication of where the next hamlet would be. The flies would tell me. Each hamlet was identical, with only a small collection of stone farmhouses dotting the road. No visible farmers, no available horses or cows. Just sinister stone houses and empty, yawning barns with huge piles of fresh animal shit on the ground. And, boy, did those flies love that fresh animal shit. They also loved dive-bombing me, smacking my face, burrowing in my hair, and tunneling into my ears.

Was it my perspiration? Was it my dewy eyes and runny nose? Was I cursed? They never attacked Brie. Only me.

Brie didn't know whether to shriek in horror or bend over with laughter. Sometimes she did both.

"What the hell, Jamie? Why only you?"

"Tell me again why I had to leave that room to get better!"

"I'm sorry, Jamie," Brie giggled. "I wish I could help."

She was right about one thing, though: no guidebook or pilgrim ever mentions the flies. But, trust me; they are waiting for you in Galicia. And they want to tunnel into your ears.

The memory of Pam's death came surging back when we came upon a makeshift memorial in the woods outside the village of Barbadelo. It wasn't unique to this or any other stretch of the Camino; it was only the first one of the day. And it was substantial.

The tribute to the fallen focused on a four-foot wooden cross atop a cairn of rocks. Later pilgrims had added to it, littering it with photos of Pope Benedict and numerous personal items such as shirts, scarves, socks, and flags. Some hung off the crossbeam of the cross, some were strewn along the stone wall behind it, and some were tied on the clothesline of rope that ran from the cross to a nearby tree.

I noticed pilgrims had left behind handwritten notes addressed to their fallen Camino comrades. And that's when I set down my backpack to search for Pam's letters.

"No, Jamie—don't," Brie said with a gasp.

"I can't move on if I keep these letters."

"But they're the last words from your wife."

"I've read them a million times. I won't forget what she said."

I shuffled the letters into a small stack of pages, folded them, and placed them between two rocks at the bottom of the cairn.

"The next time it rains they'll be ruined."

"The next time it rains I still won't forget what she said."

We would pass several more cemeteries and makeshift memorials along the Camino path over the next few days. However, I never paused to weep or pay them any deferential attention. I was done with the consecration of death.

Outside the hamlet of A Brea, we passed a stone marker that announced Santiago de Compostela was officially one hundred kilometers away. This was the exact spot where the Camino officials required you to begin your journey in order to receive your cherished compostela. It wasn't much. I had expected a grand shrine, but it was just a simple plinth with a shell symbol and a "K 100" marking—along with dozens of inscriptions from pilgrim vandals over the years. Savages.

Burnsley warned that the roads from here on would be busier and the lodging opportunities in shorter supply.

There was another new wrinkle to the pilgrim proceedings as well. Officials in Santiago now requested pilgrims obtain two stamps per day for the remaining one hundred kilometers. They were targeting pilgrims who had started their journey in Sarria and maybe didn't take the Camino seriously enough. Two stamps a day meant you had to enter two historical buildings to receive them, which suggested (weakly) that you might explore each town more closely. Most pilgrims obliged; even those pilgrims who had begun their journey hundreds of kilometers farther away than Sarria.

At the twelve-kilometer mark, Brie and I stopped in a bar in Morgade for coffee and sponge cake. Take away our backpacks and my watery eyes, and we were like two old friends sharing delicious gossip and dessert mid-morning in any café in Europe.

"You look terrible," said Brie in between bites. "You need a farmacia."

"Or less cow shit."

"Why the bloody hell did you go to Gibraltar?"

"Subtle."

"I don't recall you being subtle when you asked me about my breakup with Martin."

"Fun fact: the Spanish always assume that if you stop walking the Camino for any reason, you can always pick up and finish it the following year."

"What?"

"When I was at the bus station in León, the guy in the coffee shop called me lazy, assuming that I was just taking the bus to another town on the Camino. I had to show him my swollen ankle just to get him off my back. Then he tells me to come back next year. He just assumed that I could get the time off work again, bring extra money, and return to Spain—"

"You live in Spain and you don't have a job."

"But you see my point? The Spanish just take it for granted that you can come back every year to walk another section of the Camino. Rather cheeky, don't you think?"

"Listen, you useless bugger," Brie said, jabbing the air with her cake fork. "Are you going to tell me why you went to Gibraltar, or am I going to have to get mental with this fork?"

"The first letter I got from Pam? Back in Palma? The address on the envelope was a Gibraltar address. I didn't think much about it at the time, but after reading about Ronald . . . I figured he sent it from Gibraltar."

"We always assumed Ronald was British," Brie nodded.

"But the British don't have to live in Britain, do they? I figured he lived in Gibraltar."

"Still . . . bit of a leap."

"And bit of a trip to find out, too. I first had to catch a bus to Madrid and then spend the whole next day getting there. And all I had was this old address."

"Bloody hell. Couldn't you fly?"

"Only from London. Gibraltar won't allow Spanish jets into their airport."

"So, did you find him?"

"Not right away."

"Oh, shit. What did you do? You did something horrible, didn't you? You got revenge somehow, didn't you?"

Gibraltar lies in the very southern tip of the Iberian Peninsula. It's a self-governing British territory, only three miles long and one mile wide, and home to thirty thousand people who cling to the coastline under huge limestone cliffs rising fourteen hundred feet above the Mediterranean Sea.

Located five hundred kilometers north of Morocco, "the Rock" was viewed by the Romans as the end of the world. To Muslim commander Tariq ibn Ziyad it represented access to Europe when he landed there in 711 to launch the Moor invasion of present-day Spain and Portugal. The name Gibraltar is actually a Spanish derivation of the Arab name Jabal Tariq (or mountain of Tariq).

The Kingdom of Castile eventually reclaimed the Rock in 1462, but Spain lost the territory again in 1704 to the British during the War of the Spanish Succession. Then in 1713, with the signing of the Treaty of Utrecht, Spain agreed to surrender Gibraltar to Great Britain . . . *forever*.

Naturally, Spain immediately regretted that decision and has been fighting ever since—sometimes militarily—to get it back.

Naturally, the British haven't relented. Gibraltar is just too valuable; it represents the only marine entrance between the Mediterranean Sea and the Atlantic Ocean and is home to a formidable British naval base.

Over the past fifty years, the UK government has wavered occasionally in its stance and has offered to share the territory with Spain—if its citizens agreed. However, the people of Gibraltar are just too pro-British. In a 1967 referendum, they were asked to choose between British and Spanish sovereignty. The result? Staying the course with Britain: 12,138 votes. Changing it up and ceding to Spain: 44. With such an overwhelming outcome, Gibraltar proceeded to create its own constitution in 1969.

Spain did not take this well. Francisco Franco immediately closed the border, and the territory was cut off from Spain for the next sixteen years.

Obviously, this hurt the local economy and affected the freedom of travel of its residents, but it also hurt the people of southern Spain who traveled to Gibraltar to work the manual-labor jobs in the naval dockyards—jobs the Gibraltar citizens were loath to do. Solution? Give those dirty jobs to the nearby Moroccans, until Spain reopened its border in 1985.

Then in 2002, Gibraltar held another referendum and, once again, the people voted 98.48 percent to remain British. Spain again did not take it well, especially after Gibraltar sank boats and dumped concrete blocks in its harbor to create an artificial reef to boost its marine life, which would, in turn, boost its own tourism as a scuba diving destination.

Spain complained to the EU that this was a deliberate obstacle to Spanish fishing vessels that sometimes drifted into the still-disputed territorial waters off the coast. The Rock held firm. After all, Gibraltar had already issued a total ban of commercial fishing in the area.

The two nations continue to squabble at sea, and on land, about Gibraltar. Whenever Madrid feels particularly annoyed with the Gibraltar government, it instructs its Spanish border guards to perform more thorough searches of everyone crossing the border. Suddenly, a busy crossing that usually takes a matter of minutes would take several hours due to longer traffic lineups (which once again hurts its own Spanish citizens who might be returning from a day of work in Gibraltar).

Brie cared little about the history of Gibraltar, of course. Her nagging question (and rightly so) was whether I had sought revenge and done something terrible to Ronald.

"He's not dead, if that's what you're wondering."

"I should bloody well hope not! But there are massive amounts of shit things you can still do, Jamie!"

"Can I just tell the story my way?"

I didn't mind the scolding (which got louder and more intense as we moved along). And I didn't mind the implication that I would tell Brie everything that had happened—because I knew I would. I really did want to tell her everything. Just not *that* morning.

My reluctance was never meant to frustrate her or tease her. It was simply my well-earned safety net from the flood of emotions I knew was ready to flow once I got to the crux of my confrontation.

I couldn't properly cope. Not yet. It was still too soon after I had shared the news of Pam's death back in my Sarria hotel room. I needed more miles under my feet to toughen myself up. I wanted to tell Brie everything—but without sobbing and, more importantly, without her smothering me with more sympathy.

I had to be stoic, measured, unflappable. She had to be levelheaded, restrained, relieved. She had lost her mind when she witnessed my allergy attacks; how was she going to react when I told her about my emotional battle with Ronald?

20

GIBRALTAR ROADBLOCKS

After Morgade, we remained on a high ridge with the Galician mountains greeting us in the south. Our pretty country lane led us through a corridor of timber, frequently interrupted by wide pastures of green populated by small flocks of Galician cattle. The villages were few and uninspiring, and the hamlets remained nameless and deserted. It was also deathly quiet, apart from our boot falls, my vigorous sneezes, and my murderous mutterings whenever a cloud of flies rained down on my sorry head.

"Right! So you took a train from Madrid to Gibraltar—"

"Actually, I had to take the morning train from Madrid to Algeciras, all the way on the other side of the bay from Gibraltar."

Residents of Algeciras would like to remind visitors that their town was once an elegant port. However, after Francisco Franco closed the border to Gibraltar it became an industrial center designed to absorb the manual laborers no longer working in the Gibraltar shipyards. Today, it's a mere ferry stop for Moroccan tourists and migrant workers.

"Right, so you're stuck in Algeciras—"

"No, I got out of there as fast as I could. I went straight to the bus station to catch a bus to La Línea de la Concepción."

"Brilliant. So now you're in La Linea de la . . . whatever. Then what?"

"I walked across the border."

There was something seductive and intimidating about the Rock, which loomed so large behind Gibraltar's border control.

Its perpendicular western face was jagged in a light shade of gray. Then it sloped eastward with a green tablecloth of trees butting the edge of the cliffs. Nothing obscured it: not another hill, not a manmade skyscraper. It could be seen from miles at every vantage point and served as a constant reminder to everyone in the Bay of Gibraltar that the Rock was the monolithic heavyweight in a depressed area light on any real economic progress.

Armed with my passport, it had taken me just seconds to get through the border patrol. The guard barely glanced at the passport, and he certainly didn't ask me any questions. He just waved me in; there was no need for a stamp.

Large photos of Kaiane Aldorino, 2009's Miss Gibraltar, who was later crowned Miss World in Johannesburg, South Africa, lined the hallway. Five years later, and the government had felt no need to remove them. As seductive as the peninsula's limestone cliffs were, this former human resources clerk (now deputy mayor) seemed to represent the territory's most impressive achievement to date.

And if you still needed proof that you'd just entered a British territory, there was a red telephone box just outside passport control. And the first road that greeted you on the other side of the border was named Winston Churchill Avenue.

But first, you had to walk across the airport runway. That's right. There were no other roads or walkways or tunnels. You simply strolled inside the painted white lines and crossed the actual runway.

Don't worry. You wouldn't have to look both ways to see if a plane was approaching. If an airplane was in the sky, a siren would sound and the barrier arms would come down at the gates on either side of the airport. Then security officials would inspect the grounds before giving the radio tower the "all-clear" signal. It was all rather straightforward and uncomplicated, like a school crossing guard helping children cross the road in a suburban neighborhood.

You just needed to remember to walk between the painted white lines. When I strayed off the path to marvel at the Rock, I was reprimanded by a security official on Winston Churchill Avenue.

I seized the opportunity to show him my Gibraltar envelope with the mysterious return address, and he pointed me in the right direction. I didn't even have to enter town.

After the village of Mercadoiro, the pebbly country lane gave way to asphalt as Brie and I dropped steeply toward our destination of Portomarin; the Minho River and its manmade reservoir were visible on our right.

Back in Gibraltar, the multipurpose Victoria Stadium, immodestly situated just meters from the airport runway, had also been visible on my right as I followed the guard's instructions.

Bayside Road led to Gibraltar's western marina. There were no cars, no pedestrians; just granite buildings past their prime with neglected scaffolding from roof to sidewalk, no crews in sight, no sunlight penetrating the apartment windows. It was as gray and dreary as the western face of Tariq's mountain.

Next to this weary wasteland was the shiny white elephant called Ocean Village. Glimmering and glamorous in the setting sun, it was an eyesore and not indicative of what Gibraltar actually looked like.

It was like the town of Cancun in Mexico or the fake Eiffel Tower in Las Vegas. There was nothing historic or authentic about it; it was just a luxurious parking lot for old-money yachts owned by pasty-white Brits peacocking along the promenade.

I inspected my Gibraltar envelope again—"O'Reilly's, Leisure Island, Ocean Village, Gibraltar"—and asked a White Peacock if he knew the way to O'Reilly's. He sniffed the air as though I had offended his better senses and limply pointed down the dock.

It turns out O'Reilly's referred to O'Reilly's Irish Pub. I just had to plod past the gigantic casino and the monstrous luxury cruise ship that was operating as a dockside hotel.

There was nothing gauche or gaudy about O'Reilly's. It was like any Irish pub you might find on any street anywhere else in the world: Bourbon Street, Broadway, the Champs-Élysées—anywhere except authentic Ireland.

Inside the pub, a few yachties sipped cocktails by the windows and admired their boats. A few drunken louts in the next corner hollered at the TV screen showing a football match from the previous week.

I approached the bar and flagged a bemused young waiter.

"Excuse me. Is Ronald here?"

"Ronald?"

I presented my Gibraltar envelope and pointed at the handwritten inscription. "This is the address he used."

"Hold on, I'm new. Paul?"

Paul, the older bartender, was bent over, filling his refrigerators with bottles of beer. He straightened up and inspected my envelope.

"No Ronald here. Sorry."

"Oh, maybe he doesn't work here. Maybe he's a regular?"

"I only work the day shift. Carol?"

Carol, the manager, who had been filling out paperwork at a nearby table, approached the bar and inspected my envelope as well.

"No Ronald I've heard of."

The young waiter then blurted, "Ronnie, maybe?"

"Yeah, maybe Ronnie," Paul agreed. "He comes in with that tunnel lot."

"Yeah, Ronnie. He comes here all the time," Carol confirmed.

"Do you know if Ronald . . . Ronnie . . . ever walked the Camino?"

"What? Up in Spain?" asked the young waiter.

"Yeah, he walked it," Paul confirmed. "He's mentioned it loads of times. You met him on the Camino?"

"No, I never met him. I'm just looking for him."

"Cheeky, he used this place," Carol chuckled, handing back the envelope.

"He probably didn't want me to find him."

"Why? What's he done?" wondered the young waiter.

"He should have left it blank," said Carol.

"The post office probably required it."

"Cheeky, though—"

"So, he comes here all the time?"

"Who, Ronnie? Yeeeeah," said Paul.

"When can I expect him?"

"Can't say."

"Well, what does he look like?"

"Look like? Well, he's Ronnie, isn't he?"

"Well, what color's his hair? Let's start with that."

"Well, it's brown, I think, innit?" Paul wasn't sure.

The young waiter tried to help. "Brownish?"

"More blond, I thought," chimed in Carol.

"Well, in the summertime, yeah," Paul agreed.

"Look, it doesn't matter. Do any of you know where I can find him . . . like, right now?"

"He's in with that tunnel lot," Paul repeated.

"Okay, where's that?"

"You got to go to the top," the younger waiter answered.

"The top? The top of what?"

"The top of the Rock. The tunnels."

All three of them pointed to the sky.

Brie was not amused. "You might have skipped that story."

"You didn't want to hear about O'Reilly's? That's the whole mystery back in Palma," I teased.

"You could have gone straight to the tunnels."

"I'm just making a point: Ronald didn't want to be found that easily."

"Straight to the tunnels you could have gone," Brie muttered and shook her head. "You do rabbit on, don't you?"

"Look, I'm telling you the story. But I'm not going straight to the part where I'm crying and wanting to hit Ronald."

"So you did do something terrible, then?"

"I'm getting to that . . ."

We turned for the modern bridge that would lead us to Portomarin. The area had been inhabited for centuries, but it was the Romans who had formally occupied it. With the later popularity of the Camino in the Middle Ages, the town briefly thrived and was protected by several orders of knights, including the Knights Templar. This explained why its twelfth-century church, the Church of San Nicolas, looked more like a fortress than a church.

In the 1950s, Francisco Franco wanted to harness the power of the Minho River and build a hydroelectric dam. However, in doing so, the low-lying Portomarin would be completely flooded. So the townspeople were offered financial compensation to move to another town. Instead, the people of Portomarin decided to rebuild their beloved town farther up the slope.

In the 1960s, while the river was dammed to create the reservoir, the citizens chose which historical buildings they wanted to salvage and moved them up the hill to drier ground, brick by brick and stone by stone. Outside the fortress church you can still see numbers carved into the bricks to help with the building's reconstruction.

The rest of the new town was constructed as needed. That means the old village and its medieval bridge are completely underwater, and when the dam levels are low enough, the tops of some of the buildings that were left behind can be seen poking out of the water.

None of the underwater village could be seen when Brie and I crossed the modern bridge over the Minho River, although we did climb the stone staircase that had once connected the abandoned town with the Camino on the other side of the river. Then we turned for the "new" town center, a half kilometer up the hill.

While Brie and I had by now reduced our reliance on Burnsley, he was correct that the lodging opportunities after Sarria would be fewer. Only four central hotels were mentioned in the guidebook, and we visited them all.

Hotel #1 was full. Hotel #2 would accept only one more person. Hotel #3 said the same. When we finally agreed to split up for the night, Brie stayed behind in hotel #3 and I headed to hotel #4 at the edge of the square. There was room for me, but I had to share a bathroom down the hall with four others. And there would be no television. It was the barest of rooms, but it was mine and it was quiet. (Burnsley also listed seven albergues, but Brie and I had both retired from the dormitories of doom.)

I didn't mind separating from Brie for the rest of the afternoon. It was my longest walk in two weeks, and I was expectedly tired from the 22.4-kilometer trek. I was also worn out from all the talking. And there was so much more to tell!

We had already agreed on a dinner time, so my only responsibility now was locating an open pharmacy to shut down my allergies. I couldn't find one before the siesta. Maybe the town didn't have one. Maybe the pharmacy was left behind and remained at the bottom of the reservoir. I would have to fight the sneezes and the watery eyes for another day.

The streets were empty when I strolled back to my hotel. Despite its thousands of years of history, apart from a few historical structures the rest of the town was only half a century old. So . . . why wasn't it prettier? Even the "new" buildings hadn't aged well. *Had the town run out of handymen? And where were the painters? Where's your pride, Portomarin? Plant a tree. Grow some flowers. You had a second chance in re-creating your community . . . and you shit the bed.*

When I got to my hotel, I took advantage of the unoccupied bathroom and quickly washed myself and my clothes. I didn't need to hurry. No one was around. In fact, there was no evidence of any other visitor on my floor. Was the hotel really full? Or was that a story they told all the desperate pilgrims who needed a room?

I wasted away the rest of the afternoon with a long nap. It had become my key coping mechanism over the past several days, and I was still a slave to the routine: a long walk followed by a long nap. A bed in a bare room was all I needed.

When I escaped the deserted inn for my dinner date with Brie, it was stifling hot, hovering well past the thirty-degree mark. That was always the heat of the day in Spain—not midday at the start of siesta, but late in the day just before sunset.

It was another reason to complain about this ridiculous time-waster. Why not shut down the town during the hottest hours? That made sense. Why close everything of convenience in the early afternoon right after the tourists arrived? Shut it down at five and reopen when the sun goes down (*if* you had to close it down at all). As it was, stepping outside after a siesta snooze felt like a slap in the face with a heating pad.

Portomarin's main square, with its twelfth-century fortress/church, was as deserted as my hotel. Everyone was huddled under the colonnade at the far end of the plaza, rummaging through the dining options that lined the square.

Brie waved me over to the pizza patio. It was the only restaurant that had expanded beyond the colonnade and provided umbrellas to protect patrons from the searing sun. Brie quickly ordered us beers and pizza. She was all business and in no mood to slow down the proceedings by consulting the menu.

"So, you had to go to the tunnels. Then what?"

"What?"

"To find Ronald. That's where you stopped in your Gibraltar story. Go on."

"Can I wait for my beer?"

"It's coming. Go on."

I couldn't resist teasing Brie for a few extra moments. "Did you know that Gibraltar has monkeys?"

"What? Monkeys?"

"Yeah, Barbary macaques. Now no one knows how they got there. They think they were brought there from North Africa by the Moors as pets, but nobody knows for sure. Anyway, they're the only wild primates left in continental Europe. Isn't that crazy?"

"Listen." Brie spoke slowly and menacingly. "Unless Ronald was a Barbary ape—"

"Barbary macaque. They have tails; they're just so small you can hardly see them. So they're actually monkeys and not apes—"

Brit gritted her teeth. "Unless Ronald was a small-tailed Barbary macaque, I don't give a toss—"

"They're all over the place. Well, not in the town, actually. But they're all over the nature reserve at the top of the Rock. And they're not afraid of tourists, either. There are signs everywhere not to feed them. In fact, you shouldn't even have food with you . . . because those little bastards will jump right on you and steal the food right out of your hand."

Brie sighed and gave me a closed-mouth stare. Just like a Barbary macaque would do if he or she were annoyed.

The waiter dropped off our pints of beer and promised that our pizzas would be ready in a few minutes. Brie was polite but impatient for him to leave. The moment his back was turned, she leaned into me.

"So, you had to go to the tunnels."

"Shall we eat first?" I teased.

"Start talking, *you*."

"All right. So I left O'Reilly's . . . "

Leaving the Ocean Village monstrosity, I walked through the tunnel at Montagu Bastion, where enterprising retailers had set up shop in the lookout points and military storerooms where soldiers had once huddled and scoured the horizon for approaching ships. I emerged in Grand Casemates Square, which was built as a fortification chamber to fire cannons and house the military. Today it houses restaurants and shops to entertain tourists.

The square was the entry to Gibraltar's main street—appropriately named Main Street; there was no need to overthink it—with more bars, restaurants, and shops. This was more like it. This felt like a British territory. This was built for the people, not the gleaming white peacocks. When I asked a pedestrian for the location of the tunnels, he didn't sniff the air and act offended; he pointed me to Bell Lane.

From here, I walked up the slope leading to the Nature Park Reserve. Main Street was where the citizens shopped; the slope was where they lived. The road led me past homes and apartments, some grand and inviting, some small and tucked away from view.

The climb became progressively more tiring and inspiring, and when I reached the Castle Steps the views behind me improved with every stride. The steps then ended at Willis's Road, which brought me to the Great Siege Tunnels.

Throughout the eighteenth century, Great Britain, France, and Spain fought many battles for the protection of their colonies all over North America and the Atlantic. In June 1779, however, Spain specifically declared war on Great Britain to regain Gibraltar and loosen British control of the Mediterranean Sea.

Having failed to mount any formidable attack on the well-secured territory, the Spanish fleets soon blockaded Gibraltar and cut off its food supply.

Now, of course, the British had always taken advantage of the Rock's impressive height to volley cannon fire at the Spanish troops below. But it wasn't until 1782 that the decision was made to dig a tunnel inside that mountain and hollow out galleries into the limestone in order to mount bigger guns.

Work was slow and difficult, and it took five weeks to dig a tunnel that measured eight feet high and twenty-seven yards long—enough space to load a couple of cannons and further protect their territory.

Then in February 1783, the Spanish crown finally gave up, and the siege was lifted—and Gibraltar remained with Britain.

Even after the siege was over, the British continued to dig passageways inside the mountain, and by 1790 the Rock was excavated with four thousand feet of tunnels. This excavation continued over the years but began again in earnest during World War II, when Britain was certain Gibraltar would be attacked by the Germans. By the end of the war, there were thirty-three miles of tunnels inside the Rock, with room for sixteen thousand men to survive with enough supplies to last an entire year. The attack never came.

Today, you can explore those tunnels and read about the mountain's military history once you pay your admission fee to the ticket-taker inside the Great Siege Tunnel entrance. When I approached the booth, I encountered a tired bald man with long gray hair rimming his head. He looked like Benjamin Franklin.

"Hi. I'm looking for Ronald . . . Ronnie?"

"Ronnie Donaldson?"

"His name is Ronald Donaldson?"

"Well, you can see why he goes by Ronnie."

"Brownish hair? A little blond in the summertime?"

"Brownish? Yeah, alright. What's this all about?"

"We met on the Camino?"

Benjamin Franklin said nothing and looked me over.

"Last year? I thought I'd surprise him? It's like a reunion."

Benjamin Franklin said nothing and looked me over again.

"I was in the area . . ."

"That Camino really buggered him up. And I don't mean the leg."

"It was a challenge, all right," I said in my friendliest available tone.

"Don't mean that. Something else. Ronnie hasn't been the same since he got back. Anyway, that's for him to say."

"Is he here?"

"Off today. Off for the week, I think."

"I don't suppose he lives nearby."

Benjamin Franklin chuckled. "Back down the Rock, I'm afraid, mate. And then across the border. He's in La Linea."

"Brie, is that you?"

"Look who it is!"

"Mind if we join you?"

Brie wore that annoyed-Barbary-macaque expression again as several of her pilgrim friends suddenly invaded our table.

Even without introductions I could guess who the intruders were: Harriet, the sixty-year-old Aussie, with her thick glasses and sharp tongue, and Naomi, the fifty-year-old Brit with the wild hair and the permanent frown.

"I can't believe we caught up to you. It's been ages," said Harriet.

"My feet are on fucking fire," moaned Naomi.

"Who are you?" asked Harriet with a devilish twinkle. "The boyfriend? Brie, you've been hiding him! How's your feet?"

"Mine are on fucking fire," moaned Naomi again.

Oh, shit, it was happening. First my feet, then my sleep, my diet, my Camino experience... I wasn't ready for any of this! I was finally comfortable enough to disclose everything to Brie, but not to *these people*! I knew it instantly. My heart was racing. Inflammatory words were already foaming around my mouth. And I was dangerously close to embarrassing Brie.

"I have to go."

Brie instantly understood my discomfort. "I'll go with you."

"You're not going anywhere," interjected Harriet.

"Yes, please stay," said Naomi.

Harriet even tugged on Brie's arm. "You can't go, Brie. We have to catch up."

"I'm exhausted," I explained, although Harriet and Naomi really weren't that interested in what I had to say.

"Brie, we'll meet here in the morning at six-thirty, okay?"

Brie nodded and seemed resigned to stay behind.

"We could all meet here at six-thirty," suggested Harriet.

Something was still troubling Brie. "Jamie, did you get that address? From that man in the booth?

"Well, now we know this one's Jamie," muttered Harriet.

"It took some persuading," I said to Brie. "But, yeah; I got it."

Brie eased back into her chair. She was satisfied . . . for now.

The next morning was complicated by a series of small setbacks. My nightly slumber was ravaged by feverish dreams of empty Camino landscapes and never-ending roads—and the lone figure of my wife escaping my grasp every time I got close to her, then vanishing and reappearing miles ahead on abandoned bluffs.

When I finally settled into a peaceful sleep, it was almost dawn—and I slept through the alarm of my little-used travel clock. Or, more accurately, I had forgotten to set my little-used travel clock and, unfortunately, had no one to wake me up. It was the downside to staying in a private room; there was no one around to back you up.

I hurried across the plaza, but I was already too late. It was seven-thirty, and Brie was nowhere to be found. Had she waited? Should I?

I couldn't blame her for leaving. Our plan wasn't very solid, and she didn't know where I was staying. Plus I was sixty minutes late. It wasn't a tragedy; I could safely assume we would meet that afternoon at Burnsley's recommended destination of Palas de Rei. It only meant that I would be leaving Portomarin alone.

The small café next door to the pizza place, thankfully, provided the basic pilgrim breakfast. After my lukewarm coffee and bland toast, I descended the deserted streets and crossed the bridge to rejoin the Camino. This time I veered to the right and climbed through the oak forest until I reached the senda path that ran parallel to the highway.

Aymery Picaud had written in his Codex Calixtinus that a brothel had once greeted the pilgrims after they cleared the trees. If it was still standing, I might have visited it for a few minutes, if only to take a time-out from my allergy crying and sneezing.

That morning I noted a change in the overall mood of the Camino. Ever since Sarria I noticed that passing pilgrims had stopped offering greetings of "Hola" and "Buen Camino." These used to be automatic. Were the Camino veterans tired of being tactful? Or was this due to the presence of all these Sarria rookies who didn't know the refined rules of the road? *We used to be polite pilgrims!*

Marching into the village of Gonzar, 7.8 kilometers outside of Portomarin, I was ready for a proper coffee, but all the shops were closed. For the next three kilometers, the Camino track widened and ramped up through woodland with a thick mat of scrubs clinging to the road and a narrow alley of evergreens lining up as far as the eye could see.

The next few villages on the path—Castromaior, Hospital de la Cruz, and Ventas de Narón—also mocked me with their closed cafés. Flies, sneezes, tears, rude pilgrims, and a sudden coffee shortage on the Camino . . . I was not having an enlightening adventure.

I hardly noticed the top of the ridge at Sierre Ligonde before the path gently descended again. The flies kept me preoccupied and my tears blurred my vision, but there was no hiding the fact that it was a lovely stretch of scrubland over rolling hills.

The next village of Ligonde looked promising for a cup of coffee, if only because I saw living, breathing locals tending to their small farms and engaging in hushed conversations with their neighbors. But this town, just like all the others, remained stubbornly closed to the thirsty traveler.

It was only the hamlet of Portos, 19.5 kilometers outside Portomarin, that offered me an open café. Long past my need for a hot coffee, I gulped down an icy soda and devoured a slice of cake as what can only be described as a spiteful snack. *I was near the end of my walk, and now the Camino finally offers me something to drink?* I should have been grateful, but it felt like a slap in my fly-infested face.

One more push through woodland and I arrived at Palas de Rei. I felt no immediate appreciation for its history, nor any urgency to find comfort in a hotel or the company of Brie. I needed drugs.

I found a pharmacy with seconds to spare before siesta. One look at my red, swollen eyes and one conveniently timed sneezing fit led the pharmacist to pick out, presumably, the strongest medication. At any rate, she warned me to take only one pill a day. I nodded and swallowed my first pill before I even reached for my wallet.

Palas de Rei (loosely translated as the King's Palace), like many of the other towns on the Camino, lost its luster long ago. In the Middle Ages, it was a formidable military base that housed the eighth-century palace of the Visigoth king, Witiza, who later acquired the nickname Witiza the Wicked after he killed all his rivals for the throne, including a pair of worthy relatives.

The palace was long gone, and nothing of note had replaced it. The church on the top of the hill, the Iglesia de San Tirso, featured a Romanesque façade from the thirteenth-century, but little else.

The church did prove useful in allowing me to acquire one of the two stamps needed for my credencial, with the nosy parishioner insisting I first sign a daily guest book noting how far I had come in my journey. When I wrote down "Pamplona," I noticed most of the other pilgrims had walked only from Sarria (with Saint-Jean-Pied-de-Port a distant second).

My stamp duty out of the way and my allergy pill presumably working its magic (I had already stopped sneezing), I searched for a hotel. I didn't have far to roam. Palas de Rei was primarily composed of three parallel streets mounted on the side of a hill, with the busy highway encircling the town in its noisy embrace.

I found a bed on my fourth hotel attempt. My room was spotless and featured a leafy view down the slope of the hill and a television set with dozens of Spanish channels to numb my brain. Although a wasteful afternoon of TV chatter and fitful dreams tempted me, I only wanted to find Brie.

I didn't know where to start. The main square, the Praza do Concello, was vacant and uninviting, completely stripped of any pleasant accoutrements that might make a local linger. The noxious highway that snaked around it like a chokehold probably had something to do with that.

I tramped up and down the town's three signature streets, poking my head into every hotel, café, bar, and restaurant, searching for my cherished companion. Was she doing the same? Despite the town's much smaller size, the exercise reminded me of the futility I'd experienced in looking for Brie back in Logroño.

I temporarily gave up and enjoyed a late lunch in my hotel bar before embarking on another search. I had a drink here, a look over there, a snack here, followed by another walkabout, then another drink. This continued for the rest of the day. By the time I returned to my room in the evening, I was well fed, passably drunk, and completely worn out. I also knew exactly where to find Brie . . . the next morning.

21

CAMINO CONNECTION IN LA LINEA

I WOKE UP at precisely five forty-five only to be astonished by the morning darkness. Was it always this dark? Why would anyone start walking at this point of the day? Verifying the time with several TV channels, I hopped out of bed. My travel alarm had done its job.

Fifteen minutes later, I stood at the bottom of Rúa de Peregrino, the only road out of Palas de Rei if you're a walking pilgrim. Brie and I had never left any Camino town at this ungodly hour, so I was fairly certain I could intercept her as soon as she headed out for the day's destination of Ribadiso do Baixo.

There was little to do but wait. Early-bird pilgrims marched past me without acknowledgement. I nevertheless greeted each one with a "Buen Camino," startling some, confusing others. I even chirped at the menacing biking bullies who buzzed past me in their fluorescent shirts and skintight pants. With Santiago de Compostela only sixty-eight kilometers away, they would arrive at their final destination by noon.

I didn't move. I wanted to eat something, but I didn't move. I wanted to track down a cup of coffee, but I didn't move. More and more early-morning pilgrims paraded past me . . . but still no Brie.

Then I noticed several taxi driver signs posted on a nearby wall: local hustlers advertising their phone numbers for any pilgrim who wanted a ride. These advertisements had been increasing in number since Sarria. Was it because the new Sarria pilgrims hadn't anticipated the stress and strain of the journey? Or because the long-term pilgrims were now suffering from stress and strain on their bodies? Would Brie take one? No!

It was almost seven o'clock when I spied her trundling down Rúa de Peregrino. She wasn't alone. Harriet and Naomi were right behind her, with enough early-morning frowns to demoralize anyone.

"Well, look who it is! Jamie, the boyfriend!" snorted Harriet.

Brie rolled her eyes and stopped short of hugging me, if only to deflect Harriet's habit of calling me "the boyfriend."

"Where were you yesterday?" Brie whispered, careful not to sound cross but loud enough to sound worried.

"I fucked up my travel alarm. I'm sorry. I walked fast; I barely stopped. And I looked for you all day."

"Me, too." Brie smiled and subtly pinched my arm to tell me all was forgiven.

Harriet and Naomi brushed past us and took the lead. "All water under the bridge, you two. Let's go."

"Just like Portomarin, eh?" chimed Naomi, and the two friends cackled at the little joke that only a pilgrim might find funny.

I didn't. I gave Brie a disapproving look and she patted me on the shoulder. "They walk so slow we'll pass them soon."

It was a lovely path through woodland as the trail clung to the highway and passed through the village of Carballal and the hamlet of A Laguna—although I doubt Naomi found any of it pleasant, often complaining about her blistered feet and her nagging knee.

Brie remained quiet, sticking close to me, and punctuating every Naomi complaint with a forced smile or a bemused frown.

It was Harriet who did most of the talking. Since she was leading our group, she decided to impress me with her local knowledge.

"Do you know about the eucalyptus trees, Jamie? They're not native to Galicia."

"Nope."

After deforestation and too many forest fires, Galicia had imported the trees from Australia to help its local pulp industry. But they had grown too fast in too many areas and now threatened the entire indigenous ecosystem because they ruined the soil and harmed the wildlife . . . or something like that. I couldn't follow Harriet's rambling explanation once I tuned out.

"Interesting, huh?" asked Harriet when she was done.

"Yeah."

A few seconds later, Harriet started up again. "Do you know those little windowless huts you see on the farms, Jamie?"

"Yeah."

"They're corn cribs. Used to store corn. They make everything with corn here. They put all their corn in these huts to keep it dry in the winter and out of reach from all the animals . . . like rats."

"Oh."

This went on during the next hour. Even when there was no more local trivia to share, Harriet always thought of something to say. "You been following the World Cup, Jamie? Playoffs start today."

After so much early interest in the tournament, I was now completely ill-informed and indifferent—like many Spanish football fans. The Spanish team had placed third in their group, after a humiliating defeat to the Dutch and a heartbreaking shutout to the Chileans, and were now eliminated from the competition.

The tournament was never much of a critical concern on the Camino. The national team, El Selección, was more of a fanatical fascination in the big cities, like Madrid and Barcelona. The smaller Camino towns would rather support their local teams. Regional pride always trumped national interest, especially in a splintered country loosely connected by so many autonomous communities.

When we reached the village of San Xulián do Camino, Naomi's aching feet begged us to stop for breakfast.

Ignoring my own need for a caffeine fix, Brie and I begged

off joining Harriet and Naomi for coffee and promised to meet them later for dinner in Ribadiso—a promise I had no intention of keeping.

Brie and I followed the trail down to the Pambre River, where it gently climbed again through a wall of venerable oak.

"You're sneezing less."

"The drugs are doing their job."

"You're crying less."

"Once again, the drugs are doing their job."

"So, Ronald was in La Linea, yeah?"

Brie's concern for me was real, but it was only a very short matter of time before she had to steer me back to my story.

If the climb to the top of Gibraltar's Rock had been tiring and inspiring, the walk back down was painless and relatively quick. Stomping down Main Street, I even stopped for a pint of English ale in one of the pubs. Call it liquid courage before my potential confrontation with Ronald.

I hadn't really planned what I was going to do with Ronald when I met him. Fight him? Hit him? Scold him? Or try to rip out his heart? Perhaps the ale would tell me. It didn't. Nor did the next one. Or the next two. When I returned to the airport runway, I had added a sway to my step and had to concentrate to remain between the painted lines.

Crossing the border back into Spain was an even easier process than crossing into Gibraltar. At least the Gibraltar guard had waved me in. The Spanish guards were too busy inspecting the lineup of Spanish cars returning home and the British cars escaping for a holiday. A lonely pedestrian like me was of no concern. I walked right past the open border gate back to La Línea de la Concepción.

The town's name is a unique mix of religion and geography, referring to both the boundary line (*La Linea*) separating Spain from Gibraltar and the Immaculate Conception of Mary, the mother of Jesus (*de la Concepción*).

No one had taken up permanent residence in the area until

Spain's military campaigns against Gibraltar in the eighteenth century. The frequent battles made La Linea unsafe, and fortifications (long-dismantled) had to be built to keep the British at bay.

After hostilities between the two territories calmed down, La Linea endured as a fishing village until its population exploded, thanks to new jobs in both Gibraltar and Algeciras, especially after World War I and World War II.

Now La Linea has a population of sixty-five thousand people and serves as a major supplier of fruit and vegetables as well as a manufacturer of cork and liquor. It's also a source of play for the good people of Gibraltar, with its fourteen kilometers of enviable beaches.

Sounds fun, right? Well, not always. The World Health Organization has also reported that La Linea has the worst air quality in the entire country, thanks to its nearby oil refinery, the largest in Spain.

I didn't notice any of La Linea's poor air quality, but I did note the lower quality of its housing as I walked west along the highway. My instructions from Benjamin Franklin were simple: walk along the highway and turn right on Avenida del Ejército. Ronald reportedly lived in one of the red buildings beyond the Asur Hotel Campo de Gibraltar, the only four-star hotel in town.

Avenida del Ejército was completely unimpressive, despite its entry point into La Linea's main square, the Plaza de la Constitution. Though it was less than a kilometer away, La Linea was nothing like Gibraltar. There was nothing resembling the glimmering and glamorous Ocean Village, or even the yellow-and-pink-hued apartment buildings off Main Street. No, this section of town was more reminiscent of the granite buildings of Bayside Road.

Ronald's cluster of red buildings looked like neglected community housing. Despite the hot day, all the windows were closed and many were shuttered. Some of the apartments had balconies, but none of them were used for sitting; rather, they were being used for storage or as a convenient place to hang wet laundry.

The patches of lawn were left long and unkempt. The imported palm trees looked forlorn and forgotten. The only stirrings of life came from the old men in sleeveless undershirts, sitting on scattered benches between the buildings, fanning themselves with their hands and grumbling about the humid weather. And every one of them stared me down as though I had just interrupted an important private confession.

Benjamin Franklin hadn't been sure which building Ronald resided in, but he knew his balcony faced the Avenida del Ejército; Ronald had often complained about the beeps and blares of the morning traffic. That suggested the north building.

He also hadn't been sure which floor Ronald lived on, but, again, the noise complaint suggested a lower floor, where the traffic din would be more disturbing.

I approached the north building's intercom system. No names were listed, which would have simplified my search. I had to push several buttons and endure a few painful conversations with confused La Linea locals. It was when I hit 3A that my intercom investigation finally showed some promise.

"Sí?"

"Hola. I'm looking for Ronald Donaldson?"

"Sí, Ronald. *Quién es?*"

"Ummm, I'm a friend . . . an amigo from the Camino."

After a short pause, "Camino?"

"Yes! Uh, sí."

The good ol' Camino proved to be the magic entry word, because the front door suddenly clicked open.

I slipped inside the building. With adrenaline coursing through my body, I bounded up the stairs for the third floor. *What was that smell? And was that a cockroach that scampered across my foot? Did they even have cockroaches in southern Spain? Seriously, what was that smell?*

I stood in front of the door labeled 3A. I still hadn't planned what I was going to do with Ronald when I met him. Fight him? Hit him? Scold him? Or try to rip out his heart? But first . . . was he even home?

I knocked and waited. Fight him? Hit him? Scold him? I couldn't decide. *What was I going to do?*

The door opened, and a lovely La Linea woman waved me inside. My contempt for Ronald would have to wait. I had to begin with a peaceful and calm inauguration into his life. First, step inside his apartment. Then, decide whether to fight, hit, or scold him.

The apartment was clean and cozy, which didn't reflect the building's rough exterior or raw entryway. There was nothing rough or raw about the woman, either. She was short, with raven hair, and casually dressed in shorts, a T-shirt and no socks or shoes.

I pegged her to be in her mid-thirties and probably very beautiful when she was a teenager. Scratch that. She was beautiful right *now*. Her warm smile disarmed me, as did the framed photographs hanging on the walls, just out of my viewing range.

Was Ronald in those photos? Was I really this close to getting a good look at my wife's lover? A few days ago, I had never heard of Ronald. Now I was standing in his clean and cozy apartment ready to confront him about his affair with my wife.

But wait . . . who was this woman with the piercing brown eyes? Ronald's wife? His old girlfriend? His *new* girlfriend?

She asked me a couple of brief questions, but the only word I understood was "Camino."

I nodded. Was that enough? Had I answered her questions? How many more would I have to answer to remain in this room and wait for Ronald? I had been in this apartment for just fifteen seconds and I was already out of ideas.

My panic was brief—because a man then entered the room from the kitchen. He was dressed in a T-shirt and shorts, like the La Linea woman. It had to be Ronald. He was tall like me. Perhaps a few years older, but he wore them better. A square jaw, big hands and sturdy legs. And damn me if his hair wasn't brownish.

This was the moment. Fight him, hit him, scold him.

I did none of those things. I didn't know what to say, but I somehow spoke first and said the only thing that came to mind.

"My name is Jamie Draper. I believe you met my wife, Pam, on the Camino."

Ronald nodded. He wasn't upset or angry. He didn't flinch or need to sit down. He simply stared back at me, as though he had been expecting me; if not today, then at some point in the uncertain future. If I could speculate as to what he was feeling at that very moment, it might have been . . . relief.

"What did you do, Jamie? You did something horrible, didn't you?!" Brie suddenly shrieked.

"I wasn't there to get revenge, Brie," I sighed.

"Then why were you there?"

"To get some answers. I needed to know what happened to her. *I* wasn't there for my wife when she was in pain. But *he was*!"

We had been walking through a dreamy landscape of woodland and farmland up and down rolling hills and had somehow missed an important crossroad in the hamlet of O Coto.

After convincing Brie that no, I had not attacked Ronald inside his La Linea apartment, I finally noticed that we hadn't seen a Camino shell or a yellow arrow for several minutes.

"Let's go back," I suggested.

"Enough stalling. What happened next?"

"I'm talking about the Camino. I don't see any yellow arrows."

We turned around and were intercepted by an American and a pair of Germans who had been following us. They had been staying at a nearby albergue and were just now beginning their morning walk. They had just assumed we knew where we were going.

A few hundred meters later, we found the crossroad where we'd gone wrong and the small Camino sign pointing us in the proper direction.

We walked as a loose-knit group, although we offered only a polite exchange of countries and relationships. The American was a divorcée. The Germans were a widow and her college-age daughter. And, no, I explained; Brie and I were just friends and not a couple.

No names. Not even a discussion of our feet. I would have called it a comfortable crew except for Brie's increasing agitation that I refused to continue my story in front of strangers.

She saw her chance for separation outside the village of Furelos. A lovely medieval bridge spanned the Furelos River, and everyone was stopping for photos. The village on the other side of the river completed the pretty picture with its quaint stone houses and red-tiled roofs.

While our new friends paused to reach for their cameras, Brie reached for my arm and dragged me across the bridge.

"We do have to crack on, sorry!" she yelled back as we shuffled along. "Buen Camino!"

We still hadn't eaten anything that morning, but Brie was not about to stop in Furelos.

"Are you sure you don't want a coffee?"

"How long you think those pictures last? They'll be on us in a minute. Carry on! What did Ronald say?"

After a few ominous seconds staring at each other in his La Linea living room, Ronald had gathered himself and said, "Not here. Okay, mate?"

His British accent was more polished than Brie's, like a radio announcer's working for the BBC. Another part of London, perhaps? Better schooling? An upper-class upbringing? I wasn't sure how it all worked, but I knew Pam would have liked it. In four words, I knew Pam could listen to Ronald talk all day.

A small boy now emerged from the bedroom hallway and entered the room. How many more people were hiding in this apartment?

The boy ran to Ronald, clutched his legs and glared up at the stranger standing in front of his . . . father? Stepfather? Mother's new "friend?" I didn't dare ask. Not yet. It wasn't why I was here.

"Do they understand English?" I asked.

"Enough."

I was still calm. Still unsure of what to do with myself—and my hands. They were clenched, but I was in no position to start throwing punches. How could I? Not with that La Linea woman smiling at me and that small boy clutching Ronald's leg. I wasn't here to destroy a family. Were they a family? I didn't ask. Not yet. Regardless of their relationships with each other, they were an immovable distraction. I had half-prepared for a confrontation with Ronald. Alone. With clenched fists.

Then a flurry of Spanish filled the room as the La Linea woman offered lunch so Ronald and I could reminisce about our Camino adventures, while the boy begged Ronald to come see what he had been working on in his bedroom. Ronald denied them both and insisted he needed to speak to me in private because of some unfinished business we had arranged on the Camino.

He kept his steely eyes trained on me. Wondering what I was going to do. Wondering what I was going to say.

"We can meet in the square," he finally said. "The small one 'round the back. I'll tell you how to get there, and I can see you in twenty minutes. I promise."

I nodded. I was still angry but no longer seething. I was still upset but no longer inconsolable. And, in a small way, I also felt relief. I still didn't know exactly what to say to Ronald, and this bought me more time, thankfully, far from further domestic distractions.

The short climb to Melide was my current distraction. The town started out promisingly, with a medieval section of narrow winding streets serving up the local specialty of octopus. No one seemed to question why Melide, so very far from the coastline, would find its fame with eight-legged appetizers from the sea. It was simply accepted as a fun food fact in every guidebook. "Try the octopus in Melide." Full stop. (These same guidebooks also never warned you about the ferocious flies of Galicia.)

Brie and I were in no mood for Camino "calamari" for our first meal of the day. We stuck to the dirt road that connected the Old Town with the modern Melide, where we were accosted by exhaust fumes, honking cars, and squealing brakes. We hurried through town, anxious for food but more anxious to escape the noise. We finally stopped for coffee and croissants at one of the last bars on the suburban fringe.

Melide was also significant as a meeting point of two ancient routes, the Camino Francés and the *Camino Primitivo*. Originating out of Oviedo in northern Spain, the Camino Primitivo represented the original pilgrim route, forged in the ninth century when the rest of Spain was still under Moorish rule. Due to its length of only 308 kilometers, few foreign pilgrims embark on its two-week journey.

"Was that woman Ronald's wife?" asked Brie in between bites of her croissant. "And was that his son? Did Ronald come 'round? Oh, bloody hell; you don't even know Pam's dead yet, right? I can't even imagine what that was like when he told you. Wait, did he tell you? Sorry, I am keen; sorry . . ."

Outside the apartment building, the grumpy old men on the benches had gaped at me while I paused to inspect Ronald's directions handwritten on the back of a napkin. Our parting had been quick and frightfully awkward. I had ignored the boy and barely thanked the woman for letting me inside her home.

No, the moment Ronald had handed me the napkin, I backed out of the room, rushed down the hallway, and bounded down the stairs.

The grumpy old men were talking about me. I was too fascinating a topic to ignore. Who was this white man standing outside their building reading a napkin? What does he want? And why did he just run out of the building and slam the door?

I ignored them and marched toward Plaza de la Constitución. It should have been a central showcase for La Linea, but the town was more interested in advertising its underground parking. The square was vast and empty with some dodgy cafés scattered on the edges, and some pale-brown apartments tightly stacked like Lego bricks on the northern perimeter. While most Spanish towns took pride in their public spaces, La Linea presented neglect. To make matters worse, Gibraltar's majestic Rock loomed large in the south, squashing the square into insignificance.

Navigating with Ronald's napkin, I found an archway off the eastern side of the plaza that led me through a tunnel to the smaller, more people-friendly square, the Plaza del Pintor Cruz Herrera. This space was small, but dining and drinking options were abundant.

When Ronald arrived a few minutes later, we predictably played it safe and chose Molly Bloom's Irish Pub. Settling into a booth, we remained silent, neither of us taking our eyes off the other. Maybe Ronald was worried I might hit him, because he kept looking at my hands and flinched whenever I fidgeted in my seat.

I was more focused on the entire package, checking Ronald out from head to toe, comparing every physical feature to my own, and trying to determine exactly what Pam liked about him beyond his posh accent.

The waiter arrived and Ronald dismissed him with a shake of his head. We weren't ready to talk, and we certainly weren't ready to examine a menu.

Finally, Ronald took a big breath and exhaled. "Listen, I know you want to kill me—"

"I'm not here to kill you—"

"I appreciate that. But, look, I don't know if you know this . . . and I don't know how to tell you this . . . but your ex-wife is dead."

"What? That was his opener?!"

I nodded to Brie.

"I know you want to kill me? Your ex-wife is dead?"

I nodded again.

"You must have been gutted . . . "

"Remember when you met me in Sarria? In my room?"

"Of course!"

"That was nothing."

Brie reached across the table and squeezed my hand. "You poor bugger."

"It wasn't pretty. Ronald had to keep dismissing the waiter because I was such a sobbing mess. Of course everyone stared at us, too. One woman dropped off some tissues while another couple had to escape to the other side of the room. My sadness was ruining their happy hour, I guess."

Brie took it all in and shook her head.

"Eventually I stopped, and Ronald ordered two Irish whiskeys. He drank them both and then ordered another one for me. That bought me some time."

"I can't imagine it. I really can't."

"The funny thing is . . . I knew it. I knew it the moment I saw that word 'cancer' in her letter. But I kept walking. And I kept expecting I would see Pam again—"

"Of course you did."

"I was lying to myself."

"No, no; you were just being hopeful. Of course you were. Why wouldn't you be? I was."

"No, I knew. I didn't say it. And sometimes I didn't even want to think about it . . . but I knew. Hope is for other people, not for me."

"Don't say that—"

"Anyway, the crying stopped. And then I had to face Ronald again. You think getting hysterical in a pub is awful? How about getting hysterical in front of your wife's lover? Try that for a laugh." I hesitated. "Are you crying?"

Brie withdrew her hand and wiped away tears from her eyes. "Oh, just a little. Who cares?"

"I'm going to stop for a minute, then—"

"No, no, go ahead—"

"No way. Your crying is going to make me cry. And I'm done with that for now."

22

ARZÚA CROSSROADS

AFTER MELIDE, the Camino wound its way through more shaded forests of pine, oak, chestnut, and eucalyptus, occasionally broken by haunted hamlets such as Carballal and Raido.

Brie and I walked in comfortable silence.

I was pleased about the performance in my storytelling. My well-earned safety net had held firm, and I hadn't allowed a new flood of raw emotion to derail our day. By now I had walked enough miles for a substantial callus to have formed around my heart.

Brie was also more resilient. She was still sympathetic . . . but not smothering. Endearing but not meddling.

After we crossed the Boente River, the forest path widened into a country road. It would climb into the village of Castañeda before winding its way back down into another eucalyptus forest that led us toward the Iso River and the day's destination of Ribadiso do Baixo.

As we walked over the short sixth-century bridge, I developed a bad feeling about Ribadiso. Sure, it was a lovely hamlet alongside a babbling river, with lush trees and adorable stone houses, but it was far too small to entertain us for more than a minute. Burnsley mentioned only two albergues and one nameless restaurant. It didn't sound promising. So we moved forward to the next town.

"So much for our nosh-up with Harriet and Naomi in Ribadiso," mused Brie.

Arzúa, with a population of seven thousand and a roster of seven albergues and numerous hotels, was only three kilometers farther down the road. Sure, you had to walk uphill under the scalding sun, but now we'd have hotel options and unlimited dining choices. Plus it was the last sizeable town of comfort remaining on the Camino. Once again, the romanticism of the rural had clouded Burnsley's judgment.

Arzúa had no landmarks of note or monuments of interest, but it did have cheese. Made from Galican cow's milk, Arzúa-Ulloa cheese is soft and creamy and known around the world for its Denomination of Origin status (similar to the classification system used by respected winemakers). Arzúa even hosts a cheese festival every March.

Arzúa is also known as the meeting point of the Camino Francés and the *Camino del Norte*, the Northern Way, originating out of the border town of Irún in the Basque Country. Running along the Spanish coastline, it is considered a more difficult trail due to its mountain obstacles and fewer accommodations. Older than the Camino Francés, it is also a little longer, at 825 kilometers.

Considering it was the intersection of two popular routes, Arzúa also presented challenges in finding a place to sleep. We needn't worry. Strolling into town on the main road of Rúa de Lugo, we stopped at the first *pensión*, the Don Quijote, and inquired about a room. No problem, said the clerk. He had one room left.

When Brie and I entered the room, we discovered it had only one double bed.

"Oh," I mumbled.

"Is this a problem?" asked Brie matter-of-factly.

"I can sleep on the floor."

"Don't be daft."

"We could try another hotel."

"We're here now."

"So, this isn't a problem?"

"Not for me."

"We could just get drunk and it won't matter."

"Sounds like a proper plan."

Our ensuing Camino routine was quiet and cordial. While Brie washed her clothes and cleaned up in the bathroom, I watched TV. While I washed my clothes and cleaned up the bathroom, Brie watched TV. She didn't even change the channel.

And neither of us touched the bed. If either of us sat down, we sat down in the room's only chair. If we needed something from our backpack, we kneeled down on the floor. The bed was completely off-limits.

When we left the room in search of wine and adventure, Brie breathed a sigh of relief as soon as I shut the door. Out of sight and out of mind. She could finally ignore our cozy sleeping arrangement . . . for now.

Lacking a map of any kind, we kept it simple and walked farther down Rúa de Lugo, settled into the first appealing bar, and ordered a bottle of wine.

"Peregrino menu?" sighed the waitress, clearly bored with cheapskate pilgrims sticking to their tightfisted budgets so close to the Camino finish line.

We surprised her with an order of chicken wings and a sample plate of expensive regional cheeses.

"*Excelente!*" she cried.

Brie and I drank and ate quietly at first, often gazing through the window at the street activity or looking overhead to watch the Netherlands compete against Mexico on the television screens.

"Playoffs?"

"Sorry?"

Brie pointed to the TV. "Harriet said it was now the World Cup playoffs."

"Round of sixteen," I nodded. "Winner goes to the quarter-finals."

"Oh."

I had to put an end to the awkwardness. "Is it the bed?"

"The bed? No! I said it isn't a problem."

"Is it my wife? Ronald? You ready to hear more?"

"No! I mean, yes, I want to hear more. It's not that either. "

"Say it."

"Well, it *is* the bed, in a way, because obviously we're becoming closer without even saying anything about it. And it hit me today that we're almost done. And I don't know what happens after that. I don't know *anything* about me except I'm going home. And I don't know anything about you. Where are you off to? Back to Palma? Back to Canada? And should I even care? It's not that I'm even asking for anything. And it also feels sort of wrong to think anything about "you and me," because you're also telling me some incredibly sad shit about the death of your wife. So who am I to even blather on about me and you? And at the same time, I also know that I'm really mad for all of this. The Camino would be quite shit without you, even when you're crying in your room or having an eppy fit at the flies. Now, maybe the Meseta was massive loads of shit. But you had cleared off and that made it more massively shitty. Because I still know that deep down that you're a decent bloke who is much better to me than any bloke I know, and I feel so stupid that I wasted so much of my life with Martin."

"Oh."

"Don't say anything about it, Jamie. Honestly, you have to finish your story about Pam first. You have to get that all out, yeah? And then . . . and then you can have a proper think about I just said. But that's how I feel."

"I don't even know where to start—"

"You don't start anywhere. I told you: you finish that story first. Don't even think about anything I just said. Just finish your story. Then if you want to chip in about anything . . . I'm up for it."

Despite her plea for me to not think about the future—with or without her—I still struggled to conjure up some comforting words.

Brie grabbed my hand and smiled. "Thank you, Jamie. I could never say all that to Martin. But I can with you. So, cheers."

"I feel like an asshole sitting over here saying nothing—"

"Don't—"

Our suddenly very friendly waitress interrupted us by clapping her hands and wondering if we wanted another bottle of wine. When I nodded, she once again shrieked.

I then turned my attention to the older couple at the next table. She had a kindly face and wore her bifocals on a chain; he had a shock of white hair and a perpetual frown. He also wore a Toronto Blue Jays hat and caught me peeking at it.

"You from Toronto?" he asked.

"How did you know?"

"Everybody else ignores the hat. Except people from Toronto."

"I don't even follow baseball."

"Neither do I," the woman chuckled.

That did it. We were Camino friends for the rest of the night. When they sat down, the Dutch were playing the Mexicans in the early game. By the time they bid us good night, Costa Rica had beaten the Greeks in the followup match.

He was Darren, she was Linda. They had both wrapped up long careers as accountants and were enjoying their first trip as a retired couple of leisure.

"I said golf in the Caribbean. She said, 'Let's walk across Spain.'"

"I always get my way," quipped Linda.

"She always gets her way," agreed Darren.

They both had suffered minor injuries but were grateful for the training they had done in Toronto in the springtime.

"That saved us, honestly," said Linda.

"The worst part was walking over the same streets over and over again," griped Darren.

"This was so much better, don't you think?"

"Well, of course it is, dear. This is the Spanish countryside."

This went on throughout our dinner and our bottles of wine. I enjoyed Darren and Linda's gentle bickering and the love that glowed beneath it. They were a team, and nothing could break them apart. If they had any fights, they were minor. If they had issues, they were quickly solved. They seemed happy.

Brie said little as we talked about our lives back in Toronto.

The good: the alleged harmony inside a diverse ethnic patchwork that stretched across the city. The bad: the transportation problems trying to get across that city. And the indifferent: for a city so large, why didn't it have more interesting landmarks?

"Toronto is the Arzúa of North America," I mused.

"Yes! Excellent!" yelped Darren.

"And on that note, we should go. We're old," explained Linda.

"You're old," corrected Darren.

"You're two years older than me and you have a bad knee," winked Linda.

"This is why I said golfing in the Caribbean. But she's right. We're old."

"And I always get my way."

"And she always gets her way."

Darren and Linda left us with hugs and handshakes and a round of "Buen Caminos." Brie looked off in the distance with a mischievous grin slowly creeping across her face.

"What?" I asked.

"I practically love them."

"Nice people."

"Do you miss it? Home?"

I thought about it for a moment and then shook my head. "Not my job, obviously. Not my friends, unfortunately. They were more Pam's friends, as it turns out. Definitely not my apartment." I looked back at Brie. "I'm good right here."

Brie nodded and beamed. She was good right here, too.

"I'm sorry for dominating the conversation with Darren and Linda—"

"Don't be. It was good to see you smile again."

"Did I? Are you sure?" I teased. "That doesn't sound like me at all."

Back in our room, the bed was no longer off-limits. We were drunk enough; I was lazy enough. While Brie freshened up in the bathroom, I kicked off my shoes and climbed right in.

I closed my eyes when Brie entered the room to give her some "privacy" as she busied herself with invisible tasks. Zippers zipped, drawers opened and closed, items were dropped, items were retrieved; it never ended.

"Seriously, what are you doing?" I asked, keeping my eyes tightly shut.

"Seriously, never mind," Brie yawned.

We were the younger version of Darren and Linda, gently bickering with a comfort level that superseded anything as simple as new friends who had recently met on the Spanish Camino.

"You want to hear more about Ronald right now?"

"Oh, Jamie, not now. Don't get me all riled up with some story about you punching up some bloke you just met."

"That's just it. After I cried, I had nothing left. I was in no shape to do *anything*. Here was the man who had slept with my wife . . . my ex-wife—shit, is it *that* ever hard to say—and I had, seriously . . . nothing left."

The light switched off.

"I had been a complete, utter mess. Ten minutes before, I was a wreck. And then . . . completely fucking calm. He could say anything to me now. And what could I do?"

The sheets rippled a little as Brie slipped into bed.

"If you walked into Molly Bloom's that night—I mean, after my crying fit, of course—you would think it was just two old friends swapping stories and sharing drinks."

I paused and listened to Brie's breathing. Slow. Rhythmic. Peaceful. Was she already asleep?

"I haven't forgotten about your speech at dinner, by the way. I mean, I don't have an answer for you or anything, but I haven't forgotten. Listen, Brie. I don't know what I'm going to do after this walk. I was so focused on finding my wife, then finding out what happened, then grieving about what happened. I haven't had much time to think about . . . what's next. The truth is, I don't know. That's another question for the road, I guess. Right? Right?"

Brie was fast asleep. She was right. The single bed was no problem after all.

Brie's travel alarm beeped loudly, shaking me from yet another stressful dream. Pam's ghost didn't appear in this one, and neither did the long and winding road of the Camino. I was in high school again, running down the hallways, unable to find the classroom to take my algebra exam. In my dream world, I hadn't taken a class all semester, and yet I still felt confident I could somehow fake my way through the math calculations. If I could only find that classroom . . .

Pam had always enjoyed discussing our dreams. She believed that our subconscious selves were trying to teach us something in the real world. So I knew what that algebra exam meant. It meant I was lacking the ability to move onto the next stage of my life. Damn it.

Brie was out of bed and inside the bathroom before I fully opened my eyes. As I waited, I examined my Burnsley.

Since we had bypassed his earlier recommendation of Ribadiso do Baixo, we were already a few kilometers closer to the day's destination of O Pedrouzo. From Arzúa it was only nineteen kilometers, leaving us with twenty kilometers the following day.

On any other pilgrim day, that would sound satisfactory. However, the pilgrim goal was to arrive in Santiago de Compostela early in the morning. You absolutely had to line up to pick up your compostela, you likely had to line up to get your hotel bed, and, realistically, you had to line up if you wanted to explore the cathedral. No, twenty kilometers was too far to walk on our last day. We would have to walk beyond O Pedrouzo and establish a better base for our final approach.

I explained all this to Brie as we got ready. She nodded along without much input. It all sounded fine to her.

It was difficult to judge her mood. Had she heard my late-night confession about my uncertain future? Was she relieved that sharing a bed together hadn't led to further complications?

We walked in silence down Rúa de Lugo and turned for Rúa

do Carmen, the pilgrim path that would lead us out of town. We stopped for breakfast at the first open bar. Eight young men were still drinking. The disinterested bartender was still serving. It was seven o'clock in the morning!

Just like the Spanish bartenders who were unaware of the North American concept of "just browsing," they seemed equally inept at saying "Sorry, we're closed; you have to go now."

We were, thankfully, ignored by the young customers. Brie and I drank our coffee and ate our day-old sandwiches as they ordered another round of beer. The bartender even poured one for herself.

Back on the road, Brie shook her head and laughed.

"You have to admire their commitment to drinking," I said.

"It's Monday morning."

"Means nothing if you're committed to drinking."

"Fair play."

The morning route was another pleasing stroll through wooded areas dominated by the leafy eucalyptus, occasionally dipping down into shallow riverbeds and periodically passing empty farmlands and haunted hamlets.

"Okay, you. My eyes are dry. I have a stale sandwich digesting in my belly. You're not sneezing. The flies are sleeping. And nobody can hear us. Out with it."

I didn't argue with her. Barring short breaks here and there, I started to describe everything in detail for Brie. *Everything . . .*

"Feeling all right, mate?"

A few short hours earlier, I had been debating the merits of pummeling Ronald and ripping out his heart. Now he was checking up on me so we could talk like calm, civilized men.

I really wanted to leave that table. I really did. Ronald had just told me that Pam was dead. Everything I had hoped to gain on the Camino—a reunion with my estranged wife, a chance to show her I had changed, an opportunity to prove I could be a better husband and a better person—all vanished. My plans were ruined. Even if I had had only a vague idea of what I would do and what I would say to her if I ever saw her again, that was destroyed, too.

What was the point of staying now? Punch Ronald and leave.

But I stayed. I had to know more. I had to know . . . *everything*.

"What took you so long to find me?" asked Ronald.

"Well, I went to Gibraltar first . . ." *Was my voice cracking? Steady on, old boy.* I swallowed my shot of Irish whiskey and ordered two more glasses from the approaching waiter.

"I don't mean *here*. We—Pamela and I—walked the Camino last *October*. It's now the middle of June."

"I got that first letter two weeks ago."

Ronald said nothing, but his expression gave away his surprise.

"You may have walked the Camino last October. But did you *send* that letter last October?" I asked, slowly gaining my strength.

Ronald hesitated but, after a short pause, said, "No. No, I didn't."

The waiter dropped off the drinks and picked up the empty glasses. He followed with a perfunctory explanation of menu selections and dinner specials. Ronald and I shook our heads and waited for him to leave.

Ronald glanced around to see if anyone else was listening before leaning forward. "It took me a while to send it. Yes." Then he grew stern. "I didn't want to get involved and have this *particular* conversation. Right? As you saw, I have a family to protect now."

I waved that off for the moment and returned the focus back to the letter. "In October, I was already in Mallorca."

"Mallorca?" Now Ronald was completely bewildered.

"My mother-in-law let it slip that Pam had gone to Mallorca." I let that sink in for a moment before confirming. "Yeah, that's right. So I quit my job and came looking for her."

Ronald's eyes darted from side to side as he pieced the new timeline together. "I sent that letter to you in Toronto. That was the address Pamela gave me."

"Good for you. I was already in Spain."

"So it just . . . stayed there?"

"My mother-in-law probably went over to the apartment eventually to check my mail. *She* sent it to me in February."

"But you said you only got it two weeks ago—"

"Yeah, she didn't have a proper address for me, so she sent it to a friend of mine. Long story, okay? He forgot about it, we're not really close . . . Look, it doesn't matter. I just got it."

Ronald leaned forward again, suddenly excited to share something positive. "Pamela knew you'd come straight away. Sacking your job and moving to Mallorca? That is brilliant! She knew you'd come. She really did. I wasn't so sure, but she always talked you up. This is so mad; she was walking the Camino, you're in Mallorca. Neither one of you knew you were in the wrong spot!"

"Forget October. I didn't get that first fucking letter until two weeks ago."

"Right, sorry."

We certainly weren't acting like natural adversaries. We were two colleagues working on a puzzle, too concerned about making sense of the timeline rather than dealing with the emotional fallout of a failed marriage and an adulterous scandal.

At the eight-kilometer mark, Brie and I were completely ensconced in woodland. On most days we would have welcomed the reprieve from the blazing sun, but today was cloudy and the only day I could remember where I didn't have to stop in the shade to apply a thick layer of sunscreen.

We passed more hamlets of little significance, pausing only to consider a snack in Salceda before noticing the lineup of hungry pilgrims outside the café.

Soon we reached another tribute to the fallen. Unlike other makeshift memorials in the woods, this one was much more permanent. A bronzed pair of shoes and a plaque marked the spot where British pilgrim William Watt had succumbed to a heart attack at the age of sixty-nine.

Brie slowed down, waiting to see what I would do.

I marched past, only offering it a respectful glance.

Two kilometers later, there was another equally permanent stone memorial to Mariano Sanchez-Coursa Carro, who had died one month after William Watt back in 1993.

I marched past with a similar solemn response.

I asked myself if I had grown callous to the pain of other pilgrims. I concluded I had simply accepted the fact that many had died on the peregrino path, and that I could no longer be swayed to weep for each and every one. In fact, I had already wept for all of them.

"Were you with Pam the entire time?" I had asked Ronald. "The entire time she was writing me?"

"Oh, no. I met her in Nájera. I don't know which letter that was, but that's where I met her. Remember that square in Nájera?"

The Plaza de España. The castle ruins atop the red rock cliffs. The majestic monastery. The remains of a twelfth-century albergue. I had called the place magnificent. It was also where I had reunited with Brie after losing her in Los Arcos. How could I forget it?

"She was sitting on a bench feeling sorry for herself, and I walked over. She was worried she wasn't going to finish the Camino. I nattered on about my bum knee and said I wasn't going to finish it either. I asked her if she was going to quit, and she said no way. The Camino was too important."

I waved him off again and took another sip of my Irish whiskey. "I don't need . . . I don't want to hear about your Camino small talk with my wife, all right? You met her in Nájera. That's all I need to know."

Ronald understood. "She was going to send you that first letter from Santiago, you know. That was her plan. Walk the Camino and send that letter. I got involved at the end only because she asked me to."

"Send that first letter from Santiago and then what? Wait for me?"

"Maybe. Maybe say goodbye to your face? She never told me.

All I know is that she wanted you to walk that bloody Camino so you'd be ready."

"Ready for what?"

"To move on." I gave Ronald a nasty look, and he shrugged. "Healing of the road and all that, mate. It was Pamela's thinking, not mine."

He stopped for a moment to sip his whiskey. "And then when she decided she wasn't going to make it to Santiago, she changed her mind and wrote that Pamplona letter."

Ronald slammed the empty glass on the table. "You know I had to go all the way back there and convince that bar manager at Café Iruña to keep that letter for you? Cost me a hundred euros. And then I had to buy him a shovel."

"You really got involved, didn't you, Ronald?"

"Just that one part, mate. Drop off that Pamplona letter and mail you the first one—"

"Which you fucked up—"

"Which I fucked up, as it turns out!"

"Some of those other letters were damaged . . . and one of them was even missing—"

"I never read them, if you're asking me that, mate. I don't know what she wrote. It was all very private, I swear. But you got enough details from the ones you *did* read, didn't you, mate? Because we're both sitting here right now."

At the fifteen-kilometer mark in O Empalme, Brie and I sat down for a cold can of soda and a slice of chocolate cake. Our snacks on the road were always far from healthy. The processed sugar was in direct defiance to all the plain water we consumed on the Camino and all the bland food we were offered on those pilgrim dinner menus.

Burnsley's recommended destination of the day, O Pedrouzo, was now only four kilometers away. It was still late morning, and it seemed pointless to stop for the night. We were making good time, and we really wanted to position ourselves better for our final push to Santiago, although we agreed to keep an open mind when we reached O Pedrouzo. If it was pretty and welcoming, we'd stay.

It had been far from pretty when I had turned to Ronald and asked him about the Los Arcos letter. There was no need to mention how Mrs. Landerrain threw it away and accosted me in the street. I just called it "missing."

"The letter that was missing was about her cancer, I think."

"Nasty business. I don't know much about it. I can only tell you what Pamela told me."

I didn't nod; I didn't move. But my silence egged him on.

"She said there were no early symptoms. One day, she felt healthy. The next day, she was not. By the time they found anything, it had already spread and attacked other areas."

"What kind of cancer was it?"

"She didn't say?"

"I could never read that part."

"I don't know, either. Pamela didn't want to talk about it. And I thought it was extremely rude to ask. So I . . . didn't . . . "

I finished my whiskey and spun the glass between my fingers. "Her dad died of cancer. He went fast, too."

"I guess genetics plays a factor. But don't listen to me; I'm no expert."

"Pam and I never discussed her father. Nothing substantial, anyway. He just vanished from her life, and the discussion was over. It was all about her mom after that. Helping her out, avoiding her, struggling to get along with her. I never thought she could get it from her father. Maybe *she did* . . . I don't know . . . "

"Well, like I said: there were no early symptoms."

"Did she . . . ?" I couldn't spit out the next word. But Ronald instinctively knew what it was.

"Suffer? She took medication to manage the pain. It couldn't cure her . . . but it made things . . . manageable. Sometimes her back hurt. But she did manage okay. She didn't complain much, at any rate. She just . . . cracked on."

"She was only forty. Isn't that fucking young to get cancer?" I suddenly demanded.

Now Ronald was quiet and pensive. "Genetics? Again: I don't know, mate."

"No wonder she was depressed before she left me. Maybe it was the marriage too, but . . . " I let that sentiment hang in the air without a resolution. It wasn't the time to discuss the breakdown of our marriage. That would involve my input and my failings. This exact moment was about Pam and only Pam.

"She was losing weight, too, but nobody noticed. We were all losing weight because of the walk."

"Couldn't she have had chemotherapy or something?"

"Oh, she said she was offered all that. Chemotherapy, radiotherapy. But there was no cure anymore, she said. And she didn't want to spend the rest of her life in bed with people feeling sorry for her. She had one more adventure left in her."

"It could have extended her life."

"By a few months, by her account. Believe me, Pamela took all that into consideration before she left you."

The waiter moved toward us and my arm shot up to order two more whiskeys.

"She was selfish to leave you like that. She told me so."

"I could have comforted her."

"No, mate. She had to do *this* on her own. She needed the time and isolation to make peace with herself."

"Isolation? What about you?"

"That's where it gets a tad more complicated."

23

THAT NIGHT IN LA LINEA

BRIE AND I CONTINUED on the woodland path into Santa Irene, the first town of the day with a population big enough to offer both albergue accommodations and a church sanctuary. Neither was currently needed, so we dipped down the gravel road toward the hamlet of A Rúa.

O Pedrouzo was next . . . in theory. However, the walking trail bypassed the town completely, requiring a six-hundred-meter detour off the Camino path. Those six hundred meters might as well have been six hundred miles, because neither of us was tempted to visit the troublesome town to find out if it was pretty and welcoming enough according to our tough Camino standards.

We consulted Burnsley to make sure. Five albergues were listed, along with several hotels, plus an adequate number of bars and restaurants. There was also a warning that an early start was needed in order to attend the noon Pilgrim Mass the following day inside the Santiago cathedral. That sealed the deal. We were standing our ground by sticking to the walking trail.

I had been likewise standing my ground when the La Linea waiter dropped off two more Irish whiskeys and I motioned for him to deliver two local beers next. Ronald begged off, but I insisted. I needed the liquid encouragement.

"What do you mean, it got complicated with my wife?"

"She didn't say?"

"She barely mentioned you. You were just some guy with a bad knee who smoked and drank tea—"

"I've quit smoking, by the way—"

"I'm guessing there was a lot about you in that last letter in León. But I could barely read it."

"It was the Meseta."

"What?"

"You still don't want to hear about the . . . small talk?"

"I still don't."

"Well, I'll cut to the chase and say it was in the Meseta where your ex-wife and I had that one night of sex."

He spit that out so abruptly I was stunned for a second. I mean, he had said the actual words. *They had sex.* Pam had never used those words. "Ronald was a help," she said. "He may have loved me but I didn't love him back," she said. "It was one time," she said. "I didn't give him my heart," she said. But she never used the words "we had sex." Oh, hell, maybe she did. I couldn't read much of that León letter . . .

"Is this the part where you hit me?"

Before I could answer, the waiter brought over the two pints of beer and lingered by our table just long enough to deflate any simmering tension.

"It was just one time, if that makes a difference," Ronald finally explained. "I mean, it was the fucking Meseta! You walked it; you know what it was like."

"I got hurt in Burgos and took a bus to León. So, no, I *don't.*"

"Well, let me tell you, then: it was bleak and raining every fucking day we were on it. It was the worst stretch of road on the whole trip. Not physically. But all you could do was think and walk. No distractions. No fun . . . *anywhere.* Plus accommodations were always dodgy. And it was all packed out. So, we stayed in a hotel from time to time. And then one night . . . we shared a bed. She complained about her back, I massaged it a little, and then . . . well . . . "

I drank my last whiskey and must have instinctively clenched my fists, because Ronald noticeably flinched.

"I think she just needed the relief, mate. Something else to think about for a while, you know? We never had a proper chat about it; before it or after it. She felt awful; I felt awful. Not to mention I had a girlfriend back in Gibraltar."

Now I was regretting having drunk my last whiskey so fast.

"That's right, 'girlfriend.' And one day she told me she was pregnant. Just like that. So what was I going to do about it? The baby wasn't even mine!"

I had nothing enlightening to say. I masked my new discomfort by downing my beer.

"I was actually walking the Camino to sort out what I was going to do about it. You know: do I stay with her, or do I leave?"

"Wait a minute, wait a minute. She was pregnant before you left? I saw that kid. He was, like, four or five—"

"Different girlfriend, mate. The pregnant one told me to clear off the moment I told her about Pamela."

This was getting worse by the minute.

"But the one you saw today? I'm going to do right by her. The father's out of the picture and the boy has really taken to me."

I drank that beer too quickly. I was now walking the fine line between sober comprehension and inebriated confusion.

"Thanks for not blowing the gaff, by the way," Ronald said. "This is all before her time, and she doesn't need to know everything I did before I met her."

"Well, I'm not about ruining another man's life."

"Right. Well, for what it's worth, I'm sorry about your ex-wife."

"What, the dying part? Or the fucking-her part?"

Ronald didn't appreciate the sarcasm. He was walking the fine line between sober seriousness and inebriated recklessness.

"Listen, I know I got involved in a bodged-up relationship and made it worse. But she was your *ex-wife*. She left *you*. Maybe you're both responsible for not working on your marriage, but Pamela was one-hundred-percent responsible for the affair—"

"Now it's an affair—"

"Fucking hell! Like I said, it was one awful night in the fucking Meseta! It ruined my life, too! *I* lost someone, too!"

Why was I suddenly the calmest guy in the room? "Did she die?"

That knocked Ronald down a peg or two. "No." He reached for his whiskey. "Look, mate. I'm not saying our two situations are *exactly* the same. Right?" He shot the whiskey back. "So, what now? Is *this* the part where you hit me?"

"There wasn't a punch-up, was there?" asked Brie again as the gravel path, which had already led us through another eucalyptus forest and across rural farmland, tracked downward into the village of Amenal.

"No."

"It does make sense though . . . "

"What makes sense?"

"You all wound up about the bed. Back in Arzúa. Pam and Ronald shared a bed once, and look what happened—"

"It's not the same thing—"

"Right. Of course it isn't. Fair enough. Sorry . . . "

Brie apologized a few more times as we walked down the trail. More than three kilometers past O Pedrouzo, Amenal didn't appeal to our tourist tastes, either. Santiago was still 16.5 kilometers away. We could do better. It was the afternoon, we were the only pilgrims on the path, we still didn't have a place to sleep; but we could do better.

Ronald could have done better, too. Thanks to his outburst in the pub, customers were now staring at *him*. The waiter wondered what was wrong. The woman who had earlier brought me tissues gave us dirty looks. The couple who had crossed the bar to escape me now bolted for the outdoor patio.

"I'm not going to hit you," I said to Ronald. "This trip was never about revenge. And I'm not going to blame Pam one hundred percent for that o*ne awful night with you in the fucking Meseta*. I took her for granted. I didn't do my job as a husband. I blame myself just as much as I blame her."

"You keep talking about all this as a work in progress, mate. You can't fix it now. It's over."

"I know."

"And Pamela didn't fall for anybody—"

"I know."

"This whole thing . . . it didn't have any meaning—"

"I know!"

Too loud. Everyone was staring back at me again.

Ronald leaned in close and said softly, "Like I said: it was a temporary relief from her suffering, that's all."

I couldn't argue with that; I couldn't even debate it. I could only begrudgingly accept it. And I reminded myself that this wasn't a trip about revenge.

"But I get it, mate. You have to beat yourself up over it. Why not? I mean, that's what I did. After that night, I couldn't wait to get back home. But I had to walk two more days on the Camino until I got to León to catch a train. Can you imagine?"

"Did Pam—and, remember, I don't want the intimate—"

"She begged me to leave, if that's what you want to know."

I nodded. It was the smallest of victories. She had felt shame. It was incredibly petty and self-serving. But, at that very moment, it was what I needed to hear.

"She gave me those first two letters and told me what to do. So I left. I don't know what happened to her right after that. I gave her my address in case she ever wanted to reach out. And that was it; I left. I didn't know how close she was to dying. I don't think she did, either. She started the Camino to finish it."

Now that we were both calm and civil again, the waiter returned, and I ordered another beer for myself. Ronald hadn't touched his.

"Look, she had other friends on the Camino, right? I didn't just leave her by herself. I assumed she was going to write more letters and get other people to help her out. I thought she was just being safe with me, you know? Get the ball rolling with that first letter to Pamplona, that type of thing—"

We were covering old ground, and I had to cut him off. "Where did she die?"

"In a hotel. By herself, I heard. A few days after León, but they moved her body to Sarria."

"If you never heard from her again, how do you even know that she died?"

"Her mother."

Brie and I had been slowly ascending through the woodland path outside Amenal. The proof we were nearing our final destination came when we walked along the fence at the end of the runway of the Santiago de Compostela airport.

We were too far away to see the terminal or airplanes of any size taking off or landing in the area. From our vantage point, it was just a mysterious fence with assorted airfield props in the middle of the forest.

The hamlet of San Paio was next, less than a kilometer past the fence. It didn't appeal to our tourist tastes, either. Santiago was now 12.6 kilometers away. We could do better.

"How did Pam's mother know about Ronald?" asked Brie.

"I'm getting to that."

"I'm going to need a drink when you're done with this story."

"We're getting to that, too."

"How does Pam's mother know about *you*?" I had asked Ronald.

"She doesn't. Look, it was like this: it turns out Pamela kept a note with her—a note instructing whoever found her body to contact her mother as the next of kin."

"Holy shit."

"I didn't know she had it. And I don't think she had it at the beginning. But she wrote one just in case."

"So why didn't they contact me? I was still her husband—"

"They didn't know that. Pamela's note didn't mention *you*; it just mentioned her mother. Look, the Spanish authorities aren't going to get involved in all this. They just want someone to show up straight away and take care of things. Mother, separated husband . . . they don't care."

"Holy shit."

"So, her mother comes. Pamela gets cremated—" Ronald could see my agitation but dismissed it. "—I don't know why; it was in the note. Anyway, Pamela's mother does *exactly* what her daughter told her to. No questions asked."

"That's a first—"

"I mean, she follows Pamela's instructions to *the letter*. Pamela wants you to walk the Camino—instead of head straight away to Sarria to deal with all this nasty business? Then that's what her mother makes sure happens."

"How do you know all this?"

"She wrote me! She wrote me all the time. Pamela gave her my address in that note. The same address I gave her when I said goodbye in León. Look, her mother wrote you too, in case you ever came around looking for me."

Ronald produced a small folded envelope he had kept in his back pocket and tossed it on the table.

"In her own mad way, she was just as bloody adamant as her daughter that you walk the Camino before you got the news. Maybe to honor Pamela's wishes; maybe to punish you, I don't know—"

"Punish me?"

"If you two hadn't broken up, Pamela probably wouldn't have walked the Camino. Am I right? I'm sure she doesn't blame you for her death, but she might blame you for how you buggered things back at home."

"Pam made it very clear she left me *and* her mother to go to Spain. She didn't want anyone to smother her—"

"You'd have to ask Pamela's mother. Look, it's all in that letter."

Ronald slid the letter closer to me, but I still didn't touch it. I could see that it was no longer sealed.

"I'm not taking her side or anything, but she's not a happy woman, either," Ronald said as he took his first sip from his now-lukewarm beer. "First she loses a husband, then she loses her only daughter. She's suffered, too."

"She still could have done this whole thing better. So could Pam. So could I . . . "

"Why don't you read it for yourself and find out what she had to say?"

"Looks like you already read it. Is there anything in that letter you didn't tell me?"

Ronald didn't deny he had opened it. "Not really." Then he remembered something. "Something about picking herself up and going on holiday. Making up for lost time, I guess."

"She ever visit you?"

"No. But she wrote a lot. When she found out about the Camino and how Pamela had died, she put a lot of pressure on me to send that first package to you. And, like I said, eventually I did. But, also, I didn't exactly get those letters from her straight away."

Why did I feel like there was another long explanation coming?

"You see, the address I gave Pamela was the home address from my pregnant girlfriend—and I wasn't living there after she kicked me out. When I visited her a couple of months after the baby was born—you know, to be nice—she's back with the father! And then *he* shoves all these letters in my face that have been piling up from Pamela's mother. So then I read them all and found out about Pamela's death and then immediately took care of my side of things. But by now it's January."

"Which is why her stamp said February. Yeah, we covered this already—"

"So I wrote back to Pamela's mother to tell her it was all done and to stop harassing my former girlfriend."

"And I bet you used that address from the Irish pub—"

"The post office required it. And I didn't want her to send any letters to my new girlfriend's place. She doesn't need to know everything I did before we met."

"You didn't read her mother's letter?" asked Brie breathlessly.

"Nope."

"You're very stubborn, Jamie Draper."

"It's one of my best qualities."

"And one of your worst."

I gently grabbed Brie's arm and pulled her closer to me. "I know . . . but . . . I had just found out that my wife had died and there was a lot of information to process—"

"You're right—"

"And I already had huge issues with my mother-in-law, and she was the last person I wanted to deal with at that moment—"

"It's a lot to handle in one sitting—"

"And this sounds like an excuse, but I also was drinking far too much."

"Fair play. And I'm sorry about the crack about the bed."

"Again, that's okay—"

"You are not Ronald. You've been nothing but a fine, upstanding bloke the entire time I've known you."

"Okay, but—"

"Separated or not, you've been a proper prize. Pam would be proud."

Everything Brie said *sounded* like a compliment. And, yet, I could detect a hint of regret . . . or sarcasm . . . or something.

"There's still more to the story."

"Bloody hell."

"Save it for dinner?"

"Deal. And you can let go of my arm now."

Beyond the airport, the path descended with the imported eucalyptus browbeating the indigenous plants into a chaotic crush of trees.

Two kilometers later, we arrived in Lavacolla, the final important pilgrim stop before Santiago de Compostela.

In the Middle Ages, it was known as Lavamentula. Its nearby stream provided a convenient place for pilgrims to cleanse themselves of dirt and lice before they approached the sacred cathedral in Santiago—especially those who may have picked up something particularly invasive at that brothel outside Portomarin.

The loose translation of Lavamentula is "wash your private

parts" (*mentula* is Latin for phallus), and soldiers were posted on the banks to ensure that's exactly what every pious pilgrim did. *Charming.*

Today, Lavacolla (*colla* refers to scrotum, by the way) is a satellite village that mainly serves the airline trade. It certainly didn't appeal to our tourist tastes, and Burnsley didn't suggest any accommodations, but Santiago was now only 10.4 kilometers away. This was better.

In other publications, Lavacolla was advertised as "a modern town with a variety of bars and hotels." This was absolutely true, if variety meant exactly three hotels and two bars.

Brie and I opted for the three-star hotel on the highway. Although it was a Monday afternoon, there was a large party in full swing inside the dining room, with various guests wearing their Sunday best. Was it a bar mitzvah? A sweet-sixteen party? There was an awful lot of unruly tweens and teens rushing about in high pitch and plenty of adults standing around with plastic-looking faces numbed by the blur and the booze.

No one was at the front desk, and I had to crash the party in order to find a clerk. Unfortunately, my version of Sunday best was my sweaty pilgrim clothes and my dusty backpack. A sympathetic clerk approached me and led me back to the lobby. Checking her computer, she found she indeed had room for us. "Two beds or one?"

Brie and I hesitated.

"Two is better," she said.

Fate had decided our sleeping arrangements for us.

When I asked about the party, the clerk replied that the kitchen was closed for the evening and that we would have to find dinner in the town square tucked behind the Camino path along the highway.

Meanwhile, the room with the two beds was rather large and antiseptic.

"Do you want the bed closer to the window or . . . ?"

"Doesn't matter to me," said Brie.

"It can get noisier by the window, so I'll take that one. Unless . . . you want it?"

"Honestly, Jamie; it doesn't matter to me."

While Brie freshened up in the bathroom, I lay on my bed and read up on Santiago de Compostela from the tourist pamphlets left behind in the room.

The city owes its entire history as well its spiritual and secular significance to St. James. Before the alleged discovery of the saint's buried bones, the site had been a nameless Roman cemetery. The area was later settled by nomadic tribes and was once a small part of a Visigoth province, but it was forgotten beyond its borders.

The rest of the history I knew. The fortuitous hermit who followed the shower of shooting stars to the saint's grave, the construction of the holy shrine, the building of the massive church, the mass marketing by the Roman Catholic church, the establishment of the Camino route(s), the expansion of the church into a cathedral, and the visions of James as a vicious Moor slayer conveniently providing the Christian crusaders with all the divine inspiration they needed to drive the Moors back to northern Africa.

Now the city was an architectural masterpiece where art, history, and religion coincided to provide a feast for the eyes and sustenance for the soul. All the buildings and squares were hewn from the same granite stones, which gave the space a comforting uniformity. And with the banishment of cars inside the medieval quarter, a blissful blanket of peace was suspended over each and every street. In fact, the entire medieval quarter has been declared a World Heritage site by UNESCO.

The city was also completely damp. Hugging the Galician hills, Santiago receives Spain's highest annual rainfall. Brief but frequent showers arrive almost daily, meaning Santiago enjoyed only thirty completely sunny days a year.

Brie emerged from the bathroom fully dressed in her evening clothes. She was wearing a summer dress I had never seen—which seemed rather odd considering that after three days walking with anyone on the Camino, you've effectively seen every item in their limited wardrobe.

It was a basic white dress, but it had an elasticized waist that hugged her slight curves and a sweetheart neckline that gave her enough cleavage to make a Lavacolla soldier blush.

"Is that a new dress? I haven't seen it before."

"It was at the bottom of my bag," said Brie. "Last chance I get to wear it, innit? I can't wear this inside the cathedral, can I?"

I won't deny she looked gorgeous in that dress. So much of our time together had been spent in pilgrim clothes designed to prevent chafing. Nothing we wore was ever meant to make us look presentable or attractive.

"Brie . . . are you wearing makeup?"

"Just a dab. It was at the bottom of my bag with my dress."

It all seemed rather suspicious to me. Of course a woman can wear a nice dress and a little makeup on the Camino. But in Lavacolla?

The town square resembled a strip-mall parking lot more than an inspiring gathering place. Yes, there was a grandstand in the corner and a few plane trees poking out of the cement, but other than that, there were just two patio pubs keeping watch over the highway.

Brie and I chose the pub with the shorter lineup and ordered our food. For the first time in weeks, there was no pilgrim menu. Lavacolla, with its proximity to the airport, was flying under the radar of Camino protocol. Pilgrims on a budget would have to eat like the common folk. No special treatment here.

Moments after we sat down, Brie and I were bombarded by greetings from other dining pilgrims. However, the Camino conversation had completely shifted. Now no one asked about the status of your feet. It didn't matter. We were so close to the end. And no one discussed their daily diet. It didn't matter. The food would only get better in Santiago.

And no one mused about their recent Camino experience. All the usual questions had obvious answers. "What have you heard about tomorrow's journey?" It's only ten kilometers! "Are you walking the whole thing?" It's only ten kilometers!

No one even exchanged names. Names meant familiarity and pending friendships. No one had time for that now. We were near the end. We only had to declare our countries of origin to clarify our accents. So I referred to the two couples sitting at the next table as "that German couple" and "that Danish couple."

The only time it ever got intimate was the obligatory probe into everyone's occupation—if only because it offered a glimpse into the very near future that every pilgrim faced. Yes, following the conclusion of a journey of a lifetime to Santiago, many of us would have to immediately turn around and head straight back to Lavacolla to fly home—back to those same, unsatisfying jobs we had been so desperate to escape a few short weeks ago.

The German husband designed store displays. The German wife worked in sales in Basel and crossed the Switzerland border twice a day as part of her daily commute. The Danish husband had worked in computer programming for Scandinavian Airlines and had recently retired. Meanwhile, his distraught wife was too emotional to discuss her employment status; she was silently mourning the near end of her Camino journey.

There was always a common theme in talking to pilgrims about their occupations. The jobs were always in computers and software or in teaching and sales. Nobody was ever a simple tradesman. I never met a plumber or a carpenter on the trail. The Camino seemed to only attract white-collar, office-cubicle prisoners.

I, of course, made my job status much more complicated.

"So what do you do in Canada?"

"I was a high school teacher."

"Oh, nice."

"But I hated it and quit."

"Oh."

"Then I wrote detective novels."

"Oh, really? Anything I—?"

"I wasn't very good. So I quit that too."

"So . . . what now?"

"Good question. Now . . . now I'm just lost."

The others stopped asking me questions after that.

Brie fared much better. She was a bundle of energy that ignited the entire patio. Everyone loved her. Even the Danish wife brightened up a little.

Brie proudly announced that she had dumped her awful husband and was now ready to embark on a new career in art therapy. While I regarded my uncertain future as being "lost," Brie insisted her uncertain future was paved with possibilities.

"Good for you!"

"That must be a big relief!"

I found myself nodding along in agreement. This was a defining moment in Brie's life. All her past neuroses were conquered; all her previous insecurities had been vanquished. The Camino had completely healed her.

The Camino had not yet woven the same magic on me, but I was neither envious nor remorseful. I was genuinely proud of Brie and equally proud to be her friend. And damn it if she didn't sparkle in that white dress . . .

Our last supper with other pilgrims did yield one more insight. The German wife suggested booking a room in Santiago in advance, if only to check your backpack as soon as you arrived, so you could wander the city unhindered and worry-free.

I was so excited by this idea that I wanted to instantly return to our hotel and book a room.

Brie reluctantly acquiesced. She was having fun and didn't want her night of revelry to end. Where else would she find people hanging off her every word, simultaneously celebrating her recent journey *and* praising her new direction in life?

Certainly not in East London, where her alcoholic father missed her abusive ex, her fretful mother was intent on finding her a new husband, and her sister and brother-in-law were intent on never leaving England.

We soon said our goodbyes to our unnamed Lavacolla friends and walked back to our hotel.

"You don't have to come back with me. I just want to book this hotel—"

"No, it's okay. I wanted to hear more about you and Ronald. You said there was a little more . . . "

I had been just as eager to leave that bar in La Linea as I had been to leave the one in Lavacolla. I finished my beer and threw some money on the table.

Ronald signaled the waiter for the bill.

"Pamela didn't leave you with nothing, you know? She wanted to leave you with some great memories and some hard truths; that's all, mate."

"Yes, thank you." I didn't want to hear anymore. When I pushed back my chair, Ronald motioned for me to inch closer as though he were preparing to share his darkest secret.

"As much as it's been a painful day, you're free now. Her mother took care of everything. Go home, walk the rest of the Camino, go back to Mallorca. It's all up to you. But you don't have to worry about Pamela anymore."

"Is this supposed to make me feel better?"

"No. That's what the rest of the Camino is for. You have nothing but future choices. Maybe make some good ones."

Ronald lifted his glass and toasted me. I couldn't decide if he was being gracious or pretentious, but the urge to hit him returned. *Ah, fuck, he was probably right.*

"Everybody on the Camino is walking with heartbreak and regret. Now you're part of the tribe. It's the best place for you, really—until you're ready to take that next step."

"What next step?"

"Whatever it is you want to do next."

I chuckled weakly. "I always told my high school kids that the past matters; that the past completely informs you of the present and influences your future. Now you're telling me to forget it."

"Not forget it. Cherish it. But don't let it hold you back."

I nodded, tears welling up in my eyes again.

"Pamela gave you a great gift. She already got you out of that apartment. This Camino is just the start. Move forward. Lessons learned. It's not too late. It's all tragic; we both know that. But it's not too late. Not when your whole life is the long game."

"Yes, well, something to think about," I said as I rose from my chair. "And another thing: her name was Pam. Nobody who loved her called her Pamela. And I loved her."

24

SANTIAGO SHADOWS

"HE'S NOT WRONG, though," Brie said.

I glared at her for a moment. I hated it when she agreed with Ronald—especially when he was right.

"Go on. What did you do next?"

I shrugged. "I just left him there. Spent the night in that La Linea four-star and went to Sarria."

Brie didn't ask the question, but her baffled look certainly said she wondered why.

"It was the last place I knew where Pam had been."

Brie squeezed my hand and we entered our Lavacolla hotel. It was yet another sweet moment between Brie and me. Oblivious to her sentimentality, I headed directly to the hotel lobby's lone computer and promptly shooed away the Spanish kids who were playing around the desk.

I was on Camino business, I explained. "You know, the Camino?"

No, they didn't know. And they certainly weren't impressed by the gringo who was demanding to use the public computer.

Brie wasn't impressed, either, preferring to sit in a lobby chair rather than stand beside me as I booked my hotel.

A few moments later, I flopped down on the couch across from her. "I booked a room. Perfect location just outside the entrance to the old part of the city. Your turn."

Brie's earlier ebullient mood was now replaced by something that bordered on despondent.

"My turn?"

"Yeah. I booked my room, so now you can book yours. I left it on the screen so you can book it at the same hotel."

I smiled at Brie, but her expression belied nothing. Was she angry? Was she disappointed? Or just tired?

"Sorry, did I do something wrong?"

"No. You booked your room. Now it's my turn."

"Exactly. Well, I figured staying in the same room the last couple of days was a bit of a problem—"

"It was a problem?"

"Well, not a *problem*. I mean, we managed all right. I just figured, you know, on the last day you wanted some privacy?"

"Yes, Jamie, that's exactly what I want. Loads of privacy."

"Well, then, better hurry. Those kids weren't too happy about giving up the desk."

Brie slowly stood up and shuffled to the computer.

"I'll go see if I can grab a bottle of wine for the room. You have your key?"

Brie looked back and nodded. Was she still angry? Disappointed? Or just tired?

The party was winding down in the dining room. The tweens and teens were tuckered out and draped across the chairs. Their plastic parents were now stirred to retrieve coats and missing kids.

I found a waiter and inquired about a bottle of wine. He said it was impossible at this late hour. How about two full glasses? That was possible.

When I returned to the room, the lights were off and Brie was sleeping soundly, convincing me that her sullen disposition in the hotel lobby was not anger or disappointment but simple exhaustion.

When I woke the next morning, I knew instantly something was wrong. First of all, I wasn't hearing any beeps from Brie's trusted travel alarm. And something was missing. No, the two full wine glasses were where I had left them on the nightstand. But where was Brie's gear? And where was Brie?!

I scrambled out of bed and inspected the bathroom as if Brie had played an elaborate prank on me, hiding herself and her giant backpack in the bathtub until I roused from my sleep.

She was gone. Considering the time was now nine o'clock, perhaps she had been gone for an hour or more.

The only evidence of her presence was her messy bed and the note addressed to me resting on her pillow.

Dear Jamie,

I'm sorry to clear off like this. It's just that I had a proper think about it and I think you and I should walk the rest of the Camino on our own.

It's like Burgos, yeah? Back then I didn't want to hold you back whilst you were dealing with your wife's final letters.

Remember back then I said that she wanted you to walk the Camino just like she did. Well, that's not possible now, but I still think you should walk alone without me mucking it all up for you.

I heard you at dinner and you told everybody you were lost. Well, I'm not lost. Not anymore. I sorted it out, and I don't want to stop you from sorting out your next move.

Look, Jamie. I know you've been through a horrendous shit couple of weeks. Massive shit all around. And I don't want to botch up your feelings or what you're going through.

But, Jamie, darling, it's also near the very fucking end of this Camino. So I just need a first step—in some direction. It hit me in Arzúa that we were almost done and I still don't know anything about you. Well now, we're even closer and I still know bollocks!

I'm clearing off to England in a couple of days, and I know there won't be a day that goes by when I don't think about you and the Camino.

Now I'm sure your memories of the Camino might be a massive load of shit. But I just need to know if you'll <u>ever</u> think of me?

Call me selfish, but also call me scared. I was so afraid to ask you about it on our final day together and even more afraid that the whole day would go tits up and be ruined. And I don't want that. Not when we're so close to the end. So like a scared little girl I wrote this note at six in the morning while you're sleeping across the room.

Bloody hell. I just need to walk alone and enjoy these final moments, you know? And I hope you will too, somehow. I'd rather walk and not know anything than walk knowing you're still in a mental state or something and months away from even stepping foot into something again.

So just like Burgos, we can meet outside the cathedral, okay? After the pilgrim mass at noon? Meet me on the north side of the church, the smaller square where it's easier to find people. 'Immaculate' or something, I don't want to rummage through my bag to find the proper word in Burnsley and wake you up.

So after the mass, yeah? I mean, if you're still interested. That's up to you. And I bloody well hope you're there!

Yours,

Always,

Brie Bletcher

I felt like a fool. A giant-sized, ridiculous fool. I let the weight of Brie's words sink in for a few minutes before I reread the letter, this time brushing back the surprising tears that had somehow crept onto my cheeks.

I wasn't too late to respond. Nor was I too far removed from a plotted course of direction for the next chapter of my life.

I only had to make a final goodbye first. With a heavy sigh and an emergent heart that desperately needed a nudge and a purpose, I whispered, "Thanks, Pam. It's time to go." And I got to work.

I prepared quickly and was on the road within minutes. Through my final stretch of solid forest, I crossed over the stream that served as the Middle Ages bathing basin when cleanliness was next to godliness thanks to the power of a soldier's sword.

I saw no one for the first fine hour of my morning. The near-by hamlet, Villamaior, did have a café, but I could find no one working behind the bar to serve me a coffee. It would have to be a caffeine-free day.

The trees then thinned out and the path narrowed. The first

signs of big-city civilization emerged as I passed a pair of (seemingly abandoned) television stations. Where was everyone?

Next came the tiny town of San Marcos, where boldly colored homes complemented the older houses made from brick and stone. Again . . . where was everyone? Were the residents hiding from me? Or was the town deserted?

Lacking Camino companionship when I needed it most, I focused on what I would find in Santiago. First and foremost, there would be its crown jewel, the Cathedral of Santiago de Compostela, whose construction began in 1075 under Alfonso VI of Castile but wasn't completed and consecrated until 1211 by Alfonso IX of León. With a length of ninety-seven meters and a total area covering ten thousand square meters, it was the largest Romanesque church in Spain (with many Gothic and Baroque modifications added in later centuries).

Every side of the building told a different story. To the south was the small Praza das Praterias, where silversmiths once sold their wares. Today, the only silver you might find were the errant coins left behind in the central fountain.

To the north was the even-smaller Praza da Immaculada, where pilgrims would strip off their worn rags, hang them on a large iron cross, and receive a new set of clothes donated by the Benedictine monks who resided across the square in the monastery of San Martiño Pinario. Today, the cross is now gone and the monks are no longer in the free-clothing business.

To the east was the Praza da Quintana, a wide-open space with a broad swath of steps separating the upper and lower sections of the square, where the poor and hungry pilgrims were once served a satisfying meal. Today, you'd better pack your own snack.

Then there was the grandeur of the west side of the cathedral, the Praza do Obradoiro, where thousands gathered to marvel at the tremendous twelfth-century façade and its two bell towers stretching seventy-five meters into the Spanish sky.

Today, that original façade is hidden behind the eighteenth-century Baroque addition meant to protect the portico from Santiago's damp weather. Once you enter the cathedral, however, you can once again observe the twelfth-century Pórtico de la Gloria—albeit the faded gray and black version, since little remains of its original colors.

Even an achromatic Pórtico de la Gloria was an immense improvement over the monstrosity that stood atop the fabled Monte do Gozo. It was the hill outside San Marcos where pilgrims could once spot the bell towers from the Santiago cathedral and cry with joy that they were near the end of their exhausting journey. (*Monte do Gozo* means mount of joy.)

Now the cries were more likely to come from pilgrims inspecting the mountain's monument, an ugly modern sculpture commemorating the 1989 visit by Pope John Paul II, who performed Mass here to thousands of believers.

And, no, you can no longer see the bell towers. The surrounding trees, the morning mist, and the suburban sprawl obscure the cathedral's once-prominent steeples.

However, I did finally encounter some pilgrims. Lots and lots of pilgrims, because Monte do Gozo also housed an albergue complex large enough to host five hundred people. Big enough to contain multiple restaurants and shops, but perhaps a little too close to the finish line for the last-day commute.

From here, Santiago de Compostela was less than five kilometers down the road. In ancient times, pilgrims with horses would walk the rest of the way on foot while pilgrims already walking on foot would kick off their sandals or shoes and walk the rest of the way barefoot.

This was the first of several rituals ancient pilgrims would voluntarily endure upon their arrival to Santiago.

Their first step was entering the cathedral and approaching the Pórtico de la Gloria, where they'd find the statues of Christ and St. James presiding over various prophets and characters from the

Old Testament. And there, under James, they'd see five smooth holes pressed in the marble where the fingers of millions of pilgrims before them had gripped and prayed to the saint, thanking him for their safe passage on their journey. (Today it's roped off.)

Then they'd peer down to locate the small marble figure of Maestro Mateo, the chief builder of the Pórtico de la Gloria. Here the pilgrims were to bump their heads three times with the top of the statue in order to receive a tiny portion of Mateo's creative genius. (Today he's roped off).

Now they could enter the nave and behold the eyesore that is the intricate and gaudy eighteenth-century High Altar. They'd even be allowed to walk up the steps and physically embrace the thirteenth-century statue of St. James. (Today he's *not* roped off. Just don't let the statue's dead eyes and creepy bowl cut distract you when you bend down to kiss his bejeweled Liberace cape.)

Then it would be time to see the actual saint. Well, the saint's alleged bones. Or, at least, the box containing the saint's alleged bones. All the pilgrim had to do was follow the crowd down a few stairs beneath the altar. There they would find a small silver coffin, tucked inside a crypt, behind a solid set of iron bars. (Today, it's even further protected by a pane of Plexiglass.) They each would get a few precious seconds to revel in the saintly sighting. Maybe enough time to say a quick prayer. Then it was time to move on and allow someone else a glimpse of Biblical greatness.

Now the pilgrims would be free to confess their numerous sins to a priest in one of the confessional boxes or celebrate Christ's sacrifice at the Pilgrim Mass held at noon. If they had already received their compostela, the priest might even read off their nationality and point of departure (previously acquired by a clerk from the Pilgrim's Office).

And if the pilgrims were lucky, they might even get to witness the swinging of the *Botafumeiro*. Utilizing an elaborate pulley system, eight priests would raise an immense incense burner, filled with burning charcoal and melted incense, up to the church rafters and proceed to swing it wildly above the heads of the faithful, producing a thick, perfumed cloud of smoke (*botafumeiro* is Galician for smoke expeller).

While it's the highlight of the service, the original intent of the incense was probably to fumigate the dirty pilgrims, who not only visited the cathedral but slept there for a few days until more comfortable accommodations started sprouting up across the city.

The Botafumeiro was now used sparingly, unless it happened to be a Holy Year (whenever July 25, St. James Day, falls on a Sunday), and then the incense insanity would occur more frequently. But 2014 was not a Holy Year—so I didn't expect to see it.

Nor did I expect to perform any of the above rituals. I just wanted my compostela—and to somehow find Brie among the hundreds of pilgrims happily invading Santiago that morning.

For now, there were just dozens of us descending Monte do Gozo on a pavement path, relishing our final approach to Santiago.

Soon we were walking across a pedestrian bridge over the busy highway and entering the Santiago suburb of San Lázaro. Beyond a lone Peregrino Templar statue and a monument erected for the historical figures who had previously walked the Camino (such as Pope John Paul II, whose bas-relief barely made the bottom rung of the monolith), there was no big welcome for the weary pilgrim. It was business as usual for the Galician capital.

During the Middle Ages, peregrinos would have been harassed by musicians, magicians, money-changers, hustlers, and beggars. Today, we were free to roam without alarm or acknowledgement. The only sound to break the morning silence was the clickety-click from pilgrims' trekking poles. (Even though we were now in the city, old Camino habits die hard.)

We quietly followed the yellow arrows on Rúa de San Pedro deeper and deeper into the heart of Santiago as the street narrowed, the buildings aged, and the asphalt turned to slate and then to cobblestone.

Outside the medieval quarter, I broke off the Camino course and walked along Rúa da Virxe da Cerca, where sturdy apartments stood on the east side of the street and a formidable wall of medieval stone blanketed the west, providing housing for hundreds of locals.

My hotel was on Rúa das Trampas, a cruel Santiago trick linking my backpack drop-off point with the despised walkers of the Camino. Tiptoeing down the slanted street, I could picture Madrid Paola averting her eyes from her smartphone and screaming "La tramposo! La tramposo!"

I had little hope of finding Brie at my hotel, since she had not told me where she was staying. But that didn't stop me from pestering the hotel clerk about the whereabouts of a Brie Bletcher, or a Brie Baxter, or a slim-toned British woman with sandy curls and scars across her forehead. No luck.

Walking back along Rúa da Virxe da Cerca, I felt light and free. Was it because I was unhindered by my backpack? Or because I was finally roaming the streets of Santiago de Compostela? Or because . . . I was close to reuniting with Brie?

"Meet me on the back side of the church, the smaller square where it's easier to find people. . . . So after the mass, yeah? I mean, if you're still interested. That's up to you. And I bloody well hope you're there!"

I retraced my steps back to the Porta do Camino, the traditional entry point into the medieval quarter. Despite its dramatic epithet, it was neither a door nor an archway but, rather, a simple opening in the street.

The disappointment faded as I traipsed up Rúa das Casas Reias. Cars were banned and the pedestrian was king. Stone and brick buildings nuzzled medieval mansions. Quaint shops sold souvenirs. Cafés beckoned with nibbles and delights. Romance was in the air while piety splashed the streets. It was clean and crisp and completely curated for the soul.

I still had one hour before the start of the noon Pilgrim Mass, so I opted to retrieve my compostela. It was more important than any nourishment. I needed my final stamp of approval. I needed an official acknowledgment from a higher power that I had plodded across the country in good faith, following my ex-wife's instructions.

Whatever happened with Brie, I wanted my Camino confirmation in my hand to testify I had completed one important task in my life. The rest of my life's journey was still open-ended. This pilgrim part was done.

I headed directly for the Pilgrim's Office located on Rúa do Vilar, north of the church. Much to my horror, a long lineup of pilgrims spilled out of the office, snaked across the courtyard, and sprawled down the street.

In each and every other circumstance on the Camino, I would have turned around and attempted to do something else—anything else—that didn't require a long wait. However, this wait was for the compostela! There was no way around it. And with each additional second I hesitated, more surprised travelers joined the end of the line.

I waited and I agonized. One step here, two steps there, an eternity not moving at all, then suddenly four steps forward; there was no rhythm, no pattern, and no predictable pace.

What did make the indefinite wait somewhat tolerable was watching the pilgrims exit from the Pilgrim's Office with their compostelas, their diploma rolled up inside a tough tube of cardboard. Some shrieked. Some wept. Some looked for somebody to embrace: a relative, a friend, a stranger—it didn't matter. Some simply stared wild-eyed in joyous relief.

An American ahead of me commented to her friend that she was anxious to get her compostela if only because she still had a lot of walking to do that day. For some pilgrims, Santiago de Compostela was not the end of their journey. They would continue to walk for three or four extra days to the town of Finisterre, eighty-seven kilometers west of Santiago, once viewed as the very edge of the world.

I couldn't imagine walking any farther. How anticlimatic after the power and the glory of Santiago.

However, back in the Middle Ages, Santiago de Compostela had only been the halfway point of the entire pilgrim exercise.

Then they had to turn around and walk back! Fortunately, having a compostela in their hands did grant pilgrims special privileges. Dining halls would serve them better wine and bigger meal portions. Innkeepers would allow them to wash with *warm* water for the first time. Life was good—maybe even better than back home.

Today, most pilgrims enjoyed their day in Santiago and then took the twenty-minute bus ride back to Lavacolla to fly home. Most Europeans would be back in their beds in a few short hours (over a distance that had taken them weeks to walk).

When I finally reached the Pilgrim's Office, it was long past noon. But I didn't panic. Brie's meeting request had been for *after* the twelve o'clock Mass. This Mass with all its pomp and circumstance had to be an hour, right? *Right?*

No matter. The ensuing proceedings were frighteningly brief. I didn't know what to expect when I reached the end of the line, but the Pilgrim's Office was clearly that: a modern office space with posters of Spain on the wall and piles of tourist brochures on the tables.

Several clerks sat behind a long counter, and one of them waved me over. She smiled and asked for my credencial. I proudly presented it to her with a little flourish and opened it to the inside page. That's when I realized I had failed to procure two stamps a day since Sarria. Was I breaking the religious rules? Would this be an issue?

The clerk checked my starting point and nodded. "Pamplona." That was it. The number of stamps didn't impress her. The gap in my dates didn't raise any concerns. And the supposed two-stamp policy after Sarria wasn't a requirement.

The clerk then produced a cream-colored sheet of paper decorated along its edges with colorful flowers and a four-fingered St. James figure. The body of the modern-day parchment was in Latin text announcing my completion of the Camino. All the clerk had to do was print my name in Latin and add the date. She didn't even have to stamp it. The watermark of St. James's casket was already on the paper.

She handed me my compostela and whispered, "Congratulations" before waving over the next anxious pilgrim.

The entire operation had taken a total of forty-five seconds.

Unlike all the other peregrinos, when I emerged from the Pilgrim's Office I didn't shriek, weep, or look for somebody to embrace. I also didn't express any wild-eyed joyous relief. I was dispassionate and in a hurry. (I even forgot my protective canister.)

I soon sat on the short stack of steps outside the Praza da Immaculada (. . . *the smaller square where it's easier to find people* . . .) with my folded compostela in my back pocket. Tourists and pilgrims milled about the plaza, taking photos and admiring the cathedral, while I pivoted my head in all directions. Where would Brie emerge? Around this corner? Or that one? Or maybe behind me?

Then the church doors suddenly opened, and tourists and pilgrims alike scrambled for the entrance, pressing hard against one another to earn a glimpse inside the cathedral. The noon Mass was near its conclusion, and the *tiraboleiros* were raising the Botafumeiro off the floor!

Why the door was opened for us was a mystery. Why the Botafumeiro was being celebrated during a non-Holy Year was a puzzle. Nevertheless, it was a tremendously auspicious occasion, and everyone was willing to fight for the best position to get the perfect photograph. If someone's toes had to be stepped on, too bad. If someone else's view was being blocked, tough luck; you should have arrived earlier.

I rose from my seat but didn't join the melee. I stood safely behind the mass of humanity and admired the view. And it got better. Because, just as everyone else was poking and prodding to get closer to the action, one pilgrim was pushing back to get out of the way.

Brie!

Suddenly, my heart skipped a beat. Suddenly, I felt a rush of adrenalin that made my knees slightly buckle. That's when I knew. That's when I knew this was better than receiving my compostela. *This* was my wild-eyed moment of joyous relief.

When Brie nudged past the crowd and emerged from the church, I kept my cool and handed her the small bouquet of flowers I had bought from a street vendor around the corner. The flowers displayed on my compostela had given me the idea. And something Pam had said in one of her first letters about the time I had brought her flowers after she had had a bad day at the retail store.

I didn't know what to say, and I didn't know what Brie had to say. All I knew was that I had to be completely in the moment. Say nothing, and there was no risk of spoiling the occasion. Just be there for her. I presented Brie the flowers and took her hand.

With the Botafumeiro rising to the ceiling, Brie raised the bouquet to cover her face and burst into tears.

"I didn't mean to make you cry."

"Oh, shut up, you big idiot."

"That was my first instinct, too! But listen, Brie. There is one more thing Ronald said that I have to tell you . . ."

When I had gotten up to leave our table in La Linea, fresh tears were stinging my eyes as Ronald explained that Pam had given me a great gift; that the Camino was just the start of my adventures; that living one's life well was part of the long game.

"Don't hold onto your mistakes, mate. You have to let go of those shadows."

"What shadows? What are you talking about?"

"Don't be like those people who can't escape their past. You have to let go, mate. It's like your shadow, right? You can never escape it. Your past—*your shadow*—is holding you back. You can only be happy again if you find some way, or some person, to help you move on."

Brie lowered the bouquet from her face and squeezed my hand. "I think I like that. Martin was like a bad shadow. I'm free from him now. Ready to move on and all that. And you helped, that's for sure."

Cameras clicked, flashes flared, a choir of angelic voices sang as the Botafumeiro soared toward the church ceiling and swung wildly from vault to vault.

I barely noticed, and Brie had her back to the whole proceedings. We just stared into each other's eyes and smiled.

"So . . ." I started.

"Don't say anything, Jamie. I know it's soon. I wasn't being fair. I just wanted to know—"

"Look, Brie, I don't know what happens next—"

"Of course you don't—"

"But we *could* keep walking."

"What? Walking? To where? To Finisterre? You must be joking—"

"I hear the walking's good in England too."

"What?"

"Brie, I don't know what the future holds. I don't even know *where* my future is. I just know I don't have to go anywhere and be anywhere. I'm completely free. So maybe . . . my place is in London right now."

Brie held her breath.

"I just know whatever I do and wherever I go, I want it to be with you."

Now Brie didn't know what to say. Now Brie was silently living the moment.

And then I kissed her. And it wasn't like our parting peck back in Burgos. This time our kiss was slow . . . and deep . . . and purely affectionate. And we savored every second of it as the angelic voices soared higher and higher.

ALSO BY JOHN MEYER

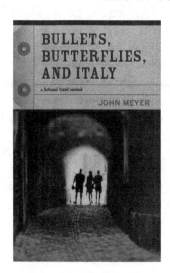

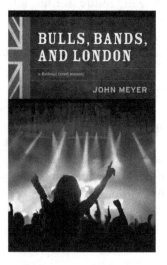

www.johnmeyerbooks.com